The CMS

Hospital Conditions *of* Participation *and* Interpretive Guidelines

HCPro

The CMS Hospital Conditions of Participation and Interpretive Guidelines is published by HCPro, a division of BLR.

No claim to original U.S. government work.

All rights reserved. Printed in the United States of America.   5   4   3   2   1

Download the additional materials of this book at *www.hcpro.com/downloads/12041.*

ISBN: 978-1-61569-376-4

HCPro, a division of BLR, provides information resources for the healthcare industry.

HCPro, a division of BLR, is not affiliated in any way with The Joint Commission, which owns the JCAHO and Joint Commission trademarks.

Jay Kumar, Editor
Rebecca Hendren, Product Manager
Erin Callahan, Senior Director, Product
Mike Mirabello, Graphic Artist
Matt Sharpe, Senior Manager of Production
Shane Katz, Art Director
Jean St. Pierre, Vice President, Operations and Customer Relations

Advice given is general. Readers should consult professional counsel for specific legal, ethical, or clinical questions.

Arrangements can be made for quantity discounts. For more information, contact:

HCPro, a division of BLR
75 Sylvan Street, Suite A-101
Danvers, MA 01923
Telephone: 800-650-6787 or 781-639-1872
Fax: 800-639-8511
E-mail: *customerservice@hcpro.com*

Visit HCPro online at: *www.hcpro.com* and *www.hcmarketplace.com.*

CONTENTS

INTRODUCTION

Every hospital should have a copy of up-to-date Centers for Medicare & Medicaid Services' (CMS) *Conditions of Participation* (CoP) and *Interpretive Guidelines* (IG) because surveyors use them to guide inspections, and following such guidelines helps to ensure full reimbursement. This document is also referred to as the *State Operations Manual.*

This book reproduces the CMS hospital *CoP*s and IGs verbatim. It includes CMS' survey protocol guidelines, which includes a list of questions surveyors will ask and the policies they will look for during an on-site visit.

In addition, available to download are the Emergency Medical Treatment and Labor Act (EMTALA) regulations, also reprinted verbatim. Medicare participating hospitals must meet these regulations, which require hospitals (including critical access hospitals) with emergency departments to provide a medical screening examination to any individual who comes to the emergency department and requests such an examination.

Our goal is to make it easier for you to understand the *CoP* requirements and have a successfully survey and receive full reimbursement. We hope you will find this book to be an essential resource to help you comply with CMS regulations.

Summary of recent changes

On August 27, 2013, CMS released significant changes impacting several areas of the *Conditions of Participation (CoP)*. Interestingly, the information included in Transmittal 88 on August 27 rescinded and replaced a relatively recent update, Transmittal 86, on July 19 2013. According to the official CMS documentation:

> *Transmittal 86, dated July 19, 2013, is being rescinded and replaced by Transmittal 88, dated August 27, 2013 to reflect the deletion of sections 5140.1 through 5140.4 on the transmittal page as this information has been moved to new sections 5170.1 through 5170.3. Additionally, in the table of contents, sections 5171.1 through 5171.3 have been corrected to 5170.1 through 5170.3. All other information remains the same.*

Let's take a look at where the most extensive of changes occurred in the language of the August 2013 transmittal.

Post-survey procedures Section 5110

Significant language was added under the header of post-survey procedures, specifically under 5110.1, Substantial Compliance. This language states that if condition-level deficiencies are not citied in a CMS survey, the provider is in substantial compliance with federal requirements. The new language also details the review process even if no deficiencies were cited, demonstrating that a survey was conducted to evaluate compliance with the listed requirements and that no deficiencies were identified in these areas.

Condition-level, Immediate Jeopardy Section 5110.2

The changes also impacted 5110.2, discussing condition-level and Immediate Jeopardy findings. If deficiencies pose an Immediate Jeopardy and that situation is removed while the surveyors are on-site, the deficiency citations are made at the condition-level. Condition-level deficiency procedures must then be followed. The CMS forms must indicate that an Immediate Jeopardy situation was cited even if it was removed with surveyors still on-site. The details of the Immediate Jeopardy and steps taken to remove it must be documented, and said documentation must include the date the surveyors verified the Immediate Jeopardy was removed prior to completion of the survey.

However, if the Immediate Jeopardy is not removed while surveyors are on-site, the deemed provider is placed on a 23 calendar day termination track. The provider is notified of the termination date and a request is issued for an acceptable plan of correction within five calendar days of the notice. The provider is advised it will be surveyed after the receipt of the acceptable plan of correction and prior to the termination date.

This notice also states that deemed status is removed. The new language does note that while deemed status is technically removed, because it is expected that deemed status will be restored once corrections are made and verified, no changes are made in the CMS ASPEN system to the provider's deemed status.

The new information goes on to describe the follow through process by CMS, including what occurs when:

- No acceptable plan of correction is submitted

- The Immediate Jeopardy is not removed at the first revisit

- The Immediate Jeopardy is removed and substantial compliance awarded after the first revisit

- The Immediate Jeopardy is removed and substantial noncompliance still remains after the first revisit

- And occurrences of substantial compliance or substantial noncompliance after the second revisit

The transmittal goes into full detail about these visits and follow up actions, which can be found under 5110.2.

Condition-level, non-Immediate Jeopardy Section 5110.3

This category, covered under 5110.3, discusses the procedures followed when the regional office does not require a full survey after a complaint survey, as well as when the regional office requires the state agency to conduct a full survey. To decide between these two options, the regional office may consider:

- The manner and degree of noncompliance identified as a result of the compliance investigation

- The provider's compliance history

- Recent changes in the provider's ownership or management

- Length of time since the provider's last accreditation survey

- Availability of state agency resources at the time required to conduct a full survey

- Advantages associated with conducting a more extensive survey compared to the advantages associated with the faster enforcement (and thus faster potential corrective action) that result when proceeding directly to enforcement action after the compliance survey

CMS regional offices have the following options after a provider fails to demonstrate substantial compliance but do not pose an Immediate Jeopardy under the updated language in the August transmittal. These options are below:

No full survey, proceed directly to termination track based on the complaint survey. As above, in this case deemed status is immediately removed but with the expectation it will be restored once corrective actions have been implemented and verified.

- The follow-up to this option depends upon the results of corrective action plans and revisits, including:

- If no timely, acceptable plan of correction is submitted, the regional office proceeds with termination of deemed status.

- Substantial compliance found on first revisit: termination is rescinded, provided substantial compliance is received and documented.

- Substantial non-compliance after first revisit: if surveyors find significant noncompliance on the first revisit, they will consult with the regional office to determine if a second revisit will occur, or if they should proceed with termination.

Full survey after the complaint survey. The regional office can order deemed status removed and a full survey conducted on an unannounced basis. The full survey must be conducted within 60 calendar days after removal of deemed status.

Full survey after complaint survey Section 5110.4

Should the regional office authorize the stage agency to conduct a full survey after a complaint survey (as detailed under 5110.4) the following can occur:

- Substantial compliance: Should the follow up survey find substantial compliance, notice of deemed status restoration is issued.

- Full survey findings: condition-level, Immediate Jeopardy. These findings run the gamut similar to those results we discussed under 5110.1, for Immediate Jeopardy conditions removed while surveyors are still on site, and Immediate Jeopardy situations not resolved with surveyors still on site.

- Full survey findings: condition-level, non-Immediate Jeopardy. Again, CMS options are similar to those already discussed for non-Immediate Jeopardy, condition-level findings.

Restraint and seclusion death reporting Section 5170

The other major changes seen in the August update involve hospital restraint/seclusion death reporting and investigation. This involves both deemed and non-deemed hospitals, critical access hospital distinct part psychiatric and rehabilitation units.

Hospitals are required to report a death associated with the use of restraint/seclusion to their CMS regional office.

The update details responsibilities of various agencies, stating that the regional office is responsible for communicating with hospitals in its region how it will accept these reports and how the data is entered in the system. The regional office should designate one person and a backup person as point of contact for reporting.

State agencies conduct complaint investigations regarding patient deaths involving restraint or seclusion but only when authorized by the regional office. The state agencies respond to requests from protection and advocacy groups and other parties.

The regional office evaluates the information reported to determine if the situation might involve a violation of CMS *CoP*s. It then authorizes an on-site investigation if there appears to be a possible violation.

With the information provided, if the regional office determines that an investigation is needed, within two days of receiving the report the regional office enters the report into the restraint/ seclusion model maintained by CMS and immediately notifies the state agency that it is authorized to conduct a complaint survey. The stage agency is expected to complete the investigation within five working days of receipt of authorization.

Simultaneously, the regional office must also provide written notification to the appropriate protection and advocacy agency with the state where the hospital is located if that organization has a data use agreement with CMS. The names and addresses for each state's protection and advocacy agency can be found online at *www.ndrn.org*.

The regional office provides the following information to the protection and advocacy agency:

- Hospital name

- Hospital address

- Name of deceased

- Copy of restraint/seclusion death report submitted by hospital

The August transmittal provides rules the protection and advocacy agency must comply with to receive this information as part of its CMS data use agreement.

The agency may request information about an on-site survey by submitting the request to the state agency. If the agency identifies a particular patient, hospital, approximate date or dates the patients was in that hospital, and makes a request for additional information related to the use of restraint or seclusion, that request is forward to the regional office.

Other areas of note

When examining this latest CMS update, we recommend looking at additional updates falling under the Interpretive Guidelines for ventilation, light, and temperature control, 482.41(c)(4).

Proper ventilation rules have been added for anesthetizing locations in accordance to NFPA rules. Humidity levels for these areas have also been addressed under the same section, stating:

> *Hospitals must maintain relative humidity (RH) levels at 35 percent or greater in each anesthetizing location; unless the hospital elects to use the CMS categorical waiver, which permits it to maintain a RH of at least 20 percent (see Appendix I, Section II for additional information). Hospitals must maintain records that demonstrate they have achieved the required levels. Although not required, CMS recommends that hospitals maintain the upper range of RH at 60 percent or less, as excessive humidity is conducive to microbial growth and compromises the integrity of wrapped sterile instruments and supplies. Each operating room should have separate temperature control. Acceptable standards such as from the Association of Operating Room Nurses (AORN) or the Facilities Guidelines Institute (FGI) should be incorporated into hospital policy.*

Hospitals will be surveyed for humidity maintenance records for anesthetizing locations to ensure, if monitoring determined humidity levels were not within acceptable parameters, that corrective actions were performed in a timely manner to achieve acceptable levels.

References:

- State Operations Manual Appendix A - Survey Protocol, Regulations and Interpretive Guidelines for Hospitals, (Rev. 84, 06-07-13) *www.cms.gov/Regulations-and-Guidance/Guidance/Manuals/downloads/som107ap_a_hospitals.pdf*

- CMS Manual System, DHHS, Centers for Medicare & Medicaid Services, Transmittal 88, Date: August 27, 2013, (Rev. 88, Issued: 08-27, 13), Revisions to Chapter 5 *www.cms.gov/Regulations-and-Guidance/Guidance/Transmittals/Downloads/R88SOMA.pdf*

- State Operations Manual, Appendix A - Survey Protocol, Regulations and Interpretive Guidelines for Hospitals, (Rev. 89, 08-30-13), *www.cms.gov/Regulations-and-Guidance/Guidance/Manuals/downloads/som107ap_a_hospitals.pdf*

Editor's note: This article was written by Elizabeth Di Giacomo-Geffers, RN, MPH, CSHA and originally ran in the November 2013 issue of **Briefings on The Joint Commission.**

CMS memos every hospital should know

Hospitals have seen the publication of many important memos by the CMS in the past year. Many of these include interpretive guidelines that every hospital should know about. Hospitals should designate one person with the responsibility to visit the CMS website once a month to check for updates. The CMS policy and memos to states and regions can be located at *http://tinyurl.com/lrqo6fh.*

Double click on "posting date" and it will bring up the most current memos. The "Memo" column will tell you if the memo affects hospitals, critical access hospitals (CAH), long-term care facilities, or other facilities. The following will discuss the most recent of these memos.

Discharge planning

CMS issued a memo rewriting all of the hospital discharge planning standards. Discharge planning is especially important in 2013. Since October 1, 2012, hospitals have forfeited $280 million because they had higher than expected readmission rates for heart attacks, heart failure, and pneumonia. Two out of every three hospitals in the U.S. have been penalized for high readmission rates.

CMS issued memo 13-32-hospital on March 17, 2013. This is the date of the memo and not the actual date on which it was placed on the CMS website. There is sometimes a delay in getting them posted. This memo is called "Revision to State Operations Manual (SOM), Hospital Appendix A-Interpretive Guidelines for 42 CFR 482.43, Discharge Planning. Appendix A is the bigger hospitals as opposed to the CAH, which generally have 25 beds or less.

This memo includes blue "Advisory Boxes," which discuss advisory practices to promote better patient outcomes. The information in the blue boxes is for reference only and hospitals cannot be cited for a deficiency for failure to comply with the recommendation. They are recommendations, not mandates. The 39-page memo reduces the number of tag numbers, or section numbers, from 24 to 13. Every hospital should review this memo and share it with social workers and discharge planners.

Blue box or advisory boxes

The hospital must have a discharge planning process for all inpatients and discharge planning policies and procedures. This is to determine early in the patient's stay whether they need post-hospital services such as home health, long term care, or other such services. CMS is encouraging all hospitals to implement a discharge planning evaluation for all inpatients. Hospitals that fail to do this must comply with many additional interpretive guidelines. Physicians can request a discharge planning evaluation if the hospital has not already implemented one. Patients also have the right to request a discharge evaluation and plan. The evaluation must include an assessment of whether the patient can do any self care or if family members are willing and available to help the patient when they go home.

Humidity in the operating room

In a memo dated April 19, 2013, CMS discussed that the humidity may now be between 20%-60% as opposed in 35%-60% in the areas specified in the memo. The 17-page memo is entitled "Relative Humidity (RH): Waiver of Life Safety Code (LSC) Anesthetizing Location Requirements; Discussion of Ambulatory Surgical Center (ASC) Operating Room Requirements." CMS has issued this waiver to the *Life Safety Code® (LSC)* to permit both new and existing ventilation systems in hospitals in anesthetizing locations. Hospitals in states with a more stringent law will have to follow their state law if it differs. The hospital does not need to file anything with CMS but are expected to have written documentation that they have elected to use the waiver. The facility must also notify the survey team at the entrance conference if the hospital has elected to use this waiver.
This memo revises tag number A-0726. It also revised Appendix I regarding the guidelines for *LSC* surveys. It also applies to ambulatory surgery centers and CAHs.

The deficiency memo

CMS issued a very important three-page memo dated March 22, 2013, that lists all of the deficiencies that hospitals received during recent complaint surveys. However, it contains the link to the Excel spread sheet that contains the detailed information. CMS has already included the full text of deficiencies for hospitals surveyed that is dated June 2013. This is located at *www.cms.gov/Medicare/Provider-Enrollment-and-Certification/CertificationandComplianc/Hospitals.html* and then scroll down to the bottom section that says "downloads."

This memo contains a treasure trove of wonderful information that details the CMS hot spots. For example, hospitals were cited for being out of compliance with the restraint and seclusion standards 362 times. In fact, patient rights were cited 950 times. This made patient rights one of the largest areas of deficiencies. This included privacy, confidentiality, care in a safe setting, grievances, advance directives, visitation, and admission status notification.

Hospitals should also be aware that the deficiency memo lists the hospital's name and address and specific deficiency. The Marketing and PR departments should be provided with this information since it is possible that some local newspapers may elect to run articles in the local press regarding these results.

Insulin pen memo

Hospitals should familiarize themselves with a CMS memo called "Use of Insulin Pens in Health Care Facilities." The memo was issued May 18, 2012 and is 3 pages long. Two recent incidents of reuse of insulin pen injectors on multiple patients occurred in January 2013 in two hospitals in New York State, resulting in hospitals having to contact more than 3,000 patients for HIV, HBV, and HCV testing.

CMS allows hospitals to use insulin pens. However, the insulin pen is for one patient use only and the patient's name should be put on the insulin pen. Ongoing reports of reuse of insulin pens have continued despite the CMS memo and warnings from both the Centers for Disease Control and Prevention and the Food and Drug Administration. Many professional organizations, such as the Institute for Safe Medication Practices (ISMP), and manufacturers have also issued warnings that insulin pen injectors cannot be used on multiple patients. Nurses should be educated on this periodically and during orientation. Hospitals should have policies and procedures that indicate that insulin pens are meant for use by a single patient only. The CDC has a free poster hospitals can put up regarding insulin pen safety along with brochures. It is located on the One and Only Campaign website at *www.oneandonlycampaign.org/content/insulin-pen-safety*. This website lists a number of excellent resources on the topic of insulin pens.

Complaint investigation manual updated

CMS issued a 37-page memo April 19, 2013 regarding the updated of the Complaint Investigation Manual. The complaint manual is used by the CMS surveyors when they go out and survey a hospital based on a complaint. However, anyone can access the complaint manual. The hospital's compliance officers may find the manual of assistance.

CMS discussed that during a complaint survey sometimes it is decided to do a full validation survey. This is mandatory in incidents in which the deficiency is found to be a condition level non-compliance where the non-compliance rises to the level of immediate jeopardy. CMS is clarifying that this results in a full survey in every case. The regional office has the discretion to make this decision. The memo discusses factors that will be considered in making this decision. CMS also discussed a recent report from the Government Accountability Office (GAO) that discussed the need for CMS to share complaint information with the accreditation organizations. Accreditation organizations include The Joint Commission, DNV Healthcare, American Osteopathic Association Healthcare Facilities Accreditation Program, and perhaps soon the Center for Improving Healthcare Quality. The regional office of CMS will now forward a copy of the findings to the accrediting organizations.

EMTALA, telemedicine, and CAH

CMS issued a five-page memo on June 7, 2013 that explains that CAHs can use telemedicine services. The title of the memo is "Critical Access Hospital (CAH) Emergency Services and Telemedicine: Implications for Emergency Services *Condition of Participation (CoP)* and Emergency Medical Treatment and Labor Act (EMTALA) On-Call Compliance." EMTALA is the federal law that requires all hospitals that receive Medicare or Medicaid reimbursement to do a medical screening exam to determine if the patient is in an emergency medical condition like a stroke or heart attack. If the patient is in an emergency medical condition, then the hospital must stabilize the patient to the best of its ability.

Some CAHs do not have physicians in the emergency department. It may be staffed by a physician assistant or a nurse practitioner with a physician on call. A physician must be immediately available by telephone or radio contact on a 24-hour per day basis to receive emergency calls, provide information on treatment of emergency patients, and refer patients. This requirement can be met by the use of a telemedicine MD/DO as well as by an MD/DO who practices on-site at the CAH.

CAH and mountainous terrain

CMS issued a 12-page memo on April 22, 2013 called "Details for Title: Clarification of the Critical Access Hospital (CAH) Criteria for Rural Location and Mountainous Terrain Distance Standard." To qualify as a CAH, the hospital must 35 miles from the nearest hospital. An exception is made in the case of mountainous terrain or in areas with only secondary roads. This memo clarified the requirements for hospitals that want to meet the requirement for mountainous terrain. Hospitals will need a letter from the state transportation or highway agency stating that the exception exists.

Luer misconnections

CMS issued a four-page memo on March 8, 2013 regarding adverse events related to luer misconnections. It is a problem when two ends fit together but don't belong together. Nurses and others can mistakenly connect the wrong device and deliver substances through the wrong route, like putting chemotherapy into an epidural line instead of the IV line. The surveyors want to see if the hospital has taken actions to ensure systems are in place to prevent this type of adverse event. Many hospitals have policies and procedures on this. Many provide education in orientation for staff. For example, after filing a report, a nurse can follow the tubing from the IV down to the insertion in the peripheral IV.

CMS encourages hospitals to report this occurrence to the FDA even if there is no adverse event. This issue has been taught in the patient safety arena for many years. This was the topic of a Joint Commission Sentinel Event Alert in 2008. The (ISMP) published many articles on this topic, including one on July 15, 2010 that mentions oxygen tubing found connected to an IV, bladder irrigation given as IV fluid, TPN administered in enteral nutrition, IV tubing connected to an ET tube or a tracheostomy tube. The Pennsylvania Patient Safety Authority released a toolkit on tubing misconnections in June 2010. This report found about one misconnection occurred per month.

The new Interpretive Guidelines

CMS issued a memo on March 15, 2013 detailing the new Interpretive Guidelines. Hospitals had waited for these for more than 10 months. These were based on the final regulations that went into effect July 16, 2012. CMS made more than two dozen changes that CMS estimated would save hospitals more than $5 billion. This is an important memo for hospitals. It included new tag numbers for the death of patients in one or two soft wrist restraints. It created new tag number 457 for standing orders and new tag numbers 412 and 413 in the nursing standards related to self-administered medication. This memo included changes to hospitals including CAHs. The new interpretive guidelines are included in the updated CMS hospital manual that was issued June 7, 2013.

Reporting adverse events into the PI system

CMS issued an eight-page memo on March 15, 2013 that reminds hospitals they are required to report adverse events into the hospital's QAPI reporting system. The memo was titled "AHRQ Common Formats - Information for Hospitals and State Survey Agencies (SAs) - Comprehensive Patient Safety Reporting Using AHRQ Common Formats."

Several reports show that nurses and others were not reporting adverse events (AE) and they were not getting into the PI reporting system. The Office of Inspector General (OIG) recommends using AHRQ common formats to help with the tracking. The OIG said it could help hospitals improve the reporting process. The OIG said 86% of all adverse events are never reported to the PI program. CMS encouraged all surveyors to develop an understanding of this tool. CMS recently changed QAPI to mean quality assessment performance improvement as opposed to quality assurance. In the CMS hospital *CoPs*, the PI section requires hospitals to track AEs and analyze the causes and implement actions to prevent them in the future. In fact, the CMS' third worksheet, issued November 9, 2012, will ask hospitals to provide documentation that they conducted three separate root cause analyses. PI, discharge planning, and infection control will be hit hard during the survey process. The third and most likely final pilot runs through the end of September 2013 and is expected to be rolled out for hospitals in 2014.

CMS requirements include the reporting of near misses. The recommended AHRQ Common Formats are evidence-based. The Common Formats allow for identification and reporting of any AE, even if rare, and includes 29 National Quality Forum "never events" such as falls and medication errors. Modules in the Common Formats include blood, pressure ulcers, surgery or anesthesia, falls, perinatal, and medications. The Common Formats are located at *https://psoppc.org/web/patientsafety.*

Editor's note: This article was written by Sue Dill Calloway RN, MSN, JD, CPHRM, CCMSCP and originally ran in the September and October 2013 issues of **Briefings on The Joint Commission.**

How to track updates

CMS provides the following instructions for tracking updates on the CMS website under Regulations and Guidance (*www.cms.hhs.gov*):

- Each appendix is a separate file that can be accessed directly from the SOM Appendix Table of Contents, as applicable.

- The appendixes are in PDF format, which is the format generally used in the SOM to display files. Click on the red button in the Download column to download a copy of any available file in PDF format.

- To return to this page after opening a PDF file on your desktop, use your browser's "back" button, because closing the file usually will also close most browsers.

The following is a list of several CMS Web pages and instructions on how they are of use:

- For tracking updates, refer to the CMS State Survey and Certification page, located at *www.cms.hhs.gov/SurveyCertificationGenInfo/.* Everyone should go in once a month and check for updates here. Save this page as a favorite and appoint someone in your facility who is responsible for doing the monthly checks. This page contains CMS survey and certification memoranda, guidance, clarifications, and instructions to state survey agencies and CMS regional offices. It is searchable by date and keyword.

- The CMS Transmittals page also provides information on important issues (*www.cms.hhs.gov/transmittals*). According to the CMS website, program transmittals are used to communicate new or changed policies and/or procedures that are being incorporated into a specific CMS program manual. The cover page (or transmittal page) summarizes the new and changed material, specifying what has been changed.

- In general, if you are working in a hospitals setting, another good place to check for updates includes the CMS' Hospital Center page, which can be found at *www.cms.hhs.gov/center/hospital.asp.* A quick check of recent updates to this page show that most of the announcements this year have been related to payment systems, but other, more accreditation-related changes are also announced here.

- The EMTALA page should also be checked. This page can be found at *www.cms.hhs.gov/EMTALA.* On this page, you will find changes and updates to regulations, manuals, and appendixes, and links back to transmittals related to EMTALA and EMTALA survey and certification letters. There is also a series of links with related and helpful material.

State Operations Manual
Appendix A - Survey Protocol, Regulations and Interpretive Guidelines for Hospitals

Table of Contents

(Rev. 89, 08-30-13)

<u>Transmittals for Appendix A</u>

§482.13(a) Standard: Notice of Rights ✓

§482.13(b) Standard: Exercise of Rights

§482.13(c) Standard: Privacy and Safety ✓

§482.13(d) Standard: Confidentiality of Patient Records ✓

§482.13(e) <u>Standard: Restraint or Seclusion</u>

§482.13(f) <u>Standard: Restraint or Seclusion: Staff Training Requirements</u>

§482.13(g) Standard: Death Reporting Requirements

§482.21 Condition of Participation: Quality Assessment and Performance ✓
      Improvement Program

§482.21(a) Standard: Program Scope

§482.21(b) Standard: Program Data

§482.21(c) Standard: Program Activities

§482.21(d) Standard: Performance Improvement Projects

§482.21(e) Standard: Executive Responsibilities

§482.22 Condition of Participation: Medical staff

§482.22(a) Standard: Composition of the Medical Staff

§482.22(b) Standard: Medical Staff Organization and Accountability

§482.22(c) Standard: Medical Staff Bylaws

§482.22(d) Standard: Autopsies

§482.23 Condition of Participation: Nursing Services

§482.23(a) Standard: Organization

§482.23(b) Standard: Staffing and Delivery of Care

§482.23(c) Standard: Preparation and Administration of Drugs

§482.24 Condition of Participation: Medical Record Services ✓

§482.24(a) Standard: Organization and Staffing

§482.24(b) Standard: Form and Retention of Record

§482.24(c) Standard: Content of Record

§482.25 Condition of Participation: Pharmaceutical Services ✓

§482.25(a) Standard: Pharmacy Management and Administration

§482.25(b) Standard: Delivery of Services

§482.26 Condition of Participation: Radiologic Services ✓

§482.26(a) Standard: Radiologic Services

§482.26(b) Standard: Safety for Patients and Personnel

Survey Protocol
Introduction

(Rev. 37, Issued: 10-17-08; Effective/Implementation Date: 10-17-08)

Hospitals are required to be in compliance with the Federal requirements set forth in the Medicare Conditions of Participation (CoP) in order to receive Medicare/Medicaid payment. The goal of a hospital survey is to determine if the hospital is in compliance with the CoP set forth at 42 CFR Part 482. Also, where appropriate, the hospital must be in compliance with the PPS exclusionary criteria at 42 CFR 412.20 Subpart B and the swing-bed requirements at 42 CFR 482.66

Certification of hospital compliance with the CoP is accomplished through observations, interviews, and document/record reviews. The survey process focuses on a hospital's performance of patient-focused and organizational functions and processes. The hospital survey is the means used to assess compliance with Federal health, safety, and quality standards that will assure that the beneficiary receives safe, quality care and services.

Regulatory and Policy Reference

- The Medicare Conditions of Participation for hospitals are found at 42CFR Part 482.

- Survey authority and compliance regulations can be found at 42 CFR Part 488 Subpart A.

- Should an individual or entity (hospital) refuse to allow immediate access upon reasonable request to either a State Agency or CMS surveyor, the Office of the Inspector General (OIG) may exclude the hospital from participation in all Federal healthcare programs in accordance with 42 CFR 1001.1301.

- The regulatory authority for the photocopying of records and information during the survey is found at 42 CFR 489.53(a)(13).

- The CMS State Operations Manual (SOM) provides CMS policy regarding survey and certification activities.

Surveyors assess the hospital's compliance with the CoP for all services, areas and locations in which the provider receives reimbursement for patient care services billed under its provider number.

Although the survey generally occurs during daytime working hours (Monday through Friday), surveyors may conduct the survey at other times. This may include weekends and times outside of normal daytime (Monday through Friday) working hours. When the survey begins at times outside of normal work times, the survey team modifies the survey, if needed, in recognition of patients' activities and the staff available.

All hospital surveys are unannounced. Do not provide hospitals with advance notice of the survey.

Tasks in the Survey Protocol

Listed below, and discussed in this document, are the tasks that comprise the survey protocol for hospital.

Task 1	Off-Site Survey Preparation
Task 2	Entrance Activities
Task 3	Information Gathering/ Investigation
Task 4	Preliminary Decision Making and Analysis of Findings
Task 5	Exit Conference
Task 6	Post-Survey Activities

Survey Modules for Specialized Hospital Services

The modules for PPS-exempt units (psychiatric and rehabilitation), psychiatric hospitals, rehabilitation hospitals and swing-bed hospitals are attached to this document. The survey team is expected to use all the modules that apply to the hospital being surveyed. For example, if the hospital has swing-beds, a PPS excluded rehabilitation unit, and a PPS excluded psychiatric unit, the team will use those three modules in addition to this protocol to conduct the survey. If the hospital is a rehabilitation hospital, the team will use the rehabilitation hospital module in addition to this protocol to conduct the survey. If the hospital is a psychiatric hospital and if the survey team will be assessing the hospital's compliance with both the hospital CoPs and psychiatric hospital special conditions, the team will use the psychiatric hospital module in addition to this protocol to conduct the survey.

Survey Team

Size and Composition

The SA (or the RO for Federal teams) decides the composition and size of the team. In general, a suggested survey team for a full survey of a mid-size hospital would include two-four surveyors who will be at the facility for 3 or more days. Each hospital survey team should include at least one RN with hospital survey experience, as well as other surveyors who have the expertise needed to determine whether the facility is in compliance. Survey team size and composition are normally based on the following factors:

- Size of the facility to be surveyed, based on average daily census;

- Complexity of services offered, including outpatient services;

- Type of survey to be conducted;

- Whether the facility has special care units or off-site clinics or locations;

- Whether the facility has a historical pattern of serious deficiencies or complaints; and

- Whether new surveyors are to accompany a team as part of their training.

Training for Hospital Surveyors

Hospital surveyors should have the necessary training and experience to conduct a hospital survey. Attendance at a Basic Hospital Surveyor Training Course is suggested. New surveyors may accompany the team as part of their training prior to completing the Basic Hospital Surveyor Training Course.

Team Coordinator

The survey is conducted under the leadership of a team coordinator. The SA (or the RO for Federal teams) should designate the team coordinator. The team coordinator is responsible for assuring that all survey preparation and survey activities are completed within the specified time frames and in a manner consistent with this protocol, SOM, and SA procedures. Responsibilities of the team coordinator include:

- Scheduling the date and time of survey activities;

- Acting as the spokesperson for the team;

- Assigning staff to areas of the hospital or tasks for the survey;

- Facilitating time management;

- Encouraging on-going communication among team members;

- Evaluating team progress and coordinating daily team meetings;

- Coordinating any ongoing conferences with hospital leadership (as determined appropriate by the circumstances and SA/RO policy) and providing on-going feedback, as appropriate, to hospital leadership on the status of the survey;

- Coordinating Task 2, Entrance Conference;

- Facilitating Task 4, Preliminary Decision Making;

- Coordinating Task 5, Exit Conference; and

- Coordinating the preparation of the Form CMS-2567.

Task 1 - Off-Site Survey Preparation

General Objective

The objective of this task is to analyze information about the provider in order to identify areas of potential concern to be investigated during the survey and to determine if those areas, or any special features of the provider (e.g., provider-based clinics, remote locations, satellites, specialty units, PPS-exempt units, services offered, etc.) require the addition of any specialty surveyors to the team. Information obtained about the provider will also allow the SA (or the RO for Federal teams) to determine survey team size and composition, and to develop a preliminary survey plan. The type of provider information needed includes:

- Information from the provider file (to be updated on the survey using the Hospital/CAH Medicare Database Worksheet), such as the facility's ownership, the type(s) of services offered, any prospective payment system (PPS) exclusion(s), whether the facility is a provider of swing-bed services, and the number, type and location of any off-site locations;

- Previous Federal and state survey results for patterns, number, and nature of deficiencies, as well as the number, frequency, and types of complaint investigations and the findings;

- Information from CMS databases available to the SA and CMS. Note the exit date of the most recent survey;

- Waivers and variances, if they exist. Determine if there are any applicable survey directive(s) from the SA or the CMS Regional Office (RO); and

- Any additional information available about the facility (e.g., the hospital's Web site, any media reports about the hospital, etc).

Off-Site Survey Preparation Team Meeting

The team should prepare for the survey offsite so they are ready to begin the survey immediately upon entering the facility. The team coordinator should arrange an off-site preparation meeting with as many team members as possible, including specialty surveyors. This meeting may be a conference call if necessary.

During the meeting, discuss at least the following:

- Information gathered by the team coordinator;

- Significant information from the CMS databases that are reviewed;

- Update and clarify information from the provider file so a surveyor can update the Medicare database using the "Hospital/CAH Medicare Database Worksheet," Exhibit 286;

- Layout of the facility (if available);

- Preliminary team member assignments;

- Date, location and time team members will meet to enter the facility;

- The time for the daily team meetings; and

- Potential date and time of the exit conference.

Gather copies of resources that may be needed. These may include:

- Medicare Hospital CoP and Interpretive Guidelines (Appendix A);

- Survey protocol and modules;

- Immediate Jeopardy (Appendix Q);

- Responsibilities of Medicare Participating Hospitals in Emergency Cases (Appendix V);

- Hospital Swing-Bed Regulations and Interpretive Guidelines (Appendix T);

- Hospital/CAH Medicare Database Worksheet, Exhibit 286;

- Exhibit 287, Authorization by Deemed Provider/Supplier Selected for Accreditation Organization Validation Survey; and

- Worksheets for swing-bed, PPS exclusions, and restraint/seclusion death reporting.

Task 2 - Entrance Activities

General Objectives

The objectives of this task are to explain the survey process to the hospital and obtain the information needed to conduct the survey.

General Procedures

Arrival

The entire survey team should enter the hospital together. Upon arrival, surveyors should present their identification. The team coordinator should announce to the Administrator, or whoever is in charge, that a survey is being conducted. If the Administrator (or person in charge) is not onsite or available (e.g., if the survey begins outside normal daytime Monday-Friday working hours), ask that they be notified that a survey is being conducted. Do not delay the survey because the Administrator or other hospital staff is/are not on site or available.

Entrance Conference

The entrance conference sets the tone for the entire survey. Be prepared and courteous, and make requests, not demands. The entrance conference should be informative, concise, and brief; it should not utilize a significant amount of time. Conduct the entrance conference with hospital administrative staff that is available at the time of entrance. During the entrance conference, the Team Coordinator should address the following:

- Explain the purpose and scope of the survey;

- Briefly explain the survey process;

- Introduce survey team members, including any additional surveyors who may join the team at a later time, the general area that each will be responsible for, and the various documents that they may request;

- Clarify that all hospital areas and locations, departments, and patient care settings under the hospital provider number may be surveyed, including any contracted patient care activities or patient services located on hospital campuses or hospital provider based locations;

- Explain that all interviews will be conducted privately with patients, staff, and visitors, unless requested otherwise by the interviewee;

- Discuss and determine how the facility will ensure that surveyors are able to obtain the photocopies of material, records, and other information as they are needed;

- Obtain the names, locations, and telephone numbers of key staff to whom questions should be addressed;

- Discuss the approximate time, location, and possible attendees of any meetings to be held during the survey. The team coordinator should coordinate any meetings with facility leadership; and

- Propose a preliminary date and time for the exit conference.

During the entrance conference, the Team Coordinator will arrange with the hospital administrator, or available hospital administrative supervisory staff if he/she is unavailable to obtain the following:

- A location (e.g., conference room) where the team may meet privately during the survey;

- A telephone for team communications, preferably in the team meeting location;

- A list of current inpatients, providing each patient's name, room number, diagnosis(es), admission date, age, attending physician, and other significant information as it applies to that patient. The team coordinator will explain to the hospital that in order to complete the survey within the allotted time it is important the survey team is given this information as soon as possible, and request that it be no later than 3 hours after the request is made. SAs may develop a worksheet to give to the facility for obtaining this information;

- A list of department heads with their locations and telephone numbers;

- A copy of the facility's organizational chart;

- The names and addresses of all off-site locations operating under the same provider number;

- The hospital's infection control plan;

- A list of employees;

- The medical staff bylaws and rules and regulations;

- A list of contracted services; and

- A copy of the facility's floor plan, indicating the location of patient care and treatment areas;

Arrange an interview with a member of the administrative staff to complete the Hospital/CAH Medicare Database Worksheet that will be used to update the provider's file in the Medicare database. The worksheet may not be given to hospital personnel for completion.

Hospital Tours

Guided tours of the hospital are not encouraged and should be avoided. While a tour of a small facility may take place in less than one-man hour, a tour of a large facility could consume several man hours of allocated survey time and resources that are needed to conduct the survey.

Initial On-Site Team Meeting

After the conclusion of the Entrance Conference, the team will meet in order to evaluate information gathered, and modify surveyor assignments, as necessary. Do not delay the continuation of the survey process waiting for information from the provider, but adjust survey activities as necessary. During the on-site team meeting, team members should:

- Review the scope of hospital services;

- Identify hospital locations to be surveyed, including any off-site locations;

- Add survey protocol modules and adjust surveyor assignments, as necessary, based on new information;

- Discuss issues such as change of ownership, sentinel events, construction activities, and disasters, if they have been reported;

- Make an initial patient sample selection (The patient list may not be available immediately after the entrance conference, therefore the team may delay completing the initial patient sample selection a few hours as meets the needs of the survey team); and

- Set the next meeting time and date.

Sample Size and Selection

To select the patient sample, review the patient list provided by the hospital and select patients who represent a cross-section of the patient population and the services provided. Patient logs (ER, OB, OR, restraint, etc) may be used in conjunction with the patient list to assure the sample is reflective of the scope of services provided by the hospital.

Whenever possible and appropriate, select patients who are in the facility during the time of survey (i.e., open records). Open records allow surveyors to conduct a patient-focused survey and enable surveyors to validate the information obtained through record reviews with observations and patient and staff interviews. There may be situations where closed records are needed to supplement the open records reviewed (e.g., too few open records, complaint investigation, etc), surveyors should use their professional judgment in these situations and select sample that will enable them to make compliance determinations. If it is necessary to remove a patient from the sample during the survey, (e.g., the patient refuses to participate in an interview), replace the patient with another who fits a similar profile. This should be done as soon as possible in the survey.

Select the number of patient records for review based on the facility's average daily census. The sample should be at least 10 percent of the average daily census, but not fewer than 30 inpatient records. For small general hospitals (this reduction does not apply to surgical or other specialty hospitals) with an average daily census of 20 patients or less, the sample should not be fewer than 20 inpatient records, provided that number of records is adequate to determine compliance. Within the sample, select at least one patient from each nursing unit (e.g., med/surg, ICU, OB, pediatrics, specialty units, etc). In addition to the inpatient sample, select a sample of outpatients in order to determine compliance in outpatient departments, services, and locations. The sample size may be expanded as needed to assess the hospital's compliance with the CoP.

If a complaint is being investigated during the survey, include patients who have been identified as part of the complaint in the sample. Issues or concerns identified through complaints may be an area of focus when selecting the patient sample.

Give each patient in the sample a unique identifier. Appropriate identifiable information should be kept on a separate identifier list. Do not use medical record numbers, Social Security numbers, care unit or billing record numbers to identify patients.

To conduct an initial survey of a hospital there must be enough inpatients currently in the hospital and patient records (open and closed) for surveyors to determine whether the hospital can demonstrate compliance with all the applicable CoP. The number of current and discharged inpatients and outpatients in relation to the complexity of care provided to patients and the length of stay of those patients needs to be large enough for surveyors to evaluate the manner and degree to which the hospital satisfies all the standards within each CoP including any CoP applying to optional services offered by the hospital. Utilize the same sample size and selection methods as previously discussed.

Task 3 - Information Gathering/Investigation

General Objective

The objective of this task is to determine the hospital's compliance with the Medicare CoP through observations, interviews, and document review.

Guiding Principles

- Focus attention on actual and potential patient outcomes, as well as required processes.

- Assess the care and services provided, including the appropriateness of the care and services within the context of the regulations.

- Visit patient care settings, including inpatient units, outpatient clinics, anesthetizing locations, emergency departments, imaging, rehabilitation, remote locations, satellites, etc.

- Observe the actual provision of care and services to patients and the effects of that care, in order to assess whether the care provided meets the needs of the individual patient.
- Use the interpretive guidelines and other published CMS policy statements to guide the survey.

- Use <u>Appendix Q</u> for guidance if Immediate Jeopardy is suspected.

General Procedures

Survey Locations

For hospitals with either no or a small number of off-campus provider-based locations, survey all departments, services, and locations that bill for services under the hospital's provider number and are considered part of the hospital.

For hospitals with many provider-based locations survey:

- All hospital departments and services at the primary hospital campus and on the campuses of other remote locations of the hospital;

- All satellite locations of the hospital;

- All inpatient care locations of the hospital;

- All out-patient surgery locations of the hospital;

- All locations where complex out-patient care is provided by the hospital; and

- Select a sample of each type of other services provided at additional provider-based locations.

On any Medicare hospital survey, contracted patient care activities or patient services (such as dietary services, treatment services, diagnostic services, etc.) located on hospital campuses or hospital provider based locations should be surveyed as part of the hospital for compliance with the conditions of participation.

During the Survey

- Observe what activities are taking place and assess the CoP that represent the scope and complexity of the patient care services located at each location, as well as, any other CoP that apply to those locations. Expand the survey activities as necessary.

- The SA and surveyors have discretion whether to allow, or to refuse to allow, facility personnel to accompany the surveyors during a survey. Surveyors should make a decision whether to allow facility personnel to accompany them based on the circumstances at the time of the survey.

- The team should meet at least daily in order to assess the status of the survey, progress of completion of assigned tasks, areas of concern, and to identify areas for additional investigations. The team meetings should include an update by each surveyor that addresses findings and areas of concern that have been identified. If areas of concern are identified in the discussion, the team should coordinate efforts to obtain additional information. Additional team meetings can be called at any time during the survey to discuss crucial problems or issues.

- All significant issues or significant adverse events must be brought to the team coordinator's attention immediately.

- Maintain open and ongoing dialogue with the facility staff throughout the survey process. Conferences with facility staff may be held in order to inform them of survey findings. This affords facility staff the opportunity to present additional information or to offer explanations concerning identified issues. Survey information must not be discussed unless the investigation process and data collection for the specific concerns is completed.

- Surveyors should always maintain a professional working relationship with facility staff.

- Surveyors need to respect patient privacy and maintain patient confidentiality at all times during the survey.

- Surveyors should maintain their role as representatives of a regulatory agency. Although non-consultative information may be provided upon request, the surveyor is not a consultant.

Patient Review

A comprehensive review of care and services received by each patient in the sample should be part of the hospital survey. A comprehensive review includes observations of care/services provided to the patient, patient and/or family interview(s), staff interview(s), and medical record review. After obtaining the patient's permission, observe each sample patient receiving treatments (e.g., intravenous therapy, tube feedings, wound dressing changes) and observe the care provided in a variety of treatment settings, as necessary, to determine if patient needs are met.

Observations

Observations provide first-hand knowledge of hospital practice. The regulations and interpretive guidelines offer guidance for conducting observations. Observation of the care environment provides valuable information about how the care delivery system works and how hospital departments work together to provide care. Surveyors are encouraged to make observations, complete interviews, and review records and policies/procedures by stationing themselves as physically close to patient care as possible. While completing a chart review, for instance, it may be possible to also observe the environment and the patients, as far as care being given, staff interactions with patients, safety hazards, and infection control practices. When conducting observations, particular attention should be given to the following:

- Patient care, including treatments and therapies in all patient care settings;

- Staff member activities, equipment, documentation, building structure, sounds and smells;

- People, care, activities, processes, documentation, policies, equipment, etc., that are present that should not be present, as well as, those that are not present that should be present;

- Integration of all services, such that the facility is functioning as one integrated whole;

- Whether quality assessment and performance improvement (QAPI) is a facility-wide activity, incorporating every service and activity of the provider and whether every facility department and activity reports to, and receives reports from, the facility's central organized body managing the facility-wide QAPI program; and

- Storage, security and confidentiality of medical records.

A surveyor should take complete notes of all observations and should document: the date and time of the observation(s); location; patient identifiers, individuals present during the observation, and the activity being observed (e.g., therapy, treatment modality, etc).

A surveyor should have observations verified by the patient, family, facility staff, other survey team member(s), or by another mechanism. For example, when finding an out-dated medication in the pharmacy, ask the pharmacist to verify that the drug is out-dated. In addition, a surveyor should integrate the data from observations with data gathered through interviews and document reviews.

Surveyors must not examine patients by themselves, although in certain circumstances, in order to determine a patient's health status and whether appropriate health care is being provided, especially to ensure a patient's welfare where he/she appears to be in immediate jeopardy, it is permissible and necessary to examine the patient. After obtaining permission from the patient, the surveyor should request that a staff member of the facility examine the patient in the surveyor's presence. The health and dignity of the patient is always of paramount concern. A surveyor must respect the patient's right to refuse to be examined.

Interviews

Interviews provide a method to collect information, and to verify and validate information obtained through observations. Informal interviews should be conducted throughout the duration of the survey. Use the information obtained from interviews to determine what additional observations, interviews, and record reviews are necessary. When conducting interviews, observe the following:

- Maintain detailed documentation of each interview conducted. Document the interview date, time, and location; the full name and title of the person interviewed; and key points made and/or topics discussed. To the extent possible, document quotes from the interviewee.

- Interviews with facility staff should be brief. Use a few well-phrased questions to elicit the desired information. For example, to determine if a staff member is aware of disaster procedures and his/her role in such events, simply ask, "If you smelled smoke, what would you do?"

- When interviewing staff, begin your interviews with staff that work most closely with the patient.

- Conduct patient interviews regarding their knowledge of their plan of care, the implementation of the plan, and the quality of the services received. Other topics for patient or family interview may include patient rights, advanced directives, and the facility's grievance/complaint procedure.

- Interviews with patients must be conducted in privacy and with the patient's prior permission.

- Use open-ended questions during your interview.

- Validate all information obtained.

- Telephone interviews may be conducted if necessary, but a preference should be made for in- person interviews.

- Integrate the data from interviews with data gathered through observations and document reviews.

Staff interviews should gather information about the staff's knowledge of the patient's needs, plan of care, and progress toward goals. Problems or concerns identified during a patient or family interview should be addressed in the staff interview in order to validate the patient's perception, or to gather additional information.

Patient interviews should include questions specific to the patient's condition, reason for hospital admission, quality of care received, and the patients knowledge of their plan of care. For instance, a surgical patient should be questioned about the process for preparation for surgery, the patient's knowledge of and consent for the procedure, pre-operative patient teaching, post-operative patient goals and discharge plan.

Document Review

Document review focuses on a facility's compliance with the CoP. When conducting a document review, document the source and date of the information obtained. When making document copies, identify the original date of the document and indicate the date and time the copies were made. Once a document review is completed, integrate the data obtained with data gathered through observations and interviews to decide if the hospital is in compliance with the CoP. Documents reviewed may be both written and electronic and include the following:

- Patient's clinical records, to validate information gained during the interviews, as well as for evidence of advanced directives, discharge planning instructions, and patient teaching. This review will provide a broad picture of the patient's care. Plans of care and discharge plans should be initiated immediately upon admission, and be modified as patient care needs change. The record review for that patient who has undergone surgery would include a review of the pre-surgical assessment, informed consent, operative report, and pre-, inter-, and post-operative anesthesia notes. Although team members may have a specific area assigned during the survey, the team should avoid duplication of efforts during review of medical records and each surveyor should review the record as a whole instead of targeting the assigned area of concern. Surveyors should use open patient records rather than closed records, whenever possible;

- Closed medical records may be used to determine past practice, and the scope or frequency of a deficient practice. Closed records should also be reviewed to provide information about services that are not being provided by the hospital at the time of the survey. For example, if there are no obstetrical patients in the facility at the time of the survey, review closed OB records to determine care practices, or to evaluate past activities that cannot be evaluated using open records. In the review of closed clinical records, review all selected medical records for an integrated plan of care, timelines of implementation of the plan of care, and the patient responses to the interventions.

- Personnel files to determine if staff members have the appropriate educational requirements, have had the necessary training required, and are licensed, if it is required;

- Credential files to determine if the facility complies with CMS requirements and State law, as well as, follows its own written policies for medical staff privileges and credentialing;

- Maintenance records to determine if equipment is periodically examined and to determine if it is in good working order and if environmental requirements have been met;

- Staffing documents to determine if adequate numbers of staff are provided according to the number and acuity of patients;

- Policy and procedure manuals. When reviewing policy and procedure manuals, verify with the person in charge of an area that the policy and procedure manuals are current; and

- Contracts, if applicable, to determine if patient care, governing body, QAPI, and other CoP requirements are included.

Photocopies

Surveyors should make photocopies of all documents needed to support survey findings. The surveyor needs access to a photocopier where he/she can make their own photocopies of needed documents. If requested by the hospital, the surveyor should make the hospital a copy of all items photocopied. All photocopies need to be dated and timed as to when photocopied, and identified such as "hospital restraint policy- 2/17/04 page 3" or "Patient # 6, progress note- 2/17/04."

Completion of Hospital/CAH Medicare Database Worksheet

Arrange an interview with a member of the administrative staff to update and clarify information from the provider file. The Hospital/CAH Medicare Database Worksheet will be used to collect information about the hospital's services, locations, and staffing by Medicare surveyors during hospital surveys. The worksheet will be completed by the surveyors using observation, staff interviews, and document review. The worksheet will not be given to hospital staff to complete. The worksheet is used to collect information that will later be entered into the Medicare database. During the interview clarify any inconsistencies from prior information or information gathered during the survey.

Task 4 - Preliminary Decision Making and Analysis of Findings

General Objectives

The general objectives of this task are to integrate findings, review and analyze all information collected from observations, interviews, and record reviews, and to determine whether or not the hospital meets the Conditions of Participation found at 42 CFR Part 482 and, as appropriate, the PPS exclusionary criteria at 42 CFR Part 412 Subpart B, and the swing-bed requirements at 42 CFR 482.66. The team's preliminary decision-making and analysis of findings assist it in preparing the exit conference report. Based on the team's decisions, additional activities may need to be initiated.

General Procedures

Preparation

Prior to beginning this Task, each team member should review his/her notes, worksheets, records, observations, interviews, and document reviews to assure that all investigations are complete and organized for presentation to the team.

Discussion Meeting

At this meeting, the surveyors will share their findings, evaluate the evidence, and make team decisions regarding compliance with each requirement. Proceed sequentially through the requirements for each condition appropriate to the facility as they appear in regulation. For any issues of noncompliance, the team needs to reach a consensus. Decisions about deficiencies are to be team decisions, with each member having input. The team should document their decisions, the substance of the evidence, and the numbers of patients impacted, in order to identify the extent of facility noncompliance. The team must ensure that their findings are supported by adequate documentation of observations, interviews and document reviews and includes any needed evidence such as photocopies. Any additional documentation or evidence needed to support identified non compliance should be gathered prior to the exit conference but at a minimum, prior to exiting the hospital.

Determining the Severity of Deficiencies

The regulations at 42 CFR 488.26 state, "The decision as to whether there is compliance with a particular requirement, condition of participation, or condition for coverage, depends upon the manner and degree to which the provider or supplier satisfies the various standards within each condition." When noncompliance with a condition of participation is noted, the determination of whether a lack of compliance is at the Standard or Condition level depends upon the nature (how severe, how dangerous, how critical, etc.) and extent (how prevalent, how many, how pervasive, how often, etc.) of the lack of compliance. The cited level of the noncompliance is determined by the interrelationship between the nature and extent of the noncompliance.

A deficiency at the Condition level may be due to noncompliance with requirements in a single standard or several standards within the condition, or with requirements of noncompliance with a single part (tag) representing a severe or critical health or safety breach. Even a seemingly small breach in critical actions or at critical times can kill or severely injure a patient, and represents a critical or severe health or safety threat.

A deficiency is at the Standard level when there is noncompliance with any single requirement or several requirements within a particular standard that are not of such character as to substantially limit a facility's capacity to furnish adequate care, or which would not jeopardize or adversely affect the health or safety of patients if the deficient practice recurred.

When a deficient practice (noncompliance) is determined to have taken place prior to the survey and the hospital states that it has corrected the deficient practice/issue (noncompliance), issues for the survey team to consider would include:

- Is the corrective action superficial or inadequate, or is the corrective action adequate and systemic?

- Has the hospital implemented the corrective intervention(s) or action(s)?

- Has the hospital taken a QAPI approach to the corrective action to ensure monitoring, tracking and sustainability?

The survey team uses their judgment to determine if any action(s) taken by the hospital prior to the survey is sufficient to correct the noncompliance and to prevent the deficient practice from continuing or recurring. If the deficient practice is corrected prior to the survey, do not cite noncompliance. However, if the noncompliance with any requirements is noted during the survey, even when the hospital corrects the noncompliance during the survey, cite noncompliance.

All noted noncompliance must be cited even when corrected on site during the survey. Citing noncompliance at the appropriate level is important to the integrity of the survey process. Citing too high a level is unfair to the hospital. Citing noncompliance at a level below the noted degree and manner of the noncompliance does not ensure that the hospital will develop acceptable plans of correction and implement corrective actions, and does not depict accurately whether the care provided adversely affects the health and safety of patients; and continued deficient practices may lead to adverse patient outcomes such as injury or death.

Gathering Additional Information

If it is determined that the survey team needs additional information to determine facility compliance or noncompliance, the team coordinator should decide the best way to conduct the additional review.

Task 5 - Exit Conference

General Objective

The general objective of this task is to inform the facility staff of the team's preliminary findings.

Prior to the Exit Conference

- The team coordinator is responsible for organization of the presentation of the exit.

- The team determines who will present the findings.

- If the team feels it may encounter a problem during the exit, they should contact their immediate supervisor.

Discontinuation of an Exit Conference

It is CMS' general policy to conduct an exit conference at the conclusion of each survey. However, there are some situations that justify refusal to continue or to conduct an exit conference. For example:

- If the provider is represented by counsel (all participants in the exit conference should identify themselves), surveyors may refuse to conduct the conference if the lawyer tries to turn it into an evidentiary hearing; or

- Any time the provider creates an environment that is hostile, intimidating, or inconsistent with the informal and preliminary nature of an exit conference, surveyors may refuse to conduct or continue the conference. Under such circumstances, it is suggested that the team coordinator stop the exit conference and call the State agency for further direction.

Recording the Exit Conference

If the facility wishes to audio tape the conference, it must provide two tapes and tape recorders, recording the meeting simultaneously. The surveyors should take one of the tapes at the conclusion of the conference. Video taping is also permitted if it is not disruptive to the conference, and a copy is provided at the conclusion of the conference. It is at the sole discretion of the surveyor(s) to determine if video taping is permitted.

General Principles

The following general principles apply when conducting an exit conference:

- The facility determines which hospital staff will attend the exit conference.

- The identity of an individual patient or staff member must not be revealed in discussing survey results. Identity includes not just the name of an individual patient or staff member, but also includes any reference by which identity might be deduced.

- Because of the ongoing dialogue between surveyors and facility staff during the survey, there should be few instances in which the facility is unaware of surveyor concerns or has not had an opportunity to present additional information prior to the exit conference.

Exit Conference Sequence

The following discusses the sequence of events in conducting an exit conference.

Introductory Remarks:

- Thank everyone for cooperation during the survey.

- Introduce all team members, mentioning any that have concluded their portion of the survey and have left the facility.

- Briefly mention the reason for the survey.

- Explain that the exit conference is an informal meeting to discuss preliminary findings.

- Indicate that official findings are presented in writing on the Form CMS-2567.

Ground Rules

- Explain how the team will conduct the exit conference and any ground rules.

- Ground rules may include waiting until the surveyor finishes discussing each deficiency before accepting comments from facility staff.

- State that the provider will have an opportunity to present new information after the exit conference for consideration after the survey.

Presentation of Findings

- Avoid referring to data tag numbers.

- Present the findings of noncompliance, explaining why the findings are a violation. If the provider asks for the regulatory basis, provide it.

- Refrain from making any general comments (e.g., "Overall the facility is very good"). Stick to the facts. Do not rank findings. Treat requirements as equal as possible.

- Do not identify unmet requirements as condition or standard level. Avoid statements such as, "the condition was not met" or "the standard was not met." It is better to state "the requirement is not met."

- If immediate jeopardy was identified, explain the significance and the need for immediate correction. Follow instructions in Appendix Q.
- Assure that all findings are discussed at the exit conference.

Closure

- Explain that a statement of deficiencies (Form CMS-2567) will be mailed within 10 working days to the hospital.

- Explain that the Form CMS-2567 is the document disclosed to the public about the facility's deficiencies and what is being done to remedy them. The Form CMS-2567 is made public no later than 90 calendar days following completion of the survey. It documents specific deficiencies cited, the facility's plans for correction and timeframes, and it provides an opportunity for the facility to refute survey findings and furnish documentation that requirements are met.

- Inform the facility that a written plan of correction must be submitted to the survey agency within 10 calendar days following receipt of the written statement of deficiencies.

- Explain the required characteristics of a plan of correction. The characteristics include:

  Corrective action to be taken for each individual affected by the deficient practice, including any system changes that must be made;

- The position of the person who will monitor the corrective action and the frequency of monitoring;

- Dates each corrective action will be completed;

- The administrator or appropriate individual must sign and date the Form CMS-2567 before returning it to the survey agency; and

- The submitted plan of correction must meet the approval of the State agency, or in some cases the CMS Regional Office for it to be acceptable.

- If the exit conference was audio or video taped, obtain a copy of the tape in its entirety before leaving the facility.

All team members should leave the facility together immediately following the exit conference. If the facility staff provides further information for review, the team coordinator should decide the best way to conduct the further review. It is usually prudent for at least two individuals to remain.

Task 6 – Post-Survey Activities

General Objective

The general objective of this task is to complete the survey and certification requirements, in accordance with the regulations found at 42 CFR Part 488.

General Procedures

Each State agency and Federal Regional Office should follow directives in the State Operations Manual. The procedures include:

- Timelines for completing each step of the process;

- Responsibilities of the team coordinator and other team members to complete the Form CMS-2567, "Statement of Deficiencies," following the "Principles of Documentation";

- Notification to the facility staff regarding survey results;

- Additional survey activities based on the survey results (e.g., revisit, forwarding documents to the Regional Office for further action/direction);

- Completion of "Hospital Restraint/Seclusion Death Reporting Worksheet," as appropriate;

- Compilation of documents for the provider file;

- Signed Authorization by Deemed Provider/Supplier Selected for Accreditation Organization Validation Survey is forwarded to RO; and

- Enter the information collected on the Hospital/CAH Medicare Database Worksheet into the Medicare database.

Plan of Correction

Regulations at 42 CFR 488.28(a) allow certification of providers with deficiencies at the Standard or Condition level "only if the facility has submitted an acceptable plan of Correction [POC] for achieving compliance within a reasonable period of time acceptable to the Secretary." Failure to submit a POC may result in termination of the provider agreement as authorized by 42 CFR 488.28(a) and §489.53(a)(1). After a POC is submitted, the surveying entity makes the determination of the appropriateness of the POC.

Psychiatric Hospital Survey Module

Background

State survey agencies are given the responsibility for conducting surveys of psychiatric hospitals to determine compliance with the two special conditions of participation. However, most are not staffed with the personnel with the psychiatric expertise necessary to conduct the surveys. In light of this, CMS has contracted out this function for many years, and a panel of contracted psychiatric consultants has conducted the majority of surveys of psychiatric hospitals.

General Procedures

When conducting a validation survey or other full survey of a psychiatric hospital using the hospital A-tags located in Appendix A of the SOM, the SA is also expected to conduct a review of the two special conditions of participation for psychiatric hospitals if:

- The State survey agency has the expertise (i.e., at a minimum a Masters prepared psychiatric nurse or an RN with inpatient psychiatric nursing experience) to serve on the team. The surveyors should conduct the survey of the two special conditions as outlined in Appendix AA of the State Operations Manual.

It is strongly recommended that when the State survey agency does not have the clinical expertise to conduct surveys of psychiatric hospitals, the SA should request, through its regional office, the assistance of the contracted psychiatric surveyors.

Regulatory Authority and Requirements for Psychiatric Hospitals

The following regulations describe the special requirements for psychiatric hospitals:

- 42 CFR 482.60 -- Special provisions applying to psychiatric hospitals;

- 42 CFR 482.61 -- Special medical record requirements for psychiatric hospitals; and

- 42 CFR 482.62 -- Special staff requirements for psychiatric hospitals.

The focus of the survey is on the "outcome" experienced by the patient and how the provider implements the plan of care. The survey process includes seven (7) tasks. When these tasks are viewed in total, they give a clear indication of how the provider is meeting or not meeting the requirements. Appendix AA of the State Operations Manual (SOM) gives detailed instructions on how to perform these tasks. The seven tasks are:

- Representative sample of patients -- selection methodology;

- Record review of individuals in the sample;

- Other record review;

- Direct patient observation;

- Interviews;

- Visit to each area of the hospital serving certified patients; and

- Team assessment of compliance.

Survey Preparation When Surveying the Two Special Conditions

When the SA is preparing to perform a survey of the special conditions while conducting a full survey (A-tags) of a psychiatric hospital, include in the preparation for the survey a review of Appendix A of the SOM, "Interpretive Guidelines and Survey Procedures for Hospitals," and a review of Appendix AA, "Interpretive Guidelines and Survey Procedures for Psychiatric Hospitals." Appendix AA includes the following exhibits:

- Exhibit 1, "Medicare/Medicaid Psychiatric Hospital Survey Data," Form CMS-724 (this form must be completed by the hospital and survey team.)

- Exhibit 2, "Surveyor Worksheet for Psychiatric Hospital Review: Two Special Conditions," Form CMS-725 (*optional)

- Exhibit 3, "CMS Death Record Review Data Sheet," Form CMS-726 (*optional)

- Exhibit 4, "CMS Nursing Complement Data," Form CMS-727 (*optional)

- Exhibit 5, "CMS Total Nursing Staff Data," Form CMS-728 (*optional)

- Exhibit 6, "Data Collection Medical Staff Coverage," Form CMS-729 (*optional)

*Although these forms are optional, they are useful for data collection purposes and will assist in determining the hospital's compliance status.

Identify all remote and satellite locations of the psychiatric hospital.

Survey Methods

Follow the interpretive guidelines and survey protocol in <u>Appendix AA</u> to determine compliance with the two special conditions. As judged appropriate by the survey team, patients selected for the survey of the two special conditions may be used to meet the patient selection requirements in the hospital survey protocol. Surveyors should select patients using the sample selection methodology in Appendix AA of the psychiatric hospital survey protocol and, using the hospital survey protocol patient selection methods, should select any remaining or additional patients needed to determine the hospital's compliance with the hospital CoP.

Identify any psychiatric hospital satellite(s), remote locations, or other provider based location(s). Record the location, name, address, and telephone number for every satellite, remote location, or provider based location on the Hospital/CAH Medicare Database Worksheet for updating the Medicare database.

Post-Survey Activities

Follow the directions and procedures in the SOM for post-survey activities. The findings for deficiencies noted for the A-tags and B-tags must be documented on separate Form CMS-2567.

Psychiatric Unit Survey Module

When conducting a full survey of an accredited or non-accredited hospital that has a PPS excluded psychiatric unit, conduct a survey of the psychiatric unit using the survey methods in this module to assess the hospital's compliance with the excluded psychiatric unit requirements.

Excluded unit surveys utilizing these methods will count as annual validation compliance surveys of the hospital's self-attestation of compliance with the excluded psychiatric unit requirements.

Background

The PPS excluded psychiatric unit is part of the hospital and is included as part of the overall hospital survey. The term "exclusion" is a reimbursement term. Patient care in a PPS excluded psychiatric unit is reimbursed at the PPS psychiatric unit excluded rate rather than the hospital PPS rate. In order for a hospital to receive the excluded rate for psychiatric care provided in its excluded unit, the unit must comply with the excluded psychiatric unit requirements found at 42 CFR 412.27.

A PPS excluded psychiatric unit is regulated by both the hospital CoP at 42 CFR 482 (also found in Appendix A of the SOM) and the PPS excluded psychiatric unit requirements at 42 CFR 412.27. The actual psychiatric unit requirements are based on the Special Conditions of Participation for Psychiatric Hospitals found in §§482.60, 482.61, and 482.62.

Requirements for PPS Excluded Psychiatric Units

- 42 CFR 482 - Conditions of Participation for hospitals;
- 42 CFR 412.25 - Excluded hospital units: Common Requirements; and

- 42 CFR 412.27 - Excluded psychiatric units: Additional Requirements

Activities Conducted Prior to Psychiatric Unit Survey

- Contact the RO to determine if the hospital has approval for a PPS excluded psychiatric unit.

- Contact the RO to determine the unit's cost-reporting period.

- If possible, establish the location or locations of the psychiatric unit. Determine if the unit has a satellite or satellites in other locations. Determination or verification of this information may have to wait until the survey team is onsite.

- Do not conduct the survey of the PPS excluded psychiatric unit requirements within 90 days of the end of the hospital's cost reporting period.

- Review the "Psychiatric Unit Criteria Worksheet," Form CMS-437.

Survey Tool

The "Psychiatric Unit Criteria Worksheet," Form CMS-437.

Survey Procedures for Determining Compliance with the PPS Excluded Psychiatric Unit Requirements

- The surveyor of the psychiatric unit requirements should be an RN.

- Select 10 percent of the unit's average daily census or a minimum of two patients for the patient sample.

- The selected patients should be included in the patient sample used for the full hospital survey.

- Hospital survey activities should be conducted concurrently with the survey of the PPS excluded psychiatric unit requirements.

- Using the "Psychiatric Unit Criteria Worksheet," Form CMS-437, verify whether the requirements have been met by checking the appropriate boxes marked "YES" and "NO." Under the column "Explanatory Statement," document specifics of the findings. Additional findings can be documented in a narrative note that should be attached to the worksheet.

- Select additional patients (open or closed records) as needed to determine compliance with the excluded psychiatric unit requirements.

- If there are patients on the unit who were admitted the day before or on the day of the survey, verify that all applicable requirements have been completed or are already in place. These patients are in addition to the number of patients needed to establish the minimum patient sample size.

- If there are no patients on the unit at the time the survey is conducted, review closed patient records of unit patients treated within 6 months of the date of the survey.

- Identify if the psychiatric unit has a satellite or satellites. Record the location, name, address, and telephone number for every satellite on the Hospital/CAH Medicare Database Worksheet for updating the Medicare database.

Exit Conference

- Inform the hospital of findings of noncompliance with the excluded psychiatric unit requirements.

- Inform the hospital that the SA will forward the completed CMS Form-437 to the hospital at the same time as the completed CMS Form-2567.

Post-Survey Activities

- Do not include the survey findings of the excluded psychiatric unit requirements on the Form CMS-2567 that is used to document the hospital survey findings.

- If there are requirements that have not been met, notify the RO. Document survey findings of PPS psychiatric unit requirements on the Form CMS-437. Submit the completed Form CMS-437 to the RO within the same time frame as the completion of the Form CMS-2567 and at least 60 days prior to the end of the hospital's cost reporting period.

- Follow the procedures in the SOM for post-survey activities.

Rehabilitation Hospital Survey Module

When conducting a full survey of an accredited or non-accredited rehabilitation hospital, conduct a survey of the hospital's compliance with rehabilitation hospital excluded requirements using the survey methods in this module.

Surveys of the PPS excluded rehabilitation hospital requirements utilizing these methods will count as annual validation compliance surveys of the hospital's self-attestation of compliance with the excluded requirements.

Background

The term "exclusion" is a reimbursement term. Patient care in a PPS excluded rehabilitation hospital is reimbursed at the PPS rehabilitation hospital excluded rate rather than at the hospital PPS rate. In order for a hospital to receive the excluded rate for rehabilitation care provided, the hospital must comply with the excluded requirements found at 42 CFR 412.

A PPS excluded rehabilitation hospital is regulated by both the hospital CoP at 42 CFR 482 (also found in Appendix A of the SOM) and the PPS excluded rehabilitation hospital requirements at 42 CFR 412.

Regulatory Authority and Requirements for PPS Excluded Rehabilitation Hospitals

- 42 CFR 482 - Conditions of Participation for Hospitals;

- 42 CFR 412.22 - Excluded hospitals and hospital units: General rules; and

- 42 CFR 412.23 - Excluded hospitals: Classifications

Activities Conducted Prior to a Rehabilitation Hospital Survey

- Contact the RO to determine if the hospital has approval for a PPS excluded rehabilitation hospital.

- Contact the RO to determine the hospital's cost reporting period.

- Do not conduct the survey of the PPS excluded rehabilitation hospital requirements within 90 days of the end of the hospital's cost reporting period.

- Identify any satellite locations of the hospital.

- Verify with the RO that the hospital is in compliance with the inpatient population percent rule, and that each satellite, if any, is independently in compliance with the inpatient population percent rule.

- Review the "Rehabilitation Hospital Criteria Worksheet," Form CMS-437B.

Survey Tool

"Rehabilitation Hospital Criteria Worksheet," Form CMS-437B.

Survey Procedures for Determining Compliance with the PPS Excluded Rehabilitation Hospital Requirements

- Survey activities to determine hospital compliance with the PPS excluded rehabilitation hospital requirements should be conducted concurrently with the full survey of the hospital's compliance with the hospital CoP.

- Using the "Rehabilitation Hospital Criteria Worksheet," Form CMS-437B, verify whether the requirements have been met by checking the appropriate box marked "YES" or "NO." Under the column "Explanatory Statement," document specifics about the findings. Additional findings can be documented in a narrative note that should be attached to the worksheet.

- Select a minimum of two current inpatients for the patient sample.

- Select additional patients (open or closed records) as needed to determine compliance with the excluded rehabilitation hospital requirements.

- The selected patients should be included in the patient sample used for the full hospital survey.

- Identify if the rehabilitation hospital has remote locations, satellites, or other provider based locations. Record the location, name, address and telephone number for every remote location, satellite, or provider based location on the Hospital/CAH Medicare Database Worksheet for updating the Medicare database.

Exit Conference

- Inform the hospital of findings of noncompliance with the excluded rehabilitation hospital requirements.

- Inform the hospital that the SA will forward the completed Form CMS-437B to the hospital at the same time as the completed Form CMS-2567.

Post Survey Activities

- Do not include the survey findings for the PPS excluded rehabilitation hospital requirements on the Form CMS-2567.

- If there are PPS excluded hospital requirements that have not been met, notify the RO. Document survey findings of the PPS excluded rehabilitation hospital requirements on the CMS 437B. Submit the completed Form CMS-437B to the RO within the same time frame as the completion of the Form CMS-2567 and at least 60 days prior to the end of the hospital's cost reporting period.

- Follow the requirements in the SOM for post-survey activities.

Inpatient Rehabilitation Unit Survey Module

When conducting a full survey of an accredited or non-accredited hospital that has a PPS excluded rehabilitation unit, conduct a survey of the rehabilitation unit using the survey methods in this module to assess the hospital's compliance with the excluded rehabilitation unit requirements.

Surveys of the PPS excluded rehabilitation unit requirements utilizing these methods will count as annual validation compliance surveys of the hospital's self-attestation of compliance with the excluded requirements.

Background

The PPS excluded rehabilitation unit is part of the hospital and is included as part of the overall hospital survey. The term "exclusion" is a reimbursement term. Patient care in a PPS excluded rehabilitation unit is reimbursed at the PPS excluded rehabilitation unit rate rather than the hospital PPS rate. In order for a hospital to receive the excluded rate for rehabilitation care provided in its excluded unit, the unit must comply with the excluded rehabilitation unit requirements found at 42 CFR 412.

A PPS excluded rehabilitation unit is regulated by both the hospital CoP at 42 CFR 482 (also found in Appendix A of the SOM) and the PPS excluded rehabilitation unit requirements at 42 CFR 412.

Requirements for PPS Excluded Rehabilitation Units

- 42 CFR 482 - Conditions of Participation for hospitals;

- 42 CFR 412.25 - Excluded hospital units: Common Requirements;

- 42 CFR 412.29 - Excluded rehabilitation units: Additional Requirements; and

- State Operations Manual, Chapter 3, §3100.

Activities Conducted Prior to Rehabilitation Unit Survey

- Contact the RO to determine if the hospital has approval for a PPS excluded rehabilitation unit.

- Contact the RO to determine the unit's cost-reporting period.

- Do not conduct the survey of the PPS excluded rehabilitation unit requirements within 90 days of the end of the hospital's cost reporting period.

- Verify with the RO that the hospital is in compliance with the inpatient population percent rule for the unit and that each rehabilitation unit satellite, if any, is independently in compliance with the inpatient population percent rule.

- If possible, establish the location or locations of the rehabilitation unit. Determine if the unit has a satellite or satellites in other locations. Determination or verification of this information may have to wait until the survey team is onsite.

- Review the "Rehabilitation Unit Criteria Worksheet," Form CMS-437A.

Survey Tool

The "Rehabilitation Unit Criteria Worksheet," Form CMS-437A.

Survey Procedures for Determining Compliance with the PPS Excluded Rehabilitation Unit Requirements

- Survey activities to determine hospital compliance with the PPS excluded rehabilitation unit requirements should be conducted concurrently with the full survey of the hospital's compliance with the hospital CoP.

- Using the "Rehabilitation Hospital Criteria Worksheet," Form CMS-437A, verify whether the requirements have been met by checking the appropriate box marked "YES" or "NO." Under the column "Explanatory Statement," document specifics about the findings. Additional findings can be documented in a narrative note that should be attached to the worksheet.

- Select 10 percent of the unit's average daily census or a minimum of two current patients for the patient sample.

- The selected patients should be included in the patient sample used for the full hospital survey.
- Select additional patients (open or closed records) as needed to determine compliance with the excluded rehabilitation unit requirements.

- If there are no patients on the unit at the time the survey is conducted, review closed patient records of unit patients treated within six months of the survey.

- Identify if the rehabilitation unit has a satellite or satellites. Record the location, name, address and telephone number for every satellite on the Hospital/CAH Medicare Database Worksheet for updating the Medicare database.

Exit Conference

- Inform the hospital of findings of noncompliance with the excluded rehabilitation unit requirements.

- Inform the hospital that the SA will forward the completed Form CMS-437A to the hospital at the same time as the completed Form CMS-2567.

Post Survey Activities

- Do not include the survey findings for the PPS excluded rehabilitation unit requirements on the Form CMS-2567.

- If there are PPS excluded unit requirements that have not been met, notify the RO. Document survey finding of the PPS rehabilitation unit requirements on the CMS-437A. Submit the completed Form CMS-437A to the RO within the same time frame as the completion of the Form CMS-2567 and at least 60 days prior to the end of the hospital's cost reporting period.

- Follow the requirements in the SOM for post-survey activities.

Hospital Swing-Bed Survey Module

When conducting a full survey of an accredited or unaccredited hospital that has swing-bed approval, conduct a survey of the hospital swing-bed requirements found at 42 CFR 482.66. These requirements, as well as interpretive guidelines, are found in Appendix T of the SOM. An optional survey worksheet, also found in Appendix T, may be used.

Background

Swing-bed patients are hospital patients who are situated in the hospital but for whom the hospital is receiving reimbursement for skilled nursing services, as opposed to acute-care reimbursement. The reference to swing-bed is a patient care and reimbursement status and has no relationship to geographic location in the facility. The patient may be in acute-care status one day and change to swing-bed status the next day. It is not necessary for the patient to change location in the hospital when the reimbursement status changes, but moving to a different location is allowed. A 3-day qualifying stay for the same spell of illness in any hospital or critical access hospital (CAH) is required prior to admission to swing-bed status. The 3-day qualifying stay does not need to be from the same facility as the swing-bed admission.

Regulatory Authority and Requirements for Hospital Providers of Extended Care Services ("Swing-beds")

Hospital swing-bed care is regulated by both the hospital requirements at 42 CFR Part 482 (reprinted at Appendix A of the SOM) and the swing-bed requirements at 42 CFR 482.66 (also in Appendix T, along with an optional surveyor worksheet). The actual swing-bed survey requirements are referenced in the Medicare Nursing Home requirements at 42 CFR Part 483.

Section 1883 of the Act authorizes payment under Medicare for post-hospital SNF services provided by any hospital that meets certain requirements. By regulation, the Secretary has specified these requirements at **42 CFR 482.66**:

- The hospital has a Medicare provider agreement;

- The facility has fewer than 100 hospital beds, excluding beds for newborns and beds in intensive care type inpatient units;

- The hospital is located in a rural area. This includes all areas not delineated as "urbanized" areas by the Census Bureau, based on the most recent census;

- The hospital does not have in effect a 24-hour nursing waiver granted under 42 CFR §488.54(c);

- The hospital has not had a swing-bed approval terminated within the two years previous to application; and

- The hospital meets the swing-bed CoP on Resident Rights; Admission, Transfer, and Discharge Rights; Resident Behavior and Facility Practices; Patient Activities; Social Services; Discharge Planning; Specialized Rehabilitative Services; and Dental Services.

Activities Conducted Prior to Swing-Bed Survey

Prior to conducting the swing-bed survey, verify the following:

- The hospital continues to be located in a rural census tract;

- The hospital does not have a 24-hour nursing waiver in place; and

- The hospital's swing-bed approval is in effect and has not been terminated within the two previous years.

Survey Procedures

In conducting the survey, verify that the hospital has fewer than 100 hospital beds, excluding beds for newborns and beds in intensive care units. A hospital licensed for more than 100 beds may be eligible for swing-bed approval if it utilizes and staffs for fewer than 100 beds. Count the staffed beds in each nursing unit. Do not count beds in recovery rooms, intensive care units, operating rooms, newborn nurseries or stretchers in emergency departments.

Assess the hospital's compliance with the swing-bed requirements at **42 CFR 482.66**, found in <u>Appendix T</u> of the SOM, and the hospital survey methods contained in the hospital survey protocol. Swing-bed requirements apply to any patient discharged from the hospital and admitted to a swing-bed for skilled nursing services. The requirements for acute-care hospitals also apply.

If swing-bed patients are present during the on-site inspection, conduct an open record review and an environmental assessment. Include patient interviews and observations of care and services. However, if no swing-bed patients are present during the on-site inspection, review two closed records for compliance with swing-bed requirements. In all cases, review policies, procedures, and contracted services to assure that the hospital has the capability to provide the services needed.

It is important for surveyors to maintain on-going documentation of their findings during the course of the survey for later reference. Surveyors may use the optional swing-bed worksheet as a note-taking tool to document and record their findings on the survey.

Exit Conference

Any findings of noncompliance may be discussed during the time of the hospital exit conference.

Post-Survey Activities

The findings for swing-bed deficiencies must be documented on a separate Form CMS-2567, even though the swing-bed survey is being conducted simultaneously with the hospital survey.

Regulations and Interpretive Guidelines

A-0001
(Rev. 37, Issued: 10-17-08; Effective/Implementation Date: 10-17-08)

§482.2 Provision of Emergency Services by Nonparticipating Hospitals

(a) The services of an institution that does not have an agreement to participate in the Medicare program may, nevertheless, be reimbursed under the program if--

(1) The services are emergency services; and

(2) The institution meets the requirements of section 1861(e)(1) through (5) and (7) of the Act. Rules applicable to emergency services furnished by non-participating hospitals are set forth in subpart G of part 424 of this chapter.

(b) Section 440.170(e) of this chapter defines emergency hospital services for purposes of Medicaid reimbursement.

Interpretive Guidelines §482.2

The statutory requirements that a hospital must meet are:

- The hospital is primarily engaged in providing, by or under the supervision of MD/DOs, to inpatients, diagnostic services and therapeutic services for medical diagnosis, treatment, and care of injured, disabled or sick persons, or rehabilitation services for the injured, disabled, or sick persons;

- The hospital maintains clinical records on all patients;

- The hospital has medical staff bylaws;

- The hospital has a requirement that every Medicare patient must be under the care of an MD/DO;

- The hospital provides 24-hour nursing services rendered or supervised by a registered professional nurse and has a licensed, practical, or registered professional nurse on duty at all times; and

- The hospital is licensed or is approved as meeting the standards for licensing, as a hospital as defined by the State.

A-0020
(Rev. 37, Issued: 10-17-08; Effective/Implementation Date: 10-17-08)

§482.11 Condition of Participation: Compliance with Federal, State and Local Laws

Interpretive Guidelines §482.11

The hospital must ensure that all applicable Federal, State and local law requirements are met.

A-0021
(Rev. 37, Issued: 10-17-08; Effective/Implementation Date: 10-17-08)

§482.11(a) The hospital must be in compliance with applicable Federal laws related to the health and safety of patients.

Survey Procedures §482.11(a)

Interview the CEO, or appropriate individual designated by the hospital, to determine whether the hospital is in compliance with Federal laws related to patient health and safety. (For example, ask if the hospital was cited since its last survey for any violation of Section 504 of the Rehabilitation Act of 1973 related to denying people with disabilities access to care. If so, verify that satisfactory corrections have been made to bring the hospital into compliance with that law.) Refer or report noted noncompliance with Federal laws and regulations to the appropriate agency having jurisdiction (e.g., accessibility issues, blood-borne pathogens, standard precautions, and TB control to OSHA; hazardous chemical/waste issues to EPA; etc.)

A-0022
(Rev. 37, Issued: 10-17-08; Effective/Implementation Date: 10-17-08)

§482.11(b) The hospital must be--

(1) **Licensed; or**

(2) **Approved as meeting standards for licensing established by the agency of the State or locality responsible for licensing hospitals.**

Survey Procedures §482.11(b)

Prior to the survey, determine whether the hospital is subject to licensure requirements and verify that the licensing agency has approved the hospital as meeting the standards for licensure as set forth by the agency of the State or locality responsible for licensing hospitals.

A-0023
(Rev. 37, Issued: 10-17-08; Effective/Implementation Date: 10-17-08)

§482.11(c) The hospital must assure that personnel are licensed or meet other applicable standards that are required by State or local laws.

Interpretive Guidelines §482.11(c)

All staff that are required by the State to be licensed must possess a current license. The hospital must assure that these personnel are in compliance with the State's licensure laws. The laws requiring licensure vary from state to state. Examples of healthcare professionals that a state may require to be licensed could include: nurses, MD/DOs, physician assistants, dieticians, x-ray technologists, dentists, physical therapists, occupational therapists, respiratory therapists and hospital administrators.

All staff must meet all applicable standards required by State or local law for hospital personnel. This would include at a minimum:

- Certification requirements;

- Minimum qualifications;

- Training/education requirements; and

- Permits (such as food handlers permits).

When telemedicine is used and the practitioner and patient are located in different states, the practitioner providing the patient care service must be licensed and/or meet the other applicable standards that are required by State or local laws in both the state where the practitioner is located and the state where the patient is located.

Survey Procedures §482.11(c)

- Verify for those personnel required to be licensed, certified, and/or permitted by the State, that the hospital has established, and follows procedures for determining that personnel are properly licensed, certified, and/or permitted.

- Verify that staff and personnel are licensed, certified, and/or permitted in accordance with State and local requirements.

- Verify that staff and personnel meet all standards (such as continuing education, basic qualifications, etc.) required by State and local laws or regulations. Verify that the hospital has a mechanism established and enforced to ensure compliance.

- Review a sample of personnel files to verify that licensure and/or other required credentials information is up to date. Verify State licensure compliance of the direct care personnel as well as administrators and supervisory personnel.

A-0043
(Rev. 84, Issued: 06-07-13, Effective: 06-07-13, Implementation: 06-07-13)

§482.12 Condition of Participation: Governing Body

There must be an effective governing body that is legally responsible for the conduct of the hospital. If a hospital does not have an organized governing body, the persons legally responsible for the conduct of the hospital must carry out the functions specified in this part that pertain to the governing body….

Interpretive Guidelines §482.12

The hospital must have a governing body which is effective in carrying out its responsibilities for the conduct of the hospital. In the absence of an organized governing body, there must be written documentation that identifies the individual or individuals that are legally responsible for the conduct of the hospital operations.

If the hospital is part of a healthcare system that includes several separately certified hospitals, each with its own Medicare provider agreement and CMS Certification Number, the governing body of the healthcare system has the option to act as the governing body of each separately certified hospital, unless doing so would conflict with State law. A hospital system also has the option to form several governing bodies, each of which is responsible for several separately certified hospitals. For example, a health system operating hospitals in many states might choose to form regional sub-boards each responsible for the hospitals in its region, or a health system that has a mixture of types of hospitals may choose to form one sub-board responsible for its short-term acute care hospitals and another for its long term care hospitals.

The Medicare program offers hospital facilities considerable flexibility regarding how they choose to participate. Based on the geographic and other institutional limitations set out in the "provider-based" regulation at §413.64, which addresses provider-based status for hospital facilities in multiple locations, hospital governing bodies make business decisions about how they want to participate in Medicare, and they indicate on their Medicare enrollment application the choices they have made. It is not uncommon to find multiple hospital campuses with one owner located in the same geographic area enrolled in Medicare as one hospital. It is also not uncommon to see a hospital system choosing to enroll its various facilities as separately certified hospitals. Various factors enter into consideration when the governing body of a system makes these decisions.

For example, some governing bodies prefer to enroll various campuses as separate hospita_____lems at one hospital's campus might jeopardize the Medica_____campuses if they were a multi-campus hospital covere_____er agreement. In other cases a governing body may see the_____il services on multiple campuses into one integrated hospita_____iding factor might be the implications for Medicare reimbu_____education, the ease of adding satellite locations, etc.

Governing body policies & procedures ✓

CMS d_____of hospitals to weigh the pertinent factors, the permiss_____siness decisions in their best interest when applying to participate in Medicare. CMS's hospital certification decisions and issuance of a provider agreement and associated CCN follow from these business decisions by a hospital's governing body. But once the "hospital," with whatever component parts, has been certified, that hospital must separately demonstrate its compliance with the CoPs, independent of any other facility. (77 FR 29040, May 16, 2012)

If a hospital system has chosen to have a one body act as the governing body for multiple separately certified hospitals, this does not alter the fact that each hospital must separately demonstrate compliance with the CoPs. Examples of what this means include, but are not limited to, the following:

- Each separately certified hospital must be separately and independently assessed for its compliance with the CoPs, through either State Survey Agency or approved national accreditation program surveys. There is no survey of a hospital "system," since the Medicare agreement and its terms are specific to each certified hospital.

✓ *This*

_____ ning body may wish to adopt identical policies and procedures for _____ a hospital's operations across all of its hospitals within the system. It _____ flexibility to do so, but the documentation of such policies and procedures _____ clear that the governing body has chosen to apply them to specifically named _____ Also, each hospital must be able to present for inspection the system _____ policies and procedures that clearly apply to that hospital. For

_____ that says "XX Healthsystem has adopted the following policy" is **not** acceptable. Instead, the document must be more specific, such as, "XX Healthsystem adopts the following policy and procedure for Hospital A, Hospital B, and Hospital C." Furthermore, the names of each hospital (Hospitals A, B, and C in this example) must correspond to the names used for their provider agreements. For example, if Hospital C is one Medicare-certified hospital with two inpatient campuses, one called "East" and one called "West," it is **not** acceptable for the policy document to state, "XX Healthsystem adopts the following policy and procedure for Hospital A, Hospital B, and Hospital East and Hospital West." It would be acceptable to state, "XX Healthsystem adopts the following policy and procedure for Hospital A, Hospital B, and Hospital C."

It also is **not** acceptable for the policy document to state, "XX Healthsystem adopts the following policy and procedure for Hospital A, Hospital B, and Hospital East, but not Hospital West." Since "Hospitals" East and West refer to separate campuses of Hospital C, which participates in Medicare as one multi-campus hospital, it is not appropriate to refer to these separate campuses of C as "hospitals," since the XX Healthsystem made a business decision to enroll them as parts of one multi-campus hospital in Medicare. CMS recognizes that, depending on the particular policy topic, it may be acceptable to have policies that vary by type of unit/department within a hospital. The system governing body could achieve this as follows: "XX Healthsystem adopts the following policy and procedure requiring that a physician be on-site 24 hours per day, seven days per week on the inpatient campuses of Hospital A and Hospital B, but within Hospital C, only for the East inpatient campus."

- Likewise, the minutes of the governing body must be written in such a manner so that it is clear when the governing body has taken actions that apply to a specific certified hospital.

- Departments of separately certified hospitals with one system governing body may not be operationally integrated. For example, if a system has chosen to operate three separately certified hospitals in relatively close proximity to each other rather than to have them certified as one multi-campus hospital, then each hospital must have its own nursing service. It may not have one integrated nursing service with one Director of Nursing who manages one nursing staff for all three hospitals, including moving them back and forth among the different hospitals. The policies and procedures the governing body has adopted for the nursing service in each hospital may be identical, but the services must operate separately. It is also permissible for the same individual to be the Director of Nursing for each hospital, provided that he or she is able to carry out all of the duties of the position in each hospital.

- Likewise, although the system may choose to operate a quality assessment/performance improvement (QAPI) program at the system level which standardizes indicators measured across system hospitals, each separately-certified hospital in the system must have a QAPI program that is specific to that hospital. This is required not only to demonstrate compliance, but also for the governing body to function effectively, since reviewing QAPI program results only at the system level would make it difficult for the governing body to identify and act upon problems that are localized to one hospital.

For example, the system may choose to use the same quality indicators or the same methodology to track adverse events across all system hospitals. But each certified hospital must have its own QAPI data with respect to these indicators and adverse events. If a system is tracking readmission rates across all of its hospitals, it must be able to separate out the hospital-specific results for the governing body's review and possible action.

The governing body must be functioning effectively and holds the ultimate responsibility for the hospital's compliance not only with the specific standards of the governing body CoP, but also with all of the CoPs. This is the case regardless of whether the regulatory text for a particular condition or standard within a condition specifically mentions responsibilities of the governing body. Substantial, i.e., condition-level, non-compliance with one of the other hospital CoPs may be an indicator that the governing body is not functioning effectively. However, it is not the policy of CMS that condition-level noncompliance with any other CoP automatically results in a condition-level citation of the governing body CoP. Surveyors must consider whether the manner and degree of the other deficiencies provide sufficient evidence to conclude that the governing body is not functioning effectively.

Survey Procedures §482.12

- Verify that the hospital has an organized governing body or has written documentation that identifies the individual or individuals that are responsible for the conduct of the hospital operations.

- If the hospital is part of a hospital system which uses one governing body for several of the hospital's separately certified within the system:

  - Review the governing body minutes to determine if it is clear which actions pertain to which hospitals.

  - Select for review several policy and procedure documents adopted by the system governing body to determine if it is clear that they apply to the hospital being surveyed.

A-0044
(Rev. 37, Issued: 10-17-08; Effective/Implementation Date: 10-17-08)

§482.12(a) Standard: Medical Staff. The governing body must:

Interpretive Guidelines §482.12(a)
The governing body must ensure the medical staff requirements are met.

A-0045
(Rev. 78, Issued: 12-22-11, Effective/Implementation: 12-22-11)

[The governing body must:]

§482.12(a)(1) Determine, in accordance with State law, which categories of practitioners are eligible candidates for appointment to the medical staff;

Interpretive Guidelines §482.12(a)(1)

The governing body must determine, in accordance with State law, which categories of practitioners are eligible for appointment to the medical staff.

The medical staff must, at a minimum, be composed of physicians who are doctors of medicine or doctors of osteopathy. In addition, the medical staff may include other types of health care professionals included in the definition of a physician in Section 1861(r) of the Social Security Act:

- Doctor of medicine or osteopathy;

- Doctor of dental surgery or of dental medicine;

- Doctor of podiatric medicine;

- Doctor of optometry; and

- a Chiropractor.

In all cases, the healthcare professionals included in the definition of a physician must be legally authorized to practice within the State where the hospital is located and providing services within their authorized scope of practice. In addition, in certain instances the Social Security Act and regulations attach further limitations as to the type of hospital services for which a healthcare professional may be considered to be a "physician." See 42 CFR 482.12(c)(1) for more detail on these limitations.

The governing body has the flexibility to determine whether healthcare professionals included in the definition of a physician other than a doctor of medicine or osteopathy are eligible for appointment to the medical staff.

Furthermore, the governing body has the authority, in accordance with State law, to appoint some types of non physician practitioners to the medical staff. Practitioners are defined in Section 1842(b)(18)(C) of the Act as a:

- Physician assistant;

- Nurse practitioner;

- Clinical nurse specialist (Section 1861(aa)(5) of the Act);

- Certified registered nurse anesthetist (Section 1861(bb)(2) of the Act);

- Certified nurse-midwife (Section 1861(gg)(2) of the Act);

- Clinical social worker (Section 1861(hh)(1) of the Act;

- Clinical psychologist (42 CFR 410.71 for purposes of Section 1861(ii) of the Act); or

- Registered dietician or nutrition professional.

Other types of licensed healthcare professionals have a more limited scope of practice and are generally not eligible for hospital medical staff privileges, unless their permitted scope of practice in their State makes them comparable to the above types of practitioners.

Physicians and non physicians may be granted medical staff privileges to practice at the hospital by the governing body for practice activities authorized within their State scope of practice without being appointed a member of the medical staff.

Survey Procedures §482.12(a)(1)

done via credentials report etc

Review documentation and verify that the governing body has determined and stated the categories of physicians and practitioners that are eligible candidates for appointment to the medical staff or medical staff privileges.

A-0046
(Rev. 37, Issued: 10-17-08; Effective/Implementation Date: 10-17-08)

[The governing body must:]

§482.12(a)(2) Appoint members of the medical staff after considering the recommendations of the existing members of the medical staff;

Interpretive Guidelines §482.12(a)(2)

The governing body determines whether to grant, deny, continue, revise, discontinue, limit, or revoke specified privileges, including medical staff membership, for a specific practitioner after considering the recommendation of the medical staff. In all instances, the governing body's determination must be consistent with established hospital medical staff criteria, as well as with State and Federal law and regulations. Only the hospital's governing body has the authority to grant a practitioner privileges to provide care in the hospital.

Survey Procedures §482.12(a)(2)

- Review records of medical staff appointments to determine that the governing body is involved in appointments of medical staff members.

- Confirm that there is evidence that the governing body considered recommendations of the medical staff before making medical staff appointments.

A-0047
(Rev. 37, Issued: 10-17-08; Effective/Implementation Date: 10-17-08)

[The governing body must:]

§482.12(a)(3) Assure that the medical staff has bylaws;

Interpretive Guidelines §482.12(a)(3)

The governing body must assure that the medical staff has bylaws and that those bylaws comply with State and Federal law and the requirements of the Medicare hospital Conditions of Participation.

Survey Procedures §482.12(a)(3)

Verify that the medical staff operates under current bylaws that are in accordance with Federal and State laws and regulations.

A-0048
(Rev. 37, Issued: 10-17-08; Effective/Implementation Date: 10-17-08)

[The governing body must:]

§482.12(a)(4) Approve medical staff bylaws and other medical staff rules and regulations;

Interpretive Guidelines §482.12(a)(4)

The governing body decides whether or not to approve medical staff bylaws submitted by the medical staff. The medical staff bylaws and any revisions must be approved by the governing body before they are considered effective.

Survey Procedures and §482.12(a)(4)

- Verify that the medical staff operates under current bylaws, rules and policies that have been approved by the governing body.

- Verify that any revisions or modifications in the medical staff bylaws, rules and policies have been approved by the medical staff and the governing body, e.g., bylaws are annotated with date of last review and initialed by person(s) responsible.

A-0049
(Rev. 37, Issued: 10-17-08; Effective/Implementation Date: 10-17-08)

[The governing body must:]

§482.12(a)(5) Ensure that the medical staff is accountable to the governing body for the quality of care provided to patients;

Interpretive Guidelines §482.12(a)(5)

The governing body must ensure that the medical staff as a group is accountable to the governing body for the quality of care provided to patients. The governing body is responsible for the conduct of the hospital and this conduct includes the quality of care provided to patients.

All hospital patients must be under the care of a practitioner who meets the criteria of 42 CFR 482.12(c)(1)and who has been granted medical staff privileges, or under the care of a practitioner who is directly under the supervision of a member of the medical staff. All patient care is provided by or in accordance with the orders of a practitioner who has been granted privileges in accordance with the criteria established by the governing body, and who is working within the scope of those granted privileges.

Survey Procedures §482.12(a)(5)

HQRB

- Verify that the governing body is periodically apprised of the medical staff evaluation of patient care services provided hospital wide, at every patient care location of the hospital.

Credentials med affairs

- Verify that any individual providing patient care services is a member of the medical staff or is accountable to a member of the medical staff qualified to evaluate the quality of services provided, and in turn, is responsible to the governing body for the quality of services provided.

A-0050
(Rev. 37, Issued: 10-17-08; Effective/Implementation Date: 10-17-08)

[The governing body must:]
§482.12(a)(6) Ensure the criteria for selection are individual character, competence, training, experience, and judgment; and

Interpretive Guidelines §482.12(a)(6)

The governing body must assure that the medical staff bylaws describe the privileging process to be used by the hospital. The process articulated in the medical staff bylaws, rules, or regulations must include criteria for determining the privileges that may be granted to individual practitioners and a procedure for applying the criteria to individual practitioners that considers:

- Individual character;

- Individual competence;

- Individual training;

- Individual experience; and

- Individual judgment.

The governing body must ensure that the hospital's bylaws governing medical staff membership or the granting of privileges apply equally to all practitioners in each professional category of practitioners.

Survey Procedures §482.12(a)(6)

- Verify that there are written criteria for appointments to the medical staff and granting of medical staff privileges.

- Verify that granting of medical staff membership or privileges, both new and renewal, is based upon an individual practitioner's meeting the medical staff's membership/privileging criteria.

- Verify that, at a minimum, criteria for appointment to the medical staff/granting of medical staff privileges are individual character, competence, training, experience, and judgment.

A-0051
(Rev. 37, Issued: 10-17-08; Effective/Implementation Date: 10-17-08)

[The governing body must:]
§482.12(a)(7) Ensure that under no circumstances is the accordance of staff membership or professional privileges in the hospital dependent solely upon certification, fellowship or membership in a specialty body or society.

Interpretive Guidelines §482.12(a)(7)

In making a judgment on medical staff membership, a hospital may not rely solely on the fact that a MD/DO is, or is not, board-certified. This does not mean that a hospital is prohibited from requiring board certification when considering a MD/DO for medical staff membership, but only that such certification must not be the only factor that the hospital considers. In addition to matters of board certification, a hospital must also consider other criteria such as training, character, competence and judgment. After analysis of all of the criteria, if all criteria are met except for board certification, the hospital has the discretion to decide not to select that individual to the medical staff.

Survey Procedures §482.12(a)(7)

Verify that written criteria for appointment to the medical staff and granting of medical staff privileges are not dependent solely upon certification, fellowship, or membership in a specialty body or society.

A-0052
(Rev.78, Issued: 12-22-11, Effective/Implementation: 12-22-11)

[The governing body must:]

§482.12(a)(8) Ensure that, when telemedicine services are furnished to the hospital's patients through an agreement with a distant-site hospital, the agreement is written and that it specifies that it is the responsibility of the governing body of the distant-site hospital to meet the requirements in paragraphs (a)(1) through (a)(7) of this section with regard to the distant –site hospital's physicians and practitioners providing telemedicine services. The governing body of the hospital whose patients are receiving the telemedicine services may, in accordance with §482.22(a)(3) of this part, grant privileges based on its medical staff recommendations that rely on information provided by the distant-site hospital.

§482.12(a)(9) Ensure that when telemedicine services are furnished to the hospital's patients through an agreement with a distant-site telemedicine entity, the written agreement specifies that the distant-site telemedicine entity is a contractor of services to the hospital and as such, in accordance with §482.12(e), furnishes the contracted services in a manner that permits the hospital to comply with all applicable conditions of participation for the contracted services, including, but not limited to, the requirements in paragraphs (a)(1) through (a)(7) of this section with regard to the distant-site telemedicine entity's physicians and practitioners providing telemedicine services. The governing body of the hospital whose patients are receiving the telemedicine services may, in accordance with §482.22(a)(4) of this part, grant privileges to physicians and practitioners employed by the distant-site telemedicine entity based on such hospital's medical staff recommendations; such staff recommendations may rely on information provided by the distant-site telemedicine entity.

Interpretive Guidelines §482.12(a)(8)&(a)(9)

"Telemedicine," as the term is used in this regulation, means the provision of clinical services to patients by physicians and practitioners from a distance via electronic communications. The distant-site telemedicine physician or practitioner provides clinical services to the hospital patient either simultaneously, as is often the case with teleICU services, for example, or non-simultaneously, as may be the case with many teleradiology services. "Simultaneously" means that the clinical services (for example, assessment of the patient with a clinical plan for treatment, including any medical orders needed) are provided to the patient in "real time" by the telemedicine physician or practitioner, similar to the actions of an on-site physician or practitioner. "Non-simultaneously" means that, while the telemedicine physician or practitioner still provides clinical services to the patient upon a formal request from the patient's attending physician, such services may involve after-the-fact interpretation of diagnostic tests in order to provide an assessment of the patient's condition and do not necessarily require the telemedicine practitioner to directly assess the patient in "real time." This would be similar to the services provided by an on-site radiologist who interprets a patient's x-ray or CT scan and then communicates his or her assessment to the patient's attending physician who then bases his or her diagnosis and treatment plan on these findings. (See 76 FR 25551-25552, May 5, 2011)

A hospital may make arrangements through written agreements either with a distant-site Medicare-participating hospital or a distant-site telemedicine entity for the provision of telemedicine services to the hospital's patients by physicians or practitioners who have been granted privileges by the distant-site hospital or telemedicine entity. For the purposes of this rule, a distant-site telemedicine entity is defined as an entity that -- (1) provides telemedicine services; (2) is not a Medicare-participating hospital; and (3) provides contracted services in a manner that enables a hospital using its services to meet all applicable CoPs, particularly those requirements related to the credentialing and privileging of practitioners providing telemedicine services to the patients of a hospital. A distant-site telemedicine entity would include a distant-site hospital that does not participate in the Medicare program that is providing telemedicine services to a Medicare-participating hospital. (See 76 FR 25553, May 5, 2011)

If a hospital enters into an agreement for telemedicine services with a distant-site hospital or telemedicine entity, the agreement must be in writing. Furthermore, the written agreement must specify, in the case of a:

- Distant-site hospital, that it is the responsibility of the governing body of the distant-site hospital to satisfy the requirements of §§482.12(a)(1) through (a) (7) with respect to those physicians and practitioners at the distant-site hospital who furnish telemedicine services under the agreement. Since the distant-site hospital must also be a Medicare-participating hospital (see §482.22(a)(3)), it has an independent obligation to comply with these governing body requirements concerning medical staff membership and privileging. Nevertheless, the written agreement between the hospital and the distant-site hospital must explicitly include a provision addressing the distant-site hospital's obligation to comply with these provisions.

- Distant-site telemedicine entity, that the written agreement specifies that they entity is a contractor providing telemedicine services to the hospital, and that, in accordance with the requirements governing services under arrangement at §482.12(e), the telemedicine entity furnishes the contracted telemedicine services in a manner that permits the hospital to comply with the Conditions of Participation, including, but not limited to, the governing body requirements of §§482.12(a)(1) through (a) (7) with respect to those physicians and practitioners at the distant-site telemedicine entity who furnish telemedicine services under the agreement.

There are additional requirements for the content of the written agreement, specified at §482.22(a)(3) and §482.22(a)(4) under the medical staff Condition of Participation, which are discussed in the interpretive guidelines for those regulations.

The hospital's governing body must grant privileges to each telemedicine physician or practitioner providing services at the hospital under an agreement with a distant-site hospital or telemedicine entity before they may provide telemedicine services. The scope of the privileges in the hospital must reflect the provision of the services via a telecommunications system. For example, a surgeon at a distant-site hospital may provide telemedicine consultation services at a hospital under agreement, but obviously would not be able to perform surgery by this means and must not have surgical privileges in the hospital as part of his/her telemedicine services privileges. If the surgeon also periodically performed surgery on-site at the hospital, then he or she would have to have privileges to do so, granted in the traditional manner provided for at §482.12(a)(1) through §482.12(a)(7) and §482.22(a)(1) and §482.22(a)(2).

In granting privileges to telemedicine physicians and practitioners, the hospital's governing body has the option of considering hospital medical staff recommendations that rely, in accordance with §482.22(a)(3) and §482.22(a)(4), upon the credentialing and privileging decisions of the distant-site hospital or telemedicine entity. With respect to the decisions of a distant-site telemedicine entity, the regulation states that this streamlined privileging option is available to the hospital for physicians and practitioners "employed" by the distant-site telemedicine entity. We are interpreting "employed" in this context to mean "utilized by" the distant-site telemedicine entity to provide telemedicine services to the hospital under an agreement. Since it is common for telemedicine entities to contract with, rather than employ, the physicians and practitioners it utilizes to provide telemedicine services, it would not be reasonable or consistent with the regulatory intent to interpret "employed" to mean that the physicians or practitioners are employees of the distant-site telemedicine entity.

When the hospital's governing body exercises the option to grant privileges based on its medical staff recommendations that rely upon the privileging decisions of a distant-site telemedicine hospital or entity, it may, but is not required to, maintain a separate file on each telemedicine physician and practitioner, or may instead have a file on all telemedicine physicians and practitioners providing services at the hospital under each agreement with a distant-site hospital or telemedicine entity, indicating which telemedicine services privileges the hospital has granted to each physician and practitioner on the list.

Relying upon the credentialing and privileging decisions of the distant-site hospital or telemedicine entity is an option available to the hospital's governing body, not a requirement. A governing body may, if it so chooses, require its medical staff to independently review the credentials of and make privileging recommendations for each telemedicine physician and practitioner in accordance with §482.22(a)(1) and §482.22(a)(2), rather than permit its medical staff to rely upon the privileging decisions of the distant-site hospital or telemedicine entity. The agreement with the distant-site hospital or telemedicine entity may not require the hospital to rely upon the distant-site organization's privileging decisions.

Survey Procedures §482.12(a)(8)&(a)(9)

- Ask the hospital's leadership whether it uses telemedicine services. If yes:

  - Ask to see a copy of the written agreement(s) with the distant-site hospital(s) or telemedicine entity(ies). Does each agreement include the required elements concerning credentialing and privileging of the telemedicine physicians and practitioners?

  - Does the hospital have documentation indicating that it granted privileges to each telemedicine physician and practitioner?

  - Does the documentation indicate that for each telemedicine physician and practitioner there is a medical staff recommendation, including an indication of whether the medical staff conducted its own review or relied upon the decisions of the distant-site hospital or telemedicine entity?

A-0057
(Rev. 37, Issued: 10-17-08; Effective/Implementation Date: 10-17-08)

§482.12(b) Standard: Chief Executive Officer

The governing body must appoint a chief executive officer who is responsible for managing the hospital.

Interpretive Guidelines §482.12(b)

The Governing Body must appoint one chief executive officer who is responsible for managing the entire hospital.

Survey Procedures §482.12(b)

- Verify that the hospital has only one chief executive officer for the entire hospital.

- Verify that the governing body has appointed the chief executive officer.

- Verify that the chief executive officer is responsible for managing the entire hospital.

A-0063

(Rev. 37, Issued: 10-17-08; Effective/Implementation Date: 10-17-08)

§482.12(c) Standard: Care of Patients

In accordance with hospital policy, the governing body must ensure that the following requirements are met:

A-0064

(Rev. 37, Issued: 10-17-08; Effective/Implementation Date: 10-17-08)

[...the governing body must ensure that the following requirements are met:]

§482.12(c)(1) Every Medicare patient is under the care of:

(i)   A doctor of medicine or osteopathy. (This provision is not to be construed to limit the authority of a doctor of medicine or osteopathy to delegate tasks to other qualified health care personnel to the extent recognized under State law or a State's regulatory mechanism.);

(ii)   A doctor of dental surgery or dental medicine who is legally authorized to practice dentistry by the State and who is acting within the scope of his or her license;

(iii)   A doctor of podiatric medicine, but only with respect to functions which he or she is legally authorized by the State to perform;

(iv)   A doctor of optometry who is legally authorized to practice optometry by the State in which he or she practices;

(v)   A chiropractor who is licensed by the State or legally authorized to perform the services of a chiropractor, but only with respect to treatment by means of manual manipulation of the spine to correct a subluxation demonstrated by x-ray to exist; and

(vi)   A clinical psychologist as defined in §410.71 of this chapter, but only with respect to clinical psychologist services as defined in §410.71 of this chapter and only to the extent permitted by State law.

Interpretive Guidelines §482.12(c)(1)

Practitioners other than doctors of medicine or osteopathy may join the medical staff if the practitioners are appropriately licensed and medical staff membership is in accordance with State law.

Every Medicare or Medicaid patient must be under the care of a licensed practitioner as defined in this requirement.

Survey Procedures §482.12(c)(1)

Verify that Medicare patients are under the care of a licensed practitioner as defined by (c)(1).

A-0065
(Rev. 37, Issued: 10-17-08; Effective/Implementation Date: 10-17-08)

[…the governing body must ensure that the following requirements are met:]

> **§482.12(c)(2) Patients are admitted to the hospital only on the recommendation of a licensed practitioner permitted by the State to admit patients to a hospital.**

Survey Procedures §482.12(c)(2)

- Verify that admitting privileges are limited to those categories of practitioners as allowed by State law.

- Verify that patients are admitted only by those practitioners who are currently licensed and have been granted admitting privileges by the governing body in accordance with State laws and medical staff bylaws.

A-0066
(Rev. 37, Issued: 10-17-08; Effective/Implementation Date: 10-17-08)

[…the governing body must ensure that the following requirements are met:]

> **§482.12(c)(2)** (continued)

> **If a Medicare patient is admitted by a practitioner not specified in paragraph (c)(1) of this section, that patient is under the care of a doctor of medicine or osteopathy.**

Interpretive Guidelines §482.12(c)(2)

CMS hospital regulations do permit licensed practitioners (e.g., nurse practitioners, midwives, etc), as allowed by the State, to admit patients to a hospital, and CMS does not require these practitioners be employed by a MD/DO. However, CMS regulations do require that Medicare and Medicaid patients admitted by these practitioners be under the care of an MD/DO. Evidence of being under the care of an MD/DO must be in the patient's medical record. If a hospital allows these practitioners to admit and care for patients, as allowed by State law, the governing body and medical staff would have to establish policies and bylaws to ensure that the requirements of 42 CFR §482 are met.

Midwife Patients

42 CFR 482.1(a)(5) states, "Section 1905(a) of the Act provides that 'medical assistance' (Medicaid) payments may be applied to various hospital services. Regulations interpreting those provisions specify that hospitals receiving payment under Medicaid must meet the requirements for participation in Medicare (except in the case of medical supervision of nurse midwife services. See §§440.10 and 440.165 of this chapter)."

Midwives are not specified at 42 CFR §482.12(c)(1).

Section 482.1(a)(5), when taken together with this requirement (42 CFR 482.12(c)(2)) means that in a State that permits midwives to admit patients (and in accordance with hospital policy and practitioner privileges), CMS requires ONLY Medicare patients of a midwife be under the care of a doctor of medicine or osteopathy. CMS DOES NOT require Medicaid or other non-Medicare patients admitted by a midwife to be under the care of a doctor of medicine or osteopathy.

Survey Procedures §482.12(c)(2)

If the hospital grants admitting privileges to these practitioners, select Medicare and Medicaid patients (select only Medicare patients for midwives) that are admitted to the hospital by these practitioners. Determine if the patient is/was under the care of an MD/DO.

A-0067
(Rev. 37, Issued: 10-17-08; Effective/Implementation Date: 10-17-08)

[…the governing body must ensure that the following requirements are met:]

§482.12(c)(3) A doctor of medicine or osteopathy is on duty or on call at all times.

Survey Procedures §482.12(c)(3)

- Verify the governing body has established and monitors the enforcement of policies that ensure a doctor of medicine or osteopathy is on duty or on call at all times to provide medical care and onsite supervision when necessary.

- Review the "call" register and documents that assure that a doctor of medicine or osteopathy is on duty or on call at all times.

- Interview nursing staff. How do they know who is on call? Are they able to call the on-call MD/DO and speak with him/her at all times? When appropriate, do on-call MD/DOs come to the hospital to provide needed care.

A-0068
(Rev. 37, Issued: 10-17-08; Effective/Implementation Date: 10-17-08)

[…the governing body must ensure that the following requirements are met:]

§482.12(c)(4) A doctor of medicine or osteopathy is responsible for the care of each Medicare patient with respect to any medical or psychiatric problem that--

    (i) Is present on admission or develops during hospitalization; and

    (ii) Is not specifically within the scope of practice of a doctor of dental surgery, dental medicine, podiatric medicine, or optometry; a chiropractor; or clinical psychologist, as that scope is--

        (A) Defined by the medical staff;

        (B) Permitted by State law; and

        (C) Limited, under paragraph (c)(1)(v) of this section, with respect to chiropractors.

Interpretive Guidelines §482.12(c)(4)

CMS hospital regulations do permit licensed practitioners (i.e., doctors of dental surgery, dental medicine, podiatric medicine, or optometry; chiropractors; or clinical psychologists), as allowed by the State, to admit patients to a hospital. However, CMS does require that Medicare and Medicaid patients who are admitted by a doctor of dental surgery, dental medicine, podiatric medicine, or optometry; a chiropractor; or clinical psychologist be under the care of a MD/DO with respect to any medical or psychiatric problem that is present on admission or develops during hospitalization that is outside the scope of practice of the admitting practitioner. If a hospital allows a doctor of dental surgery, dental medicine, podiatric medicine, or optometry, a chiropractor or a clinical psychologist to admit and care for patients, as allowed by State law, the governing body and medical staff must establish policies and bylaws to ensure that the requirements of 42 CFR §482 are met. As applicable, the patient's medical record must demonstrate MD/DO responsibility/care.

Survey Procedures §482.12(c)(4)

- Verify that an assigned doctor of medicine or osteopathy is responsible for and is monitoring the care of each Medicare or Medicaid patient with respect to all medical or psychiatric problems during the hospitalization.

- If non-MD/DOs admit patients, verify that every Medicare/Medicaid patient is being monitored by an MD/DO who is responsible for any medical or psychiatric problem outside the scope of practice of the admitting practitioners.

A-0073
(Rev. 37, Issued: 10-17-08; Effective/Implementation Date: 10-17-08)

§482.12(d) Standard: Institutional Plan and Budget

The institution must have an overall institutional plan that meets the following conditions:

(1)   The plan must include an annual operating budget that is prepared according to generally accepted accounting principles.

(2)   The budget must include all anticipated income and expenses. This provision does not require that the budget identify item by item the components of each anticipated income or expense.

(3)   The plan must provide for capital expenditures for at least a 3-year period, including the year in which the operating budget specified in paragraph (d)(2) of this section is applicable.

(4)   The plan must include and identify in detail the objective of, and the anticipated sources of financing for, each anticipated capital expenditure in excess of $600,000 (or a lesser amount that is established, in accordance with section 1122(g)(1) of the Act, by the State in which the hospital is located) that relates to any of the following:

    (i)   **Acquisition of land;**

    (ii)   **Improvement of land, buildings, and equipment; or**

    (iii)   **The replacement, modernization, and expansion of buildings and equipment.**

Survey Procedures §482.12(d)

Verify that an institutional plan and budget exist, includes items 1-4, and complies with all items in this standard. Do not review the specifics or format in the institutional plan or the budget.

A-0074
(Rev. 37, Issued: 10-17-08; Effective/Implementation Date: 10-17-08)

§482.12(d)(5) The plan must be submitted for review to the planning agency designated in accordance with section 1122(b) of the Act, or if an agency is not designated, to the appropriate health planning agency in the State. (See Part 100 of this title.)

Survey Procedures §482.12(d)(5)

Determine that the hospital's plan for capital expenditures has been submitted to the planning agency designated to review capital expenditures. In certain cases facilities used by HMO and CMP patients are exempt from the review process.

A-0075
(Rev. 37, Issued: 10-17-08; Effective/Implementation Date: 10-17-08)

§482.12(d)(5) (Continued)

A capital expenditure is not subject to section 1122 review if 75 percent of the health care facility's patients who are expected to use the service for which the capital expenditure is made are individuals enrolled in a health maintenance organization (HMO) or competitive medical plan (CMP) that meets the requirements of section 1876(b) of the Act, and if the Department determines that the capital expenditure is for services and facilities that are needed by the HMO or CMP in order to operate efficiently and economically and that are not otherwise readily accessible to the HMO or CMP because--

  (i) The facilities do not provide common services at the same site;

(ii) The facilities are not available under a contract of reasonable duration;

(iii) Full and equal medical staff privileges in the facilities are not available;

(iv) Arrangements with these facilities are not administratively feasible; or

(v) The purchase of these services is more costly than if the HMO or CMP provided the services directly.

A-0076
(Rev. 37, Issued: 10-17-08; Effective/Implementation Date: 10-17-08)

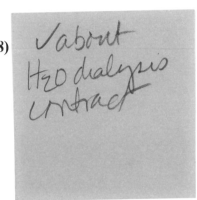

§482.12(d)(6) The plan must be reviewed and updated annually

Survey Procedures §482.12(d)(6)

Verify that the plan and budget are reviewed and updated annually.

A-0077
(Rev. 37, Issued: 10-17-08; Effective/Implementation Date: 10-17-08)

§482.12(d)(7) The plan must be prepared--

(i) Under the direction of the governing body; and

(ii) By a committee consisting of representatives of the governing body, the administrative staff, and the medical staff of the institution.

Survey Procedures §482.12(d)(7)

Verify that the governing body, administrative staff, and medical staff have participated in the development of the institutional plan and budget.

A-0083
(Rev. 37, Issued: 10-17-08; Effective/Implementation Date: 10-17-08)

§482.12(e) Standard: Contracted Services

The governing body must be responsible for services furnished in the hospital whether or not they are furnished under contracts. The governing body must ensure that a contractor of services (including one for shared services and joint ventures) furnishes services that permit the hospital to comply with all applicable conditions of participation and standards for the contracted services.

Interpretive Guidelines §482.12(e)

The governing body has the responsibility for assuring that hospital services are provided in compliance with the Medicare Conditions of participation and according to acceptable standards of practice, irrespective of whether the services are provided directly by hospital employees or indirectly by contract. The governing body must take actions through the hospital's QAPI program to: assess the services furnished directly by hospital staff and those services provided under contract, identify quality and performance problems, implement appropriate corrective or improvement activities, and to ensure the monitoring and sustainability of those corrective or improvement activities. See §482.21 QAPI.

Survey Procedures §482.12(e)

Ascertain that all contractor services provided in the hospital are in compliance with the Conditions of Participation for hospitals.

A-0084

(Rev. 37, Issued: 10-17-08; Effective/Implementation Date: 10-17-08)

§482.12(e)(1) The governing body must ensure that the services performed under a contract are provided in a safe and effective manner.

Interpretive Guidelines §482.12(e)(1)

Indirect arrangements may take into consideration services provided through formal contracts, joint ventures, informal agreements, shared services, or lease arrangements. The patient care services, and all other services, provided under contract are subject to the same hospital-wide quality assessment and performance improvement (QAPI) evaluation as other services provided directly by the hospital.

Survey Procedures §482.12(e)(1)

- Determine if the hospital has a mechanism to evaluate the quality of each contracted service and ensures that each contracted service is provided in a safe and effective manner.

- Review the QAPI plan to ensure that every contracted service is evaluated.

A-0085

§482.12(e)(2) The hospital must maintain a list of all contracted services, including the scope and nature of the services provided.

Survey Procedures §482.12(e)(2)

Review the list of contracted services and verify that there is a delineation of contractor responsibility.

A-0091
(Rev. 37, Issued: 10-17-08; Effective/Implementation Date: 10-17-08)

§482.12(f) Standard: Emergency Services

Interpretive Guidelines §482.12(f)

The hospital must ensure the emergency services requirements are met.

A-0092
(Rev. 37, Issued: 10-17-08; Effective/Implementation Date: 10-17-08)

§482.12(f)(1) If emergency services are provided at the hospital, the hospital must comply with the requirements of §482.55.

A-0093
(Rev. 37, Issued: 10-17-08; Effective/Implementation Date: 10-17-08)

§482.12(f)(2) If emergency services are not provided at the hospital, the governing body must assure that the medical staff has written policies and procedures for appraisal of emergencies, initial treatment, and referral when appropriate.

Interpretive Guidelines §482.12(f)(2)

This requirement applies hospital-wide (all on-campus and off-campus locations) to hospitals that do not provide emergency services.

Hospitals without emergency departments must have appropriate policies and procedures in place for addressing individuals' emergency care needs 24 hours per day and 7 days per week, including the following:

- **Appraisal of Persons with Emergencies:** A hospital must have medical staff policies and procedures for conducting appraisals of persons with emergencies. The policies and procedures must ensure that:

  o As required by 42 CFR 482.23(b), an RN is immediately available, as needed, to provide bedside care to any patient and that,

  o Among such RN(s) who are immediately available at all times, there must be an RN(s) who is/are qualified, through a combination of education, licensure, and training, to conduct an assessment that enables them to recognize the fact that a person has a need for emergency care.

  The policies and procedures for appraisal should provide that the MD/DO (on-site or on-call) would directly provide appraisals of emergencies or provide medical direction of on-site staff conducting appraisals.

- **Initial Treatment**: A hospital must have medical staff policies and procedures for providing the initial treatment needed by persons with emergency conditions. Among the RN(s) who must be available at all times in a hospital as required by 42 CFR 482.23(b), there must be RN(s) who are qualified, through a combination of education, licensure, and training, to provide initial treatment to a person experiencing a medical emergency. The on-site or on-call physician could provide initial treatment directly or provide medical oversight and direction to other staff. This requirement, taken together with other hospital regulatory requirements, suggests that a prudent hospital would evaluate the patient population the hospital routinely cares for in order to anticipate potential emergency care scenarios and develop the policies, procedures, and staffing that would enable it to provide safe and adequate initial treatment of an emergency.

- **Referral when Appropriate:** A hospital must have medical staff policies and procedures to address situations in which a person's emergency needs may exceed the hospital's capabilities. The policies and procedures should be designed to enable hospital staff members who respond to emergencies to: (a) recognize when a person requires a referral or transfer, and (b) assure appropriate handling of the transfer. This includes arrangement for appropriate transport of the patient. Further, in accordance with the Discharge Planning CoP at 42 CFR 482.43(d), the hospital must transfer patients to appropriate facilities, i.e., those with the appropriate capabilities to handle the patient's condition. The regulation also requires that necessary medical information be sent along with the patient being transferred. This enables the receiving hospital to treat the medical emergency more efficiently.

- **Patient Transportation and Emergency Medical Services (EMS)**

A hospital may arrange transportation of the referred patient by several methods, including using the hospital's own ambulance service, the receiving hospital's ambulance service, a contracted ambulance service, or, in extraordinary circumstances, alerting EMS via calling 9-1-1. There is no specific Medicare prohibition on a hospital with or without an emergency department calling 9-1-1 in order to obtain transport of a patient to another hospital. Use of 9-1-1 to obtain transport does not, however, relieve the hospital of its obligation to arrange for the patient's transfer to an appropriate facility and to provide the necessary medical information along with the patient.

A hospital policy or practice that relies on calling 9-1-1 in order for EMS to substitute its emergency response capabilities for those the hospital is required to maintain, as described above, is not consistent with the Medicare CoPs. For example, a hospital may not rely upon 9-1-1 to provide appraisal and initial treatment of medical emergencies that occur at the hospital. Such policy or practice should be considered as condition-level non-compliance with the applicable CoP, 42 CFR 482.55 or 42 CFR 482.12(f).

Survey Procedures §482.12(f)(2)

- Verify that the medical staff has adopted written policies and procedures for the management of medical emergencies.
- Review emergency care policies and procedures. Are they consistent with the expectations articulated above for appraisal, initial treatment, and referral? Do they address emergency procedures for all on-campus and off-campus locations?

- Interview hospital staff at various locations. Can they state their duties and what they are to do if an individual seeks or needs emergency care at their location?

A-0094
(Rev. 37, Issued: 10-17-08; Effective/Implementation Date: 10-17-08)

§482.12(f)(3) If emergency services are provided at the hospital but are not provided at one or more off-campus departments of the hospital, the governing body of the hospital must assure that the medical staff has written policies and procedures in effect with respect to the off-campus department(s) for appraisal of emergencies and referral when appropriate.
Interpretive Guidelines §482.12(f)(3)

This requirement applies to any off-campus hospital department/location that does not qualify as a dedicated emergency department in accordance with 42 CFR 489.24(b) and is part of a hospital that provides emergency services. Such departments/locations must have and must implement medical staff policies and procedures for the appraisal of emergencies and referral when appropriate.

- **Appraisal of Persons with Emergencies:** A hospital must have medical staff policies and procedures for conducting appraisals of persons with emergencies at off-campus departments/locations that are not dedicated emergency departments. The policies and procedures must ensure that clinical personnel -- who are qualified, through a combination of education, licensure, and training, to conduct an assessment that enables them to recognize the fact that a person has a need for emergency care -- are available during all hours of operation at the off-campus department/location.

- **Referral when Appropriate:** A hospital must have medical staff policies and procedures to address situations in which a person's emergency needs may exceed the capabilities of the off-campus departments/locations that are not dedicated emergency departments. The policies and procedures should be designed to enable staff members at such locations to: (a) recognize when a person requires a referral or transfer, and (b) assure appropriate handling of the transfer. This includes arrangement for appropriate transport of the patient along with the transfer of the patient's medical information so that the receiving hospital may treat the medical emergency more efficiently.

- **Initial Treatment:** Although there is no specific regulatory requirement for such off-campus departments or locations to provide initial treatment of emergencies, nevertheless they are expected to provide treatment and stabilization consistent with the complexity of services, the type and qualifications of clinical staff, and the resources available at that location. This expectation is based on the requirements of the Outpatient Services CoP that hospital outpatient services meet the needs of the patients in accordance with acceptable standards of practice, outpatient services must be appropriately organized and integrated with inpatient services, and outpatient services must have appropriate professional and nonprofessional personnel available. For example, an off-campus cardiac rehabilitation clinic would be expected to have the appropriate qualified staff, equipment (such as a crash cart), and policies and procedures in place to appropriately provide appraisal, initial interventions, and referral of a patient who experiences a cardiac emergency.

- A hospital policy or practice that relies on calling 9-1-1 in order for EMS to substitute its emergency response capabilities for those the hospital is required to maintain at its off-campus departments/locations, as described above, is not consistent with the Medicare CoPs. However, given the more limited emergency capabilities that may be present in some off-campus departments or locations, calling 9-1-1 to respond to an emergency might be appropriate.

See the hospital emergency services CoP (42 CFR 482.55) for the emergency requirements for the hospital's locations that provide emergency services.

Survey Procedures §482.12(f)(3)

- Review emergency care policies and procedures. Determine if they address emergency procedures for all off-campus locations.

- Interview off-campus hospital department staff. Can they state their duties and what they are to do if an individual seeks emergency care?

A-0115

(Rev. 37, Issued: 10-17-08; Effective/Implementation Date: 10-17-08)

§482.13 Condition of Participation: Patient's Rights

A hospital must protect and promote each patient's rights.

Interpretive Guidelines §482.13

These requirements apply to all Medicare or Medicaid participating hospitals including short-term, acute care, surgical, specialty, psychiatric, rehabilitation, long-term, children's and cancer, whether or not they are accredited. This rule does not apply to critical access hospitals. (See Social Security Act (the Act) §1861(e).)

These requirements, as well as the other Conditions of Participation in 42 CFR 482, apply to all parts and locations (outpatient services, provider-based entities, inpatient services) of the Medicare participating hospital.

Survey Procedures §482.13

Survey of the Patients' Rights Condition of Participation (CoP) should be coordinated by one surveyor. However, each surveyor, as he/she conducts his/her survey assignments, should assess the hospital's compliance with the Patients' Rights CoP.

A-0116
(Rev. 37, Issued: 10-17-08; Effective/Implementation Date: 10-17-08)

§482.13(a) Standard: Notice of Rights

Interpretive Guidelines §482.13(a)

The hospital must ensure the notice of rights requirements are met.

A-0117
(Rev. 75, Issued: 12-02-11, Effective: 12-02-11, Implementation: 12-02-11)

§482.13(a)(1) A hospital must inform each patient, or when appropriate, the patient's representative (as allowed under State law), of the patient's rights, in advance of furnishing or discontinuing patient care whenever possible.

Interpretive Guidelines §482.13(a)(1)

The hospital must inform each patient, or when appropriate, the patient's representative as allowed by State law, of the patient's rights. Whenever possible, this notice must be provided before providing or stopping care. All patients, inpatient or outpatient, must be informed of their rights as hospital patients. The patient's rights include all of those discussed in this condition, as well as any other rights for which notice is required under State or Federal law or regulations for hospital patients. (See 42 CFR 482.11.) The patient's rights should be provided and explained in a language or manner that the patient (or the patient's representative) can understand. This is consistent with the guidance related to Title VI of the Civil Rights Act of 1964 issued by the Department of Health and Human Services - "Guidance to Federal Financial Assistance Recipients Regarding Title VI Prohibition Against National Origin Discrimination Affecting Limited English Proficient Persons" (August 8, 2003, 68 FR 47311). In accordance with §482.11, hospitals are expected to comply with Title VI and may use this guidance to assist it in ensuring patient's rights information is provided in a language and manner that the patient understands. Surveyors do not assess compliance with these requirements on limited English proficiency, but may refer concerns about possible noncompliance to the Office for Civil Rights in the applicable Department of Health and Human Services Regional Office.

Hospitals are expected to take reasonable steps to determine the patient's wishes concerning designation of a representative. Unless prohibited by applicable State law:

* When a patient who is not incapacitated has designated, either orally to hospital staff or in writing, another individual to be his/her representative, the hospital must provide the designated individual with the required notice of patients' rights in addition to the patient. The explicit designation of a representative takes precedence over any non-designated relationship and continues throughout the patient's inpatient stay or outpatient visit, unless expressly withdrawn, either orally or in writing, by the patient.

* In the case of a patient who is incapacitated, when an individual presents the hospital with an advance directive, medical power of attorney or similar document executed by the patient and designating an individual to make medical decisions for the patient when incapacitated, then the hospital must, when presented with the document, provide the required notice of its policies to the designated representative. The

explicit designation of a representative takes precedence over any non-designated relationship and continues throughout the patient's inpatient stay or outpatient visit, unless the patient ceases to be incapacitated and expressly withdraws the designation, either orally or in writing.

- When a patient is incapacitated or otherwise unable to communicate his or her wishes, there is no written advance directive on file or presented, and an individual asserts that he or she is the patient's spouse, domestic partner (whether or not formally established and including a same-sex domestic partner), parent (including someone who has stood in loco parentis for the patient who is a minor child), or other family member and thus is the patient's representative, the hospital is expected to accept this assertion, without demanding supporting documentation, and provide the required notice to the individual, unless:

  - More than one individual claims to be the patient's representative. In such cases, it would be appropriate for the hospital to ask each individual for documentation supporting his/her claim to be the patient's representative. The hospital should make its determination of who is the patient's representative based upon the hospital's determination of who the patient would most want to make decisions on his/her behalf. Examples of documentation a hospital might consider could include, but are not limited to, the following: proof of a legally recognized marriage, domestic partnership, or civil union; proof of a joint household; proof of shared or co-mingled finances; and any other documentation the hospital considers evidence of a special relationship that indicates familiarity with the patient's preferences concerning medical treatment;

  - Treating the individual as the patient's representative without requesting supporting documentation would result in the hospital violating State law. State laws, including State regulations, may specify a procedure for determining who may be considered to be the incapacitated patient's representative, and may specify when documentation is or is not required; or

  - The hospital has reasonable cause to believe that the individual is falsely claiming to be the patient's spouse, domestic partner, parent or other family member.

Hospitals are expected to adopt policies and procedures that facilitate expeditious and non-discriminatory resolution of disputes about whether an individual is the patient's representative, given the critical role of the representative in exercising the patient's rights.

A refusal by the hospital of an individual's request to be treated as the patient's representative, based on one of the above-specified familial relationships, must be documented in the patient's medical record, along with the specific basis for the refusal.

In addition, according to the regulation at 42 CFR 489.27(a), (which cross references the regulation at 42 CFR 405.1205), each Medicare beneficiary who is an inpatient (or his/her representative) must be provided the standardized notice, "An Important Message from Medicare" (IM), within 2 days of admission. Medicare beneficiaries who have not been admitted (e.g., patients in observation status or receiving other care on an outpatient basis) are not required to receive the IM. The IM is a standardized, OMB-approved form and cannot be altered from its original format. The IM is to be signed and dated by the patient to acknowledge receipt. See Exhibit 16 for a copy of the IM. Furthermore, 42 CFR 405.1205(c) requires that hospitals present a copy of the signed IM in advance of the patient's discharge, but not more than two calendar days before the patient's discharge. In the case of short inpatient stays, however, where initial delivery of the IM is within 2 calendar days of the discharge, the second delivery of the IM is not required.

The hospital must establish and implement policies and procedures that effectively ensure that patients and/or their representatives have the information necessary to exercise their rights.

Survey Procedures §482.13(a)(1)

- Determine the hospital's policy for notifying all patients of their rights, both inpatient and outpatient;

- Determine that the hospital's policy provides for determining when a patient has a representative and who that representative is, consistent with this guidance and State law.

- Determine that the information provided to the patients by the hospital complies with Federal and State law;

- Review records and interview staff to examine how the hospital communicates information about their rights to diverse patients, including individuals who need assistive devices or translation services. Does the hospital have alternative means, such as written materials, signs, or interpreters (when necessary), to communicate patients' rights?

- Review records and interview staff and patients or patients' representatives (as appropriate) to examine how the hospital determines whether the patient has a representative, who that representative is, and whether notice of patients' rights is provided as required to patients' representatives.

- Ask patients to tell you what the hospital has told them about their rights;

- Does staff know what steps to take to inform a patient about their patients' rights, including those patients' with special communication needs?; and

- Review a sample of inpatient medical records for Medicare beneficiaries, to determine whether the records contain a signed and dated IM provided within 2 days of the admission of the patient. For patients whose discharge occurred more than 2 days after the initial IM notice was issued, determine whether the hospital provided another copy of the IM to the patient prior to discharge in a timely manner.

A-0118
(Rev. 37, Issued: 10-17-08; Effective/Implementation Date: 10-17-08)

§482.13(a)(2) The hospital must establish a process for prompt resolution of patient grievances and must inform each patient whom to contact to file a grievance.

Interpretive guidelines §482.13(a)(2)

The patient should have reasonable expectations of care and services and the facility should address those expectations in a timely, reasonable, and consistent manner. Although 482.13(a)(2)(ii) and (iii) address documentation of facility time frames for a response to a grievance, the expectation is that the facility will have a process to comply with a relatively minor request in a more timely manner than a written response. For example, a change in bedding, housekeeping of a room, and serving preferred food and beverage may be made relatively quickly and would not usually be considered a "grievance" and therefore would not require a written response.

The hospital must inform the patient and/or the patient's representative of the internal grievance process, including whom to contact to file a grievance (complaint). As part of its notification of patient rights, the hospital must provide the patient or the patient's representative a phone number and address for lodging a grievance with the State agency. The hospital must inform the patient that he/she may lodge a grievance with the State agency (the State agency that has licensure survey responsibility for the hospital) directly, regardless of whether he/she has first used the hospital's grievance process.

A "**patient grievance**" is a formal or informal written or verbal complaint that is made to the hospital by a patient, or the patient's representative, regarding the patient's care (when the complaint is not resolved at the time of the complaint by staff present), abuse or neglect, issues related to the hospital's compliance with the CMS Hospital Conditions of Participation (CoPs), or a Medicare beneficiary billing complaint related to rights and limitations provided by 42 CFR 489.

- "Staff present" includes any hospital staff present at the time of the complaint or who can quickly be at the patient's location (i.e., nursing, administration, nursing supervisors, patient advocates, etc.) to resolve the patient's complaint.

- If a patient care complaint cannot be resolved at the time of the complaint by staff present, is postponed for later resolution, is referred to other staff for later resolution, requires investigation, and/or requires further actions for resolution, then the complaint is a grievance for the purposes of these requirements. A complaint is considered resolved when the patient is satisfied with the actions taken on their behalf.

- Billing issues are not usually considered grievances for the purposes of these requirements. However, a Medicare beneficiary billing complaint related to rights and limitations provided by 42 CFR 489 is considered a grievance.

- A written complaint is always considered a grievance. This includes written complaints from an inpatient, an outpatient, a released/discharged patient, or a patient's representative regarding the patient care provided, abuse or neglect, or the hospital's compliance with CoPs. For the purposes of this requirement, an email or fax is considered "written."

- Information obtained from patient satisfaction surveys usually does not meet the definition of a grievance. If an identified patient writes or attaches a written complaint on the survey and requests resolution, then the complaint meets the definition of a grievance. If an identified patient writes or attaches a complaint to the survey but has not requested resolution, the hospital must treat this as a grievance if the hospital would usually treat such a complaint as a grievance.

- Patient complaints that are considered grievances also include situations where a patient or a patient's representative telephones the hospital with a complaint regarding the patient's care or with an allegation of abuse or neglect, or failure of the hospital to comply with one or more CoPs, or other CMS requirements. Those post-hospital verbal communications regarding patient care that would routinely have been handled by staff present if the communication had occurred during the stay/visit are not required to be defined as a grievance.

- All verbal or written complaints regarding abuse, neglect, patient harm, or hospital compliance with CMS requirements are considered grievances for the purposes of these requirements.

- Whenever the patient or the patient's representative requests that his or her complaint be handled as a formal complaint or grievance or when the patient requests a response from the hospital, the complaint is considered a grievance and all the requirements apply.

- Data collected regarding patient grievances, as well as other complaints that are not defined as grievances (as determined by the hospital), must be incorporated in the hospital's Quality Assessment and Performance Improvement (QAPI) Program.

Survey Procedures §482.13(a)(2)

- Review the hospital's policies and procedures to assure that its grievance process encourages all personnel to alert appropriate staff concerning any patient grievance. Does the hospital adhere to its policy/procedure established for grievances?

- Interview patients or the patient's legal representative to determine if they know how to file a complaint (grievance) and who to contact if they have a complaint (grievance).

- Is the hospital following its grievance policies and procedures?

- Does the hospital's process assure that grievances involving situations or practices that place the patient in immediate danger are resolved in a timely manner?

- Does the patient or the patient's representative know that he/she has the right to file a complaint with the State agency as well as or instead of utilizing the hospital's grievance process?

- Has the hospital provided the telephone number for the State agency to all patients/patient representatives?

- Are beneficiaries aware of their right to seek review by the QIO for quality of care issues, coverage decisions, and to appeal a premature discharge?

A-0119
(Rev. 37, Issued: 10-17-08; Effective/Implementation Date: 10-17-08)

§482.13(a)(2) (Continued)

[The hospital must establish a process for prompt resolution of patient grievances and must inform each patient whom to contact to file a grievance.] The hospital's governing body must approve and be responsible for the effective operation of the grievance process, and must review and resolve grievances, unless it delegates the responsibility in writing to a grievance committee.

Interpretive guidelines §482.13(a)(2)

The hospital's grievance process must be approved by the governing body. The hospital's governing body is responsible for the effective operation of the grievance process. This includes the hospital's compliance with all of the CMS grievance process requirements. The hospital's governing body must review and resolve grievances, unless it delegates this responsibility in writing to a grievance committee. A committee is more than one person. The committee membership should have adequate numbers of qualified members to review and resolve the grievances the hospital receives (this includes providing written responses) in a manner that complies with the CMS grievance process requirements.

Survey Procedures §482.13(a)(2)

- Determine if the hospital's governing body approved the grievance process.

- Is the governing body responsible for the operation of the grievance process, or has the governing body delegated the responsibility in writing to a grievance committee?

- Determine how effectively the grievance process works. Are patient's or the patient representative's concerns addressed in a timely manner? Are patients informed of any resolution to their grievances? Does the hospital apply what it learns from the grievance as part of its continuous quality improvement activities?

- Is the grievance process reviewed and analyzed through the hospital's QAPI process or some other mechanisms that provides oversight of the grievance process?

A-0120
(Rev. 37, Issued: 10-17-08; Effective/Implementation Date: 10-17-08)

§482.13(a)(2) (Continued)

[The hospital must establish a process for prompt resolution of patient grievances and must inform each patient whom to contact to file a grievance. The hospital's governing body must approve and be responsible for the effective operation of the grievance process, and must review and resolve grievances, unless it delegates the responsibility in writing to a grievance committee.] The grievance process must include a mechanism for timely referral of patient concerns regarding quality of care or premature discharge to the appropriate Utilization and Quality Control Quality Improvement Organization. At a minimum:

Interpretive Guidelines §482.13(a)(2)

Quality Improvement Organizations (QIOs) are CMS contractors charged with reviewing the appropriateness and quality of care rendered to Medicare beneficiaries in the hospital setting. The QIOs are also tasked with reviewing utilization decisions. Part of this duty includes reviewing discontinuation of stay determinations based upon a beneficiary's request. The regulations state the functions of the QIOs in order to make Medicare beneficiaries aware of the fact that if they have a **complaint regarding quality of care**, disagree with a **coverage decision**, or they wish to appeal a premature discharge, they may contact the QIO to lodge a complaint. The hospital is required to have procedures for referring Medicare beneficiary concerns to the QIOs; additionally, CMS expects coordination between the grievance process and existing grievance referral procedures so that beneficiary complaints are handled timely and referred to the QIO at the beneficiary's request.

This regulation requires coordination between the hospital's existing mechanisms for utilization review notice and referral to QIOs for Medicare beneficiary concerns (See 42 CFR Part 489.27). This requirement does not mandate that the hospital automatically refer each Medicare beneficiary's grievance to the QIO; however, the hospital must inform all beneficiaries of this right, and comply with his or her request if the beneficiary asks for QIO review.

Medicare patients have the right to appeal a premature discharge (see Interpretive Guidelines for 42 CFR 482.13(a)). Pursuant to 42 CFR 412.42(c)(3), a hospital must provide a hospital-issued notice of non-coverage (HINN) to any fee-for-service beneficiary that expresses dissatisfaction with an impending hospital discharge. Medicare Advantage (MA) organizations are required to provide enrollees with a notice of non-coverage, known as the Notice of Discharge and Medicare Appeal Rights (NODMAR), only when a beneficiary disagrees with the discharge decision or when the MA organization (or hospital, if the MA organization has delegated to it the authority to make the discharge decision) is not discharging the enrollee, but no longer intends to cover the inpatient stay.

Survey Procedures §482.13(a)(2)

- Review patient discharge materials. Is the hospital in compliance with 42 CFR §489.27?

- Does the hospital grievance process include a mechanism for timely referral of Medicare patient concerns to the QIO? What time frames are established?

  - Interview Medicare patients. Are they aware of their right to appeal premature discharge?

A-0121
(Rev. 37, Issued: 10-17-08; Effective/Implementation Date: 10-17-08)

[At a minimum:]

§482.13(a)(2)(i) The hospital must establish a clearly explained procedure for the submission of a patient's written or verbal grievance to the hospital.

Interpretive Guidelines §482.13(a)(2)(i)

The hospital's procedure for a patient or the patient's representative to submit written or verbal grievances must be clearly explained. The patient or patient's representative should be able to clearly understand the procedure.

Survey Procedures §482.13(a)(2)(i)

- Review the information provided to patients that explains the hospital's grievance procedures. Does it clearly explain how the patient is to submit either a verbal or written grievance?

- Interview patients or patient representatives. Does the patient, or (if he/she is incapacitated) his/her representative, know about the grievance process and how to submit a grievance?

A-0122
(Rev. 37, Issued: 10-17-08; Effective/Implementation Date: 10-17-08)

[At a minimum:]

§482.13(a)(2)(ii) The grievance process must specify time frames for review of the grievance and the provision of a response.

Interpretive Guidelines §482.13(a)(2)(ii)

The hospital must review, investigate, and resolve each patient's grievance within a reasonable time frame. For example, grievances about situations that endanger the patient, such as neglect or abuse, should be reviewed immediately, given the seriousness of the allegations and the potential for harm to the patient(s). However, regardless of the nature of the grievance, the hospital should make sure that it is responding to the substance of each grievance while identifying, investigating, and resolving any deeper, systemic problems indicated by the grievance.

Document when a grievance is so complicated that it may require an extensive investigation. We recognize that staff scheduling as well as fluctuations in the numbers and complexity of grievances can affect the timeframes for the resolution of a grievance and the provision of a written response. On average, a time frame of 7 days for the provision of the response would be considered appropriate. We do not require that every grievance be resolved during the specified timeframe although most should be resolved. 42 CFR 482.13(a)(2)(iii) specifies information the hospital must include in their response.

If the grievance will not be resolved, or if the investigation is not or will not be completed within 7 days, the hospital should inform the patient or the patient's representative that the hospital is still working to resolve the grievance and that the hospital will follow-up with a written response within a stated number of days in accordance with the hospital's grievance policy. The hospital must attempt to resolve all grievances as soon as possible.

Survey Procedures §482.13(a)(2)(ii)

What time frames are established to review and respond to patient grievances? Are these time frames clearly explained in the information provided to the patient that explains the hospital's grievance process? On average, does the hospital provide a written response to most of its grievances within the timeframe specified in its policy?

A-0123
(Rev. 37, Issued: 10-17-08; Effective/Implementation Date: 10-17-08)

[At a minimum:]

§482.13(a)(2)(iii) In its resolution of the grievance, the hospital must provide the patient with written notice of its decision that contains the name of the hospital contact person, the steps taken on behalf of the patient to investigate the grievance, the results of the grievance process, and the date of completion.

Interpretive Guidelines §482.13(a)(2)(iii)

The written notice of the hospital's determination regarding the grievance must be communicated to the patient or the patient's representative in a language and manner the patient or the patient's legal representative understands.

The hospital may use additional tools to resolve a grievance, such as meeting with the patient and his family. The regulatory requirements for the grievance process are minimum standards, and do not inhibit the use of additional effective approaches in handling patient grievances. However, in all cases the hospital must provide a written notice (response) to each patient's grievance(s). The written response must contain the elements listed in this requirement.

When a patient communicates a grievance to the hospital via email the hospital may provide its response via email pursuant to hospital policy. (Some hospitals have policies against communicating to patients over email.) If the patient requests a response via email, the hospital may respond via email. When the email response contains the information stated in this requirement, the email meets the requirement for a written response. The hospital must maintain evidence of its compliance with these requirements.

A grievance is considered resolved when the patient is satisfied with the actions taken on their behalf.

There may be situations where the hospital has taken appropriate and reasonable actions on the patient's behalf in order to resolve the patient's grievance and the patient or the patient's representative remains unsatisfied with the hospital's actions. In these situations, the hospital may consider the grievance closed for the purposes of these requirements. The hospital must maintain documentation of its efforts and demonstrate compliance with CMS requirements.

In its written response, the hospital is not required to include statements that could be used in a legal action against the hospital, but the hospital must provide adequate information to address each item stated in this requirement. The hospital is not required to provide an exhaustive explanation of every action the hospital has taken to investigate the grievance, resolve the grievance, or other actions taken by the hospital.

Survey Procedures §482.13(a)(2)(iii)

Review the hospital's copies of written notices (responses) to patients. Are all patients provided a written notice? Do the notices comply with the requirements?

A-0129
(Rev. 37, Issued: 10-17-08; Effective/Implementation Date: 10-17-08)

§482.13(b) Standard: Exercise of Rights

Interpretive Guidelines §482.13(b)

The hospital must ensure that the exercise of patients' rights requirements are met.

A-0130
(Rev. 75, Issued: 12-02-11, Effective: 12-02-11, Implementation: 12-02-11)

§482.13(b)(1) The patient has the right to participate in the development and implementation of his or her plan of care.

Interpretive Guidelines §482.13(b)(1)

This regulation requires the hospital to actively include the patient in the development, implementation and revision of his/her plan of care. It requires the hospital to plan the patient's care, with patient participation, to meet the patient's psychological and medical needs.

The patient's (or patient's representatives, as allowed by State law) right to participate in the development and implementation of his or her plan of care includes at a minimum, the right to: participate in the **development and implementation** of his/her **inpatient treatment/care plan**, **outpatient treatment/care plan**, participate in the development and implementation of his/her **discharge plan**, and participate in the development and implementation of his/her **pain management plan**.

Hospitals are expected to take reasonable steps to determine the patient's wishes concerning designation of a representative to exercise the patient's right to participate in the development and implementation of the patient's plan of care. Unless prohibited by applicable State law:

- When a patient who is not incapacitated has designated, either orally to hospital staff or in writing, another individual to be his/her representative, the hospital must involve the designated representative in the development and implementation of the patient's plan of care. The explicit designation of a representative by the patient takes precedence over any non-designated relationship and continues throughout the patient's inpatient stay or outpatient visit, unless expressly withdrawn, either orally or in writing, by the patient.

- In the case of a patient who is incapacitated, when an individual presents the hospital with an advance directive, medical power of attorney or similar document executed by the patient and designating an individual to make medical decisions for the patient when incapacitated, the hospital, when presented with the document, must involve the designated representative in the development and implementation of the patient's plan of care. The explicit designation of a representative takes precedence over any non-designated relationship and continues throughout the patient's inpatient stay or outpatient visit, unless the patient ceases to be incapacitated and expressly withdraws the designation, either orally or in writing.

- When a patient is incapacitated or otherwise unable to communicate his or her wishes, there is no written advance directive on file or presented, and an individual asserts that he or she is the patient's spouse, domestic partner (whether or not formally established and including a same-sex domestic partner), parent (including someone who has stood in loco parentis for the patient who is a minor child) or other family member and thus is the patient's representative, the hospital is expected to accept this assertion, without demanding supporting documentation, and must involve the individual as the patient's representative in the development and implementation of the patient's plan of care, unless:

  - More than one individual claims to be the patient's representative. In such cases, it would be appropriate for the hospital to ask each individual for documentation supporting his/her claim to be the patient's representative. The hospital should make its determination of who is the patient's representative based upon the hospital's determination of who the patient would most want to make decisions on his/her behalf. Examples of documentation a hospital might consider could include, but are not limited to, the following: proof of a legally recognized marriage, domestic partnership, or civil union; proof of a joint household; proof of shared or co-mingled finances; and any other documentation the hospital considers evidence of a special relationship that indicates familiarity with the patient's preferences concerning medical treatment;

- Treating the individual as the patient's representative without requesting supporting documentation would result in the hospital violating State law. State laws, including State regulations, may specify a procedure for determining who may be considered to be the incapacitated patient's representative, and may specify when documentation is or is not required; or

- The hospital has reasonable cause to believe that the individual is falsely claiming to be the patient's spouse, domestic partner, parent or other family member.

Hospitals are expected to adopt policies and procedures that facilitate expeditious and non-discriminatory resolution of disputes about whether an individual is the patient's representative, given the critical role of the representative in exercising the patient's rights.

A refusal by the hospital of an individual's request to be treated as the patient's representative, based on one of the above-specified familial relationships, must be documented in the patient's medical record, along with the specific basis for the refusal.

Survey Procedures §482.13(b)(1)

- Does the hospital have policies and procedures to involve the patient or the patient's representative (as appropriate) in the development and implementation of his/her inpatient treatment/care plan, outpatient treatment/care plan, discharge plan, and pain management plan?

- Review records and interview staff and patients, or patients' representatives (as appropriate), to determine how the hospital involves the patient or the patient's representative (as appropriate) in the development and implementation of his/her plan of care?

- Does the hospital's policy provide for determining when a patient has a representative who may exercise the patient's right to participate in developing and implementing his/her plan of care, and who that representative is, consistent with this guidance and State law?

- Is there evidence that the patient or the patient's representative was included or proactively involved in the development and implementation of the patient's plan of care?

- Were revisions in the plan of care explained to the patient and/or the patient's representative (when appropriate)?

A-0131
(Rev. 84, Issued: 06-07-13, Effective: 06-07-13, Implementation: 06-07-13)

§482.13(b)(2) The patient or his or her representative (as allowed under State law) has the right to make informed decisions regarding his or her care. The patient's rights include being informed of his or her health status, being involved in care planning and treatment, and being able to request or refuse treatment. This right must not be construed as a mechanism to demand the provision of treatment or services deemed medically unnecessary or inappropriate.

Interpretive Guidelines §482.13(b)(2)

The right to make informed decisions means that the patient or patient's representative is given the information needed in order to make "informed" decisions regarding his/her care.

Patient's Representative:

A patient may wish to delegate his/her right to make informed decisions to another person (as allowed under State law).

Hospitals are expected to take reasonable steps to determine the patient's wishes concerning designation of a representative. Unless prohibited by applicable State law:

- When a patient who is not incapacitated has designated, either orally to hospital staff or in writing, another individual to be his/her representative, the hospital must provide the designated individual with the information required to make an informed decision about the patient's care. The hospital must also seek the written consent of the patient's representative when informed consent is required for a care decision. The explicit designation of a representative by the patient takes precedence over any non-designated relationship and continues throughout the patient's inpatient stay or outpatient visit, unless expressly withdrawn, either orally or in writing, by the patient.

- In the case of a patient who is incapacitated, when an individual presents the hospital with an advance directive, medical power of attorney or similar document executed by the patient and designating an individual to make medical decisions for the patient when incapacitated, the hospital must, when presented with the document, provide the designated individual the information required to make informed decisions about the patient's care. The hospital must also seek the consent of the designated individual when informed consent is required for a care decision. The explicit designation of a representative takes precedence over any non-designated relationship and continues throughout the patient's inpatient stay or outpatient visit, unless the patient ceases to be incapacitated and expressly withdraws the designation, either orally or in writing.

- When a patient is incapacitated or otherwise unable to communicate his or her wishes, there is no written advance directive on file or presented, and an individual asserts that he or she is the patient's spouse, domestic partner (whether or not formally established and including a same-sex domestic partner), parent (including someone who has stood in loco parentis for the patient who is a minor child), or other family member and thus is the patient's representative, the hospital is expected to accept this assertion, without demanding supporting documentation, and provide the individual the information required to make informed decisions about the patient's care. The hospital must also seek the consent of the individual when informed consent is required for a care decision. Hospitals are expected to treat the individual as the patient's representative unless:

  - More than one individual claims to be the patient's representative. In such cases, it would be appropriate for the hospital to ask each individual for documentation supporting his/her claim to be the patient's representative. The hospital should make its determination of who is the patient's representative based upon the hospital's determination of who the patient would most want to make decisions on his/her behalf. Examples of documentation a hospital might consider could include, but are not limited to, the following: proof of a legally recognized marriage, domestic partnership, or civil union; proof of a joint household; proof of shared or co-mingled finances; and any other documentation the hospital considers evidence of a special relationship that indicates familiarity with the patient's preferences concerning medical treatment;

  - Treating the individual as the patient's representative without requesting supporting documentation would result in the hospital violating State law. State laws, including State regulations, may specify a procedure for determining who may be considered to be the incapacitated patient's representative, and may specify when documentation is or is not required; or

  - The hospital has reasonable cause to believe that the individual is falsely claiming to be the patient's spouse, domestic partner, parent or other family member.

  Hospitals are expected to adopt policies and procedures that facilitate expeditious and non-discriminatory resolution of disputes about whether an individual is the patient's representative, given the critical role of the representative in exercising the patient's rights.

A refusal by the hospital of an individual's request to be treated as the patient's representative, based on one of the above-specified familial relationships, must be documented in the patient's medical record must, along with the specific basis for the refusal.

Informed Decisions

The right to make informed decisions regarding care presumes that the patient or the patient's representative has been provided information about his/her health status, diagnosis, and prognosis. Furthermore, it includes the patient's or the patient's representative's participation in the development of his/her plan of care, including providing consent to, or refusal of, medical or surgical interventions, and in planning for care after discharge from the hospital. The patient or the patient's representative should receive adequate information, provided in a manner that the patient or the patient's representative can understand, to assure that the patient or the patient's representative can effectively exercise the right to make informed decisions.

Hospitals must establish processes to assure that each patient or the patient's representative is given information on the patient's health status, diagnosis, and prognosis.

Giving informed consent to a treatment or a surgical procedure is one type of informed decision that a patient or patient's representative may need to make regarding the patient's plan of care. Hospitals must utilize an informed consent process that assures patients or their representatives are given the information and disclosures needed to make an informed decision about whether to consent to a procedure, intervention, or type of care that requires consent. See the guidelines for 42 CFR 482.51(b)(2) pertaining to surgical services informed consent and the guidelines for 42 CFR 482.24(c)(2)(v) pertaining to medical records for further detail.

Informed decisions related to care planning also extend to discharge planning for the patient's post-acute care. See the guidelines at 42 CFR 482.43(c) pertaining to discharge planning for discussion of pertinent requirements.

Hospitals must also establish policies and procedures that assure a patient's right to request or refuse treatment. Such policies should indicate how the patient's request will be addressed. However, hospitals are under no obligation to fulfill a patient's request for a treatment or service that the responsible practitioner has deemed medically unnecessary or even inappropriate.

Required Hospital Disclosures to Patients:

Physician Ownership

In addition, there are certain provisions of the Medicare provider agreement rules concerning disclosures that certain hospitals are required to make which are enforced under 42 CFR 482.13(b)(2):

- 42 CFR 489.3 defines a "physician-owned hospital" as any participating hospital in which a physician or immediate family member of a physician (as defined in §411.351) has an ownership or investment interest in the hospital, except for those satisfying an exception found at §411.356(a) or (b). Surveyors are not required to make an independent determination regarding whether a hospital meets the Medicare definition of "physician-owned," but they must ask whether the hospital is physician-owned.

- 42 CFR 489.20(u)(1) requires that all physician-owned hospitals provide written notice to their patients at the beginning of each patient's hospital inpatient stay or outpatient visit stating that the hospital is physician-owned, in order to assist the patient in making an informed decision about his or her care, in accordance with the requirements of §482.13(b)(2).

  - A planned inpatient stay or outpatient visit which is subject to the notice requirement begins with the provision of a package of information regarding scheduled preadmission testing and registration for a planned hospital admission for inpatient care or for an outpatient service subject to notice. An unplanned inpatient stay or outpatient visit subject to the notice requirement begins at the earliest point at which the patient presents to the hospital.

- The notice must disclose, in a manner reasonably designed to be understood by all patients, that the hospital is physician-owned and that a list of owners or investors who are physicians or immediate family members of physicians is available upon request. If the patient (or someone on behalf of the patient) requests this list, the hospital must provide it at the time of the request.

  - However, the notice requirement does not apply to any physician-owned hospital that does not have at least one referring physician (as defined at §411.351) who has an ownership or investment interest in the hospital or who has an immediate family member who has an ownership or investment interest in the hospital. In such cases, the hospital must sign an attestation statement that it has no referring physician with an ownership or investment interest or whose immediate family member has an ownership or investment interest in the hospital. The hospital must maintain this attestation in its records.

- 42 CFR 489.20(u)(2) provides that physician-owned hospitals must require each physician owner who is a member of the hospital's medical staff to agree, as a condition of obtaining/retaining medical staff membership or admitting privileges, to disclose in writing to all patients they refer to the hospital their ownership or investment interest in that hospital or that of any immediate family member. The hospital must require that this disclosure be made at the time of the referral and the requirement should be reflected in the hospital's policies and procedures governing privileges for physician owners.

- The hospital may exempt from this disclosure requirement any physician owner who does not refer any patients to the hospital.

- 42 CFR 489.12 permits CMS to refuse to enter into a provider agreement with a physician-owned hospital applicant that does not have procedures in place to notify patients of physician ownership in the hospital as required under §489.20(u).

- 42 CFR 489.53(c) permits CMS to terminate a provider agreement with a physician-owned hospital if the hospital fails to comply with the requirements at §489.20(u).

MD/DO 24/7 On-Site Presence

42 CFR 489.20(w) mandates that **if** there is no doctor of medicine or osteopathy present in the hospital 24 hours per day, seven days per week, the hospital must provide written notice of this to all inpatients at the beginning of a planned or unplanned inpatient stay, and to outpatients for certain types of planned or unplanned outpatient visits. The purpose of this requirement is to assist the patient in making an informed decision about his/her care, in accordance with 42 CFR 482.13(b)(2). Hospitals that have an MD/DO on-site 24/7 (including residents who are MDs or DOs) do not need to issue any disclosure notice about emergency services capability**.**

- The notice must be provided to all inpatients and to those outpatients who are under observation or who are having surgery or any other procedure using anesthesia.

- The notice must be provided at the beginning of the planned or unplanned inpatient stay, or outpatient visit subject to notice.

  - A planned inpatient stay or outpatient visit which is subject to the notice requirement begins with the provision of a package of information regarding scheduled preadmission testing and registration for a planned hospital admission for inpatient care or for an outpatient service subject to notice. An unplanned inpatient stay or outpatient visit which is subject to the notice requirement begins at the earliest point at which the patient presents to the hospital.

- Individual notices are not required in the hospital's dedicated emergency department (DED) (as that term is defined in 42 CFR 489.24(b)), but the DED must post a notice conspicuously, in a place or places likely to be noticed by all individuals entering the DED. The posted notice must state that the hospital does not have a doctor of medicine or a doctor of osteopathy present in the hospital 24 hours per day, 7 days per week, and must indicate how the hospital will meet the medical needs of any patient with an emergency medical condition, as defined in 42 CFR 489.24(b) [the EMTALA definition], at a time when there is no doctor of medicine or doctor of osteopathy present in the hospital. If an emergency department patient is determined to require admission, then the individual notice requirements of 42 CFR 489.20(w) would apply to that patient.

- Before admitting an inpatient or providing outpatient services requiring notice, the hospital must obtain a signed acknowledgement from the patient stating that he/she understands that a doctor of medicine or doctor of osteopathy may not be present at all times services are furnished to him/her.

  - In the event of an unplanned surgery or inpatient admission to treat an emergency medical condition, it may in some cases be necessary in the interest of the patient's safety to proceed with treatment before the required notice can be given and acknowledgement can be obtained. In such circumstances, the hospital must provide notice and obtain acknowledgement as soon as possible after the patient's stay or visit begins.

- For a hospital that participates in Medicare with multiple campuses providing inpatient services (e.g., a main provider campus and separate satellite, remote, and/or provider-based locations) under one CMS Certification Number, a separate determination is made for each campus or satellite location with inpatient services as to whether the disclosure notice is required. For example, if a hospital has a main campus and a satellite location and a physician is present 24/7 on the main campus but not at the satellite location, the hospital is required to provide the disclosure notice only at the satellite location. No notice is required for patients presenting to the main provider campus in this case. In this same example, if the hospital also has a provider-based, off-campus ambulatory (i.e., same-day) surgery department, no notice is required at that off-campus surgery site, since the hospital's main campus does have an MD/DO present 24/7.

- 42 CFR 489.53(c) permits CMS to terminate a provider agreement with a hospital if the hospital fails to comply with the requirements at §489.20(w) when it does not have an MD or DO on-site 24/ 7.

Survey Procedures §482.13(b)(2)

- Is there a hospital policy addressing the patient's or the patient's representative (as appropriate) right to make informed decisions?

  - Does the hospital's policy provide for determining when a patient has a representative who may exercise the patient's right to make informed decisions, and who that representative is, consistent with this guidance and State law?

- Is there a hospital policy addressing the patient's right to have information on his/her medical status, diagnosis, and prognosis? Does it articulate the hospital's process for assuring that patients have this information?

- Is there a hospital policy addressing how the patient will be involved in his/her care planning and treatment?

- Is there evidence that the hospital routinely complies with its policies? Evidence would be obtained through review of medical records, interviewing current patients and/or interviewing hospital personnel to determine their understanding of the hospital's informed decision-making policies and how they are implemented. Review of evidence would be designed to determine whether patients/patient representatives are provided adequate information about the patient's medical status, diagnosis, and prognosis, and then allowed to make informed decisions about their care planning and treatment.

Assessing Required Disclosures:

Physician Ownership

- If the hospital indicates that it is physician-owned but is exempt under §489.20(v) from the disclosure requirement of §489.20(u)(2), ask to see the signed attestation that it does not have any referring physicians with an ownership/investment interest or whose immediate family member has an ownership/investment interest in the hospital. (As with any other on-the-spot correction of a deficiency during a survey, creation of an attestation at the time of a survey does not mean that there was no deficiency and that the hospital would not be cited.)

- If the hospital is physician-owned but not exempt from the physician ownership disclosure requirements:

  - Verify that appropriate policies and procedures are in place to assure that necessary written notices are provided to all patients at the beginning of an inpatient or outpatient stay.

  - Review the notice the hospital issues to each patient to verify that it discloses, in a manner reasonably designed to be understood by all patients, that the hospital meets the Federal definition of "physician-owned," that a list of owners and investors who are physicians or immediate family members of physicians is available upon request, and that such a list is provided to the patient at the time the request is made by or on behalf of the patient.

  - Determine through staff interviews, observation, and a review of policies and procedures whether the hospital furnishes its list of physician owners and investors at the time a patient or patient's representative requests it.

- Determine through staff interviews and review of policies, procedures, and staff records whether a physician-owned hospital's medical staff membership and admitting privileging requirements include a requirement that, as a condition of continued membership or admitting privileges, physician owners who refer patients to the hospital agree to provide written disclosure of their own or any immediate family member's ownership or investment interest to all patients at the time of the referral to the hospital.

MD/DO 24/7 On-Site Presence

- Determine through interviews, observation, and medical record review whether an MD/DO is present in the hospital, at each campus or satellite location providing inpatient services 24 hours/day, seven days/week.

- For each required location where an MD/DO is not present:

  - Verify that the appropriate policies and procedures are in place to assure written notices that an MD/DO is not present at all times are provided at the beginning of an inpatient stay or outpatient stay to all inpatients and to all outpatients receiving observation services, surgery or another procedure requiring anesthesia.

  - Verify that there is signed acknowledgment by patients of such disclosure, obtained by the hospital prior to the patient's admission or before applicable outpatient services were provided.

  - Ask a sample of inpatients and affected outpatients whether they were provided notice about an MD/DO not being present at all times in the hospital.

  - Verify that the hospital's emergency department has signage with the appropriate disclosure information.

  - Review the notice the hospital issues to verify that it indicates how the hospital will meet the medical needs of any patient who develops an emergency medical condition at a time when no physician is present at that hospital, including any remote location or satellite.

A-0132
(Rev. 75, Issued: 12-02-11, Effective: 12-02-11, Implementation: 12-02-11)

§482.13(b)(3) The patient has the right to formulate advance directives and to have hospital staff and practitioners who provide care in the hospital comply with these directives, in accordance with §489.100 of this part (Definition), §489.102 of this part (Requirements for providers), and §489.104 of this part (Effective dates).

Interpretive Guidelines §482.13(b)(3)

An advance directive is defined at §489.100 as "a written instruction, such as a living will or durable power of attorney for health care, recognized under State law (whether statutory or as recognized by the courts of the State), relating to the provision of health care when the individual is incapacitated." The patient (inpatient or outpatient) has the right to formulate advance directives, and to have hospital staff implement and comply with their advance directive. The regulation at 42 CFR 489.102 specifies the rights of a patient (as permitted by State law) to make medical care decisions, including the right to accept or refuse medical or surgical treatment and the right to formulate, at the individual's option, advance directives.

In the advance directive, the patient may provide guidance as to his/her wishes concerning provision of care in certain situations; alternatively the patient may delegate decision-making authority to another individual, as permitted by State law. (In addition, the patient may use the advance directive to designate a "support person," as that term is used in §482.13(h), for purposes of exercising the patient's visitation rights.) When a patient who is incapacitated has executed an advance directive designating a particular individual to make medical decisions for him/her when incapacitated, the hospital must, when presented with the document, provide the designated individual the information required to make informed decisions about the patient's care. (See also the requirements at §482.13(b)(2).) The hospital must also seek the consent of the patient's representative when informed consent is required for a care decision. The explicit designation of a representative in the patient's advance directive takes precedence over any non-designated relationship and continues throughout the patient's inpatient stay or, as applicable, outpatient visit, unless the patient ceases to be incapacitated and expressly withdraws the designation, either orally or in writing.

§489.102 also requires the hospital to:

● Provide written notice of its policies regarding the implementation of patients' rights to make decisions concerning medical care, such as the right to formulate advance directives. If an individual is incapacitated or otherwise unable to communicate, the hospital may provide the advance directive information required under §489.102 to the individual's "family or surrogate in the same manner that it issues other materials about policies and procedures to the family of the incapacitated individual or to a surrogate or other concerned persons in accordance with State law."(§489.102(e)) The guidance concerning the regulation at §482.13(a)(1) governing notice to the patient or the patient's representative of the patient's rights applies to the required provision of notice concerning the hospital's advance directive policies. Although both inpatients and outpatients have the same rights under §482.13(a)(1), §489.102(b)(1) requires that notice of the hospital's advance directive policy be provided at the time an individual is admitted as an inpatient. However, in view of the broader notice requirements at §482.13(a)(1), the hospital should also provide the advance directive notice to outpatients (or their representatives) who are in the emergency department, who are in an observation status, or who are undergoing same-day surgery. The notice should be presented at the time of registration. Notice is not required for other outpatients, given that they are unlikely to become incapacitated.

- The notice must include a clear and precise statement of limitation if the hospital cannot implement an advance directive on the basis of conscience. At a minimum, a statement of limitation should:

  - Clarify any differences between institution-wide conscience objections and those that may be raised by individual physicians or other practitioners;

  - Identify the State legal authority permitting such an objection; and

  - Describe the range of medical conditions or procedures affected by the conscience objection.

    It should be noted that this provision allowing for certain conscience objections to implementing an advance directive is narrowly focused on the directive's content related to medical conditions or procedures. This provision would not allow a hospital or individual physician or practitioner to refuse to honor those portions of an advance directive that designate an individual as the patient's representative and/or support person, given that such designation does not concern a medical condition or procedure.

    Issuance of the written notice of the hospital's advance directive policies to the patient or the patient's representative must be documented in the patient's medical record.

  - Document in a prominent part of the patient's medical record whether or not the patient has executed an advance directive;

  - Not condition the provision of care or otherwise discriminate against an individual based on whether or not the individual has executed an advance directive;

  - Ensure compliance with requirements of State law concerning advance directives and inform individuals that complaints concerning the advance directive requirements may be filed with the State survey and certification agency;

  - Provide for the education of staff concerning its policies and procedures on advance directives. The right to formulate advance directives includes the right to formulate a psychiatric advance directive (as allowed by State law); and

- Provide community education regarding advance directives and the hospital must document its efforts.

A **psychiatric advance directive** is akin to a traditional advance directive for health care. This type of advance directive might be prepared by an individual who is concerned that at some time he or she may be subject to involuntary psychiatric commitment or treatment. The psychiatric advance directive may cover a range of subjects, and may name another person who is authorized to make decisions for the individual if he or she is determined to be legally incompetent to make his/her own choices. It may also provide the patient's instructions about hospitalization, alternatives to hospitalization, the use of medications, types of therapies, and the patient's wishes concerning restraint or seclusion. The patient may designate who should be notified upon his/her admission to the hospital, as well as who should not be permitted to visit him or her. State laws regarding the use of psychiatric advance directives vary.

In accordance with State law, a psychiatric advance directive should be accorded the same respect and consideration that a traditional advance directive for health care is given. Hospitals should carefully coordinate how the choices of a patient balance with the rights of other patients, staff, and individuals in the event that a dangerous situation arises.

However, even if State law has not explicitly spoken to the use of psychiatric advance directives, consideration should be given to them inasmuch as this regulation also supports the patient's right to participate in the development and implementation of his or her plan of care. When the patient is, for whatever reason, unable to communicate his/her wishes, the preferences expressed in the psychiatric advance directive can give critical insight to the MD/DOs, nurses, and other staff as they develop a plan of care and treatment for the patient.

Survey Procedures §482.13(b)(3)

- Review the hospital's advance directive notice. Does it advise inpatients or applicable outpatients, or their representatives, of the patient's right to formulate an advance directive and to have hospital staff comply with the advance directive (in accordance with State law)? Does it include a clear, precise and valid statement of limitation if the hospital cannot implement an advance directive on the basis of conscience?

- Review the records of a sample of patients for evidence of hospital compliance with advance directive notice requirements. Does every inpatient or applicable outpatient record contain documentation that notice of the hospital's advance directives policy was provided at the time of admission or registration? Is there documentation of whether or not each patient has an advance directive? For those patients who have reported an advance directive, has a copy of the patient's advance directive been placed in the medical record?

- What mechanism does the hospital have in place to allow patients to formulate an advance directive or to update their current advance directive? Is there evidence that the hospital is promoting and protecting each patient's right to formulate an advance directive?

- Determine to what extent the hospital complies, as permitted under State law, with patient advance directives that delegate decisions about the patient's care to a designated individual.

- Determine to what extent the hospital educates its staff regarding advance directives.

- Interview staff to determine their knowledge of the advance directives of the patients in their care.

- Determine to what extent the hospital provides education for the patient population (inpatient and outpatient) regarding one's rights under State law to formulate advance directives.

A-0133
(Rev. 75, Issued: 12-02-11, Effective: 12-02-11, Implementation: 12-02-11)

§482.13(b)(4) - The patient has the right to have a family member or representative of his or her choice and his or her own physician notified promptly of his or her admission to the hospital.

Interpretive Guidelines §482.13(b)(4)

Identifying Who Is to Be Notified

For every inpatient admission, the hospital must ask the patient whether the hospital should notify a family member or representative about the admission. If the patient requests such notice and identifies the family member or representative to be notified, the hospital must provide such notice promptly to the designated individual. The explicit designation of a family member or representative by the patient takes precedence over any non-designated relationship.

The hospital must also ask the patient whether the hospital should notify his/her own physician. In the case of scheduled admissions, the patient's own physician likely is already aware of the admission. However, if the patient requests notice to and identifies the physician, the hospital must provide such notice promptly to the designated physician, regardless of whether the admission was scheduled in advance or emergent.

When a patient is incapacitated or otherwise unable to communicate and to identify a family member or representative to be notified, the hospital must make reasonable efforts to identify and promptly notify a family member or patient's representative. If an individual who has accompanied the patient to the hospital, or who comes to or contacts the hospital after the patient has been admitted, asserts that he or she is the patient's spouse, domestic partner (whether or not formally established and including a same-sex domestic partner), parent (including someone who has stood in loco parentis for the patient who is a minor child), or other family member, the hospital is expected to accept this assertion, without demanding supporting documentation, and provide this individual information about the patient's admission, unless:

- More than one individual claims to be the patient's family member or representative. In such cases it would not be inappropriate for the hospital to ask each individual for documentation supporting his/her claim to be the patient's family member or representative. The hospital should make its determination of who is the patient's representative based upon the hospital's determination of who the patient would most want to make decisions on his/her behalf. Examples of documentation a hospital might consider could include, but are not limited to, the following: proof of a legally recognized marriage, domestic partnership, or civil union; proof of a joint household; proof of shared or co-mingled finances; and any other documentation the hospital considers evidence of a special relationship that indicates familiarity with the patient's preferences concerning medical treatment ;

- Treating the individual as the patient's family member or representative without requesting supporting documentation would result in the hospital violating State law. State laws, including State regulations, may specify a procedure for determining who may be considered to be the incapacitated patient's family member or representative, and may specify when documentation is or is not required; or

- The hospital has reasonable cause to believe that the individual is falsely claiming to be the patient's spouse, domestic partner, parent or other family member.

Hospitals are expected to adopt policies and procedures that facilitate expeditious and non-discriminatory resolution of disputes about whether an individual should be notified as the patient's family member or representative, given the critical role of the representative in exercising the patient's rights. Hospitals may also choose to provide notice to more than one family member.

When a patient is incapacitated and the hospital is able through reasonable efforts to identify the patient's own physician – e.g., through information obtained from a family member, or from review of prior admissions or outpatient encounters, or through access to the patient's records in a regional system of electronic patient medical records in which the hospital participates – the hospital must promptly notify the patient's physician of the admission.

Prompt Notice

The hospital must provide the required notice promptly. "Promptly" means as soon as possible after the physician's or other qualified practitioner's order to admit the patient has been given. Notice may be given orally in person, by telephone, by e-mail or other electronic means, or by other methods that achieve prompt notification. It is not acceptable for the hospital to send a letter by regular mail.

Medical Record Documentation

The hospital must document that the patient, unless incapacitated, was asked no later than the time of admission whether he or she wanted a family member/representative notified, the date, time and method of notification when the patient requested such, or whether the patient declined to have notice provided. If the patient was incapacitated at the time of admission, the medical record must indicate what steps were taken to identify and provide notice to a family member/representative and to the patient's physician.

Survey Procedures §482.13(b)(4)

- Determine if the hospital has policies that address notification of a patient's family or representative and physician when the patient is admitted as an inpatient.

- Ask the hospital who is responsible for providing the required notice. Interview person(s) responsible for providing the notice to determine how they identify the persons to be notified and the means of notification. What do they do in the case of an incapacitated person to identify a family member/representative and the patient's physician?

- Review a sample of inpatient medical records. Do the medical records provide evidence that the patient was asked about notifying a family member/representative and his/her physician? Is there a record of when and how notice was provided? Was notice provided promptly? Is there a record of the patient declining to have notice provided to a family member/representative and his/her physician? Is there documentation of whether the patient was incapacitated at the time of admission, and if so, what steps were taken to identify a family member/representative and the patient's physician?

A-0142
§482.13(c) Standard: Privacy and Safety

Interpretive Guidelines §482.13(c)

The hospital must ensure the privacy and safety requirements are met.

A-0143

(Rev. 84, Issued: 06-07-13, Effective: 06-07-13, Implementation: 06-07-13)

§482.13(c)(1) - The patient has the right to personal privacy.

Interpretive Guidelines §482.13(c)(1)

The underlying principle of this requirement is the patient's basic right to respect, dignity, and comfort while in the hospital.

Physical Privacy

"The right to personal privacy" includes at a minimum, that patients have physical privacy to the extent consistent with their care needs during personal hygiene activities (e.g., toileting, bathing, dressing), during medical/nursing treatments, and when requested as appropriate.

People not involved in the care of the patient should not be present without his/her consent while he/she is being examined or treated. If an individual requires assistance during toileting, bathing, and other personal hygiene activities, staff should assist, giving utmost attention to the individual's need for privacy. Privacy should be afforded when the MD/DO or other staff visits the patient to discuss clinical care issues or conduct any examination or treatment.

However, audio/video monitoring (does not include recording) of patients in medical-surgical or intensive-care type units would not be considered violating the patient's privacy, as long as there exists a clinical need, the patient/patient's representative is aware of the monitoring and the monitors or speakers are located so that the monitor screens are not readily visible or where speakers are not readily audible to visitors or the public. Video recording of patients undergoing medical treatment requires the consent of the patient or his/her representative.

A patient's right to privacy may also be limited in situations where a person must be continuously observed to ensure his or her safety, such as when a patient is simultaneously restrained and in seclusion to manage violent or self-destructive behavior or when the patient is under suicide precautions.

Protecting Patient Personal Information

The right to personal privacy also includes limiting the release or disclosure of patient information. Patient information includes, but is not limited to, the patient's presence or location in the hospital; demographic information the hospital has collected on the patient, such as name, age, address, income; or information on the patient's medical condition. Such patient information may not be disclosed without informing the patient or the patient's representative in advance of the disclosure and providing the patient or the patient's representative an opportunity to agree, prohibit, or restrict the disclosure. Below is a summary of privacy issues that surveyors might encounter in hospital settings, and the related privacy requirements.

Permitted Disclosures:
A hospital is permitted to use and disclose patient information, without the patient's authorization, in order to provide patient care and perform related administrative functions, such as payment and other hospital operations.

- Payment operations include hospital activities to obtain payment or be reimbursed for the provision of health care to an individual.

- Hospital operations are administrative, financial, legal, and quality improvement activities of a hospital that are necessary to conduct business and to support the core functions of treatment and payment. These activities include, but are not limited to: quality assessment and improvement activities, case management and care coordination; competency assurance activities, conducting or arranging for medical reviews, audits, or legal services, including fraud and abuse detection and compliance programs; business planning, development, management, and administration and certain hospital-specific fundraising activities.

Hospitals must develop and implement policies and procedures that restrict access to and use of patient information based on the specific roles of the members of their workforce. These policies and procedures must identify the persons, or classes of persons, in the workforce who need access to protected health information to carry out their duties and the categories of protected health information to which access is needed.

One example of a permitted disclosure is a Facility Directory. It is common practice in many hospitals to maintain a directory of patient contact information. The hospital must inform the patient, or the patient's representative, of the individual information that may be included in a directory and the persons to whom such information may be disclosed. The patient, or the patient's representative, must be given the opportunity to restrict or prohibit any or all uses and disclosures. The hospital may rely on a patient's/representative's individual's informal permission to list in its facility directory the patient's name, general condition, religious affiliation, and location in the provider's facility. The provider may then disclose the patient's condition and location in the facility to anyone asking for the patient by name, and also may disclose religious affiliation to clergy. If the opportunity to prohibit or restrict uses and disclosures cannot be provided due to the patient's incapacity or emergency treatment circumstance, and there is no patient representative available, the hospital may disclose patient information for the facility's directory if such disclosure is in the patient's best interest. The hospital must provide the patient or the patient's representative an opportunity to prohibit or restrict disclosure as soon as it becomes practicable to do so. The hospital may use patient information to notify, or assist in the notification of, a family member, a personal representative of the patient, or another person responsible for the care of the patient of their location, general condition, or death. The hospital must have procedures in place, in accordance with State law, to provide appropriate information to patient families or others in those situations where the patient is unable to make their wishes known.

Incidental Uses and Disclosures May be Acceptable:

An incidental use or disclosure is a secondary use or disclosure of patient information that cannot reasonably be prevented, is limited in nature, and that occurs as a result of another use or disclosure that is permitted. Many customary health care communications and practices play an important role in ensuring the prompt delivery of effective care. Due to the nature of these communications and practices, as well as of the hospital environment, the potential exists for a patient's information to be disclosed incidentally. For example, a hospital visitor may overhear a health care professional's confidential conversation with another health care professional or the patient, or may glimpse a patient's information on a sign-in sheet or nursing station whiteboard. The regulation protecting patient privacy does not impede these customary and essential communications and practices and, thus, a hospital is not required to eliminate all risk of incidental use or disclosure secondary to a permitted use or disclosure, so long as the hospital takes reasonable safeguards and discloses only the minimum amount of personally identifiable information necessary. For example, hospitals may:

- Use patient care signs (e.g. "falls risk" or "diabetic diet") displayed at the bedside or outside a patient room;

- Display patient names on the outside of patient charts; or

- Use "whiteboards" that list the patients present on a unit, in an operating room suite, etc.

Hospitals are expected to review their practices and determine what steps are reasonable to safeguard patient information while not impeding the delivery of safe patient care or incurring undue administrative or financial burden as a result of implementing privacy safeguards.

Examples of reasonable safeguards could include, but are not limited to:

- Requesting that waiting customers stand a few feet back from a counter used for patient registration;

- Use of dividers or curtains in areas where patient and physician or other hospital staff communications routinely occur;

- Health care staff speaking quietly when discussing a patient's condition or treatment in a semi-private room;

- Utilizing passwords and other security measures on computers maintaining personally identifiable health information; or

- Limiting access to areas where white boards or x-ray light boards are in use, or posting the board on a wall not readily visible to the public, or limiting the information placed on the board.

Survey Procedures §482.13(c)(1)

- Conduct observations/interview patients or their representatives to determine if patients are provided reasonable privacy during examinations or treatments, personal hygiene activities and discussions about their health status/care and other appropriate situations.

- Review hospital policy and interview staff concerning their understanding of the use of patient information in the facility directory. Does the policy address the opportunity for the patient or patient's representative to restrict or prohibit use of patient information in emergent and non-emergent situations?

- Review hospital policy and conduct observations/interview staff to determine if reasonable safeguards are used to reduce incidental disclosures of patient information.

- If audio and/or visual monitoring is utilized in the med/surg or ICU setting, conduct observations to determine that monitor screens and/or speakers are not readily visible or audible to visitors or the public.

A-0144
(Rev. 37, Issued: 10-17-08; Effective/Implementation Date: 10-17-08)

§482.13(c)(2) - The patient has the right to receive care in a safe setting.

Interpretive Guidelines §482.13(c)(2)

The intention of this requirement is to specify that each patient receives care in an environment that a reasonable person would consider to be safe. For example, hospital staff should follow current standards of practice for patient environmental safety, infection control, and security. The hospital must protect vulnerable patients, including newborns and children. Additionally, this standard is intended to provide protection for the patient's emotional health and safety as well as his/her physical safety. Respect, dignity and comfort would be components of an emotionally safe environment.

Survey Procedures §482.13(c)(2)

- Review and analyze patient and staff incident and accident reports to identify any incidents or patterns of incidents concerning a safe environment. Expand your review if you suspect a problem with safe environment in the hospitals.

- Review QAPI, safety, infection control and security (or the committee that deals with security issues) committee minutes and reports to determine if the hospital is identifying problems, evaluating those problems and taking steps to ensure a safe patient environment.

- Observe the environment where care and treatment are provided.

- Observe and interview staff at units where infants and children are inpatients. Are appropriate security protections (such as alarms, arm banding systems, etc.) in place? Are they functioning?

- Review policy and procedures on what the facility does to curtail unwanted visitors or contaminated materials.

- Access the hospital's security efforts to protect vulnerable patients including newborns and children. Is the hospital providing appropriate security to protect patients? Are appropriate security mechanisms in place and being followed to protect patients?

A-0145
(Rev. 37, Issued: 10-17-08; Effective/Implementation Date: 10-17-08)

§482.13(c)(3) - The patient has the right to be free from all forms of abuse or harassment.

Interpretive Guidelines §482.13(c)(3)

The intent of this requirement is to prohibit all forms of abuse, neglect (as a form of abuse) and harassment whether from staff, other patients or visitors. The hospital must ensure that patients are free from all forms of abuse, neglect, or harassment. The hospital must have mechanisms/methods in place that ensure patients are free of all forms of abuse, neglect, or harassment.

Abuse is defined as the willful infliction of injury, unreasonable confinement, intimidation, or punishment, with resulting physical harm, pain, or mental anguish. This includes staff neglect or indifference to infliction of injury or intimidation of one patient by another. Neglect, for the purpose of this requirement, is considered a form of abuse and is defined as the failure to provide goods and services necessary to avoid physical harm, mental anguish, or mental illness.

The following components are suggested as necessary for effective abuse protection:

- **Prevent**. A critical part of this system is that there are adequate staff on duty, especially during the evening, nighttime, weekends and holiday shifts, to take care of the individual needs of all patients. (See information regarding meaning of adequate at those requirements that require the hospital to have adequate staff. Adequate staff would include that the hospital ensures that there are the number and types of qualified, trained, and experienced staff at the hospital and available to meet the care needs of every patient.)

- **Screen**. Persons with a record of abuse or neglect should not be hired or retained as employees.

- **Identify**. The hospital creates and maintains a proactive approach to identify events and occurrences that may constitute or contribute to abuse and neglect.

- **Train**. The hospital, during its orientation program, and through an ongoing training program, provides all employees with information regarding abuse and neglect, and related reporting requirements, including prevention, intervention, and detection.

- **Protect**. The hospital must protect patients from abuse during investigation of any allegations of abuse or neglect or harassment.

- **Investigate**. The hospital ensures, in a timely and thorough manner, objective investigation of all allegations of abuse, neglect or mistreatment.

- **Report/Respond**. The hospital must assure that any incidents of abuse, neglect or harassment are reported and analyzed, and the appropriate corrective, remedial or disciplinary action occurs, in accordance with applicable local, State, or Federal law.

As a result of the implementation of this system, changes to the hospital's policies and procedures should be made accordingly.

Survey Procedures §482.13(c)(3)

- Examine the extent to which the hospital has a system in place to protect patients from abuse, neglect and harassment of all forms, whether from staff, other patients, visitors or other persons. In particular, determine the extent to which the hospital addresses the following issues.

o   Are staffing levels across all shifts sufficient to care for individual patient's needs?

o   Does the hospital have a written procedure for investigating allegations of abuse and neglect including methods to protect patients from abuse during investigations of allegations?

o   How does the hospital substantiate allegations of abuse and neglect?

o   Do incidents of substantiated abuse and neglect result in appropriate action?

o   Has the hospital implemented an abuse protection program? Does it comply with Federal, State and local laws and regulations? Is it effective?

o   Are appropriate agencies notified in accordance with State and Federal laws regarding incidents of substantiated abuse and neglect?

o   Can staff identify various forms of abuse or neglect?

o   Do staff members know what to do if they witness abuse and neglect?

o   What evidence is there that allegations of abuse and neglect are thoroughly investigated?

o   Does the hospital conduct criminal background checks as allowed by State law for all potential new hires?

o   Is there evidence the hospital employs people with a history of abuse, neglect or harassment?

A-0146
(Rev. 37, Issued: 10-17-08; Effective/Implementation Date: 10-17-08)

§482.13(d) Standard: Confidentiality of Patient Records

Interpretive Guidelines §482.13(d)

The hospital must ensure the confidentiality of patient records requirements are met.

A-0147
(Rev. 84, Issued: 06-07-13, Effective: 06-07-13, Implementation: 06-07-13)

§482.13(d)(1) - The patient has the right to the confidentiality of his or her clinical records.

Interpretive Guidelines §482.13(d)(1)

The right to confidentiality of the patient's medical record means the hospital must safeguard the contents of the medical record, whether it is in paper or electronic format, or a combination of the two, from unauthorized disclosure. Confidentiality applies wherever the record or portions thereof are stored, including but not limited to central records, patient care locations, radiology, laboratories, record storage areas, etc.

A hospital is permitted to disclose patient information, without a patient's authorization, in order to provide patient care and perform related administrative functions, such as payment and other hospital operations.

- Payment operations include hospital activities to obtain payment or be reimbursed for the provision of health care to an individual.

- Hospital operations are administrative, financial, legal, and quality improvement activities of a hospital that are necessary to conduct business and to support the core functions of treatment and payment. These activities include, but are not limited to: quality assessment and improvement activities, case management and care coordination; competency assurance activities, conducting or arranging for medical reviews, audits, or legal services, including fraud and abuse detection and compliance programs; business planning, development, management, and administration and certain hospital-specific fundraising activities.

The hospital must develop policies and procedures that reasonably limit disclosures of information contained in the patient's medical record to the minimum necessary, even when the disclosure is for treatment or payment purposes, or as otherwise required by State or Federal law.

When the minimum necessary standard is applied, a hospital may not disclose the entire medical record for a particular purpose, unless it can specifically justify that the whole record is the amount reasonably needed for the purpose.

A hospital may make an authorized disclosure of information from the medical record electronically, and may also share an electronic medical record system with other health care facilities, physicians and practitioners, so long as the system is designed and operated with safeguards that ensure that only authorized disclosures are made.

The hospital must obtain the patient's, or the patient's representative's, written authorization for any disclosure of information in the medical record when the disclosure is not for treatment, payment or health care operations.

Survey Procedures §482.13(d)(1)

- Verify that the hospital has policies and procedures addressing the protecting of information in patients' medical record from unauthorized disclosures.

- Observe locations where medical records are stored to determine whether appropriate safeguards are in place to protect medical record information.

- Interview staff to determine their understanding of and compliance with the hospital's policies and procedures for protecting medical record information.

A-0148
(Rev. 37, Issued: 10-17-08; Effective/Implementation Date: 10-17-08)

§482.13(d)(2) - The patient has the right to access information contained in his or her clinical records within a reasonable time frame. The hospital must not frustrate the legitimate efforts of individuals to gain access to their own medical records and must actively seek to meet these requests as quickly as its record keeping system permits.

Interpretive Guidelines §482.13(d)(2)

The requirements of the Department of Health and Human Services with regard to the confidentiality rights of individuals are set forth in the Privacy Rule at 42 CFR 164.500 et seq., pursuant to §264 of the Health Insurance Portability and Accountability Act of 1996." The regulation at 42 CFR 164.524 specifies that patients should be allowed to inspect and obtain a copy of health information about them that is held by providers; and that providers may not withhold information except under limited circumstances. These circumstances include:

- Psychotherapy notes;

- A correctional institution or a health care provider acting at the direction of a correctional institution may deny an inmate's request for access, if providing such access would jeopardize the health or security of the individual, other inmates, or officers or employees of the correctional institution;

- The information is about another person (other than a health care provider) and the hospital determines that the patient inspection is reasonably likely to cause sufficient harm to that person to warrant withholding;

- A licensed health care professional has determined that the access requested is reasonably likely to endanger the life or physical safety of the individual or another person;

- The information contains data obtained under a promise of confidentiality (from someone other than a health care provider), and inspection could reasonably reveal the source;

- The information is collected in the course of research that includes treatment and the research is in progress, provided that the individual has agreed to the denial of access and the provider informs the individual that his or her right of access will be reinstated when the research is completed;

- The protected health information is subject to the Clinical Laboratory Improvements Amendments of 1988, 42 CFR 263a, to the extent that providing the requested access would be prohibited by law;

- The protected health information is exempt from the Clinical Laboratory Improvements Amendments of 1988, pursuant to 42 CFR 493.3(a)(2);

- The information is compiled in reasonable anticipation of, or for use in, a civil, criminal or administrative action or proceeding; and

- The request is made by an individual's personal representative (as allowed under state law) and a licensed health care professional has determined that access is reasonably likely to cause substantial harm to the individual or another person.

In general, each patient should be able to see and obtain a copy of his/her records. Record holders may not deny access except to a portion of the record that meets criteria specified above. In these cases, the record holder may decide to withhold portions of the record; however, to the extent possible, the patient should be given as much information as possible.

If the patient is incompetent, the patient record should be made available to his or her representative (as allowed under State law). Upon the patient's request, other designated individuals may access the patient's records.

The patient has the right to easily access his/her medical records. Reasonable cost-based fees may be imposed only to cover the cost of copying, postage, and/or preparing an explanation or summary of patient health information, as outlined in 42 CFR §164.524(c). The cost of duplicating a patient's record must not create a barrier to the individual's receiving his or her medical record.

Survey Procedures §482.13(d)(2)

- Does the hospital promote and protect the patient's right to access information contained in his/her clinical record?

- Does the hospital have a procedure for providing records to patients within a reasonable time frame?

- Does the hospital's system frustrate the legitimate efforts of individuals to gain access to their own medical record?

- Does the procedure include the method to identify what documents were not provided and the reason?

A-0154
(Rev. 37, Issued: 10-17-08; Effective/Implementation Date: 10-17-08)

§482.13(e) Standard: Restraint or seclusion. All patients have the right to be free from physical or mental abuse, and corporal punishment. All patients have the right to be free from restraint or seclusion, of any form, imposed as a means of coercion, discipline, convenience, or retaliation by staff. Restraint or seclusion may only be imposed to ensure the immediate physical safety of the patient, a staff member, or others and must be discontinued at the earliest possible time.

Interpretive Guidelines §482.13(e):

The intent of this standard is to identify patients' basic rights, ensure patient safety, and eliminate the inappropriate use of restraint or seclusion. Each patient has the right to receive care in a safe setting. The safety of the patient, staff, or others is the basis for initiating and discontinuing the use of restraint or seclusion. Each patient has the right to be free from all forms of abuse and corporal punishment. Each patient has the right to be free from restraint or seclusion, of any form, imposed as a means of coercion, discipline, convenience, or retaliation by staff. Restraint or seclusion may not be used unless the use of restraint or seclusion is necessary to ensure the immediate physical safety of the patient, a staff member, or others. The use of restraint or seclusion must be discontinued as soon as possible based on an individualized patient assessment and re-evaluation. A violation of any of these patients' rights constitutes an inappropriate use of restraint or seclusion and would be subject to a condition level deficiency.

The patient protections contained in this standard apply to **all hospital patients** when the use of restraint or seclusion becomes necessary, regardless of patient location. The requirements contained in this standard are not specific to any treatment setting within the hospital. They are not targeted only to patients on psychiatric units or those with behavioral/mental health care needs. Instead, the requirements are specific to the patient behavior that the restraint or seclusion intervention is being used to address.

In summary, these restraint and seclusion regulations apply to:

- All hospitals (acute care, long-term care, psychiatric, children's, and cancer);

- All locations within the hospital (including medical/surgical units, critical care units, forensic units, emergency department, psychiatric units, etc.); and

- All hospital patients, regardless of age, who are restrained or secluded (including both inpatients and outpatients).

The decision to use a restraint or seclusion is not driven by diagnosis, but by a comprehensive individual patient assessment. For a given patient at a particular point in time, this comprehensive individualized patient assessment is used to determine whether the use of less restrictive measures poses a greater risk than the risk of using a restraint or seclusion. The comprehensive assessment should include a physical assessment to identify medical problems that may be causing behavior changes in the patient. For example, temperature elevations, hypoxia, hypoglycemia, electrolyte imbalances, drug interactions, and drug side effects may cause confusion, agitation, and combative behaviors. Addressing these medical issues may eliminate or minimize the need for the use of restraints or seclusion.

Staff must assess and monitor a patient's condition on an ongoing basis to ensure that the patient is released from restraint or seclusion at the earliest possible time. Restraint or seclusion may only be employed while the unsafe situation continues. Once the unsafe situation ends, the use of restraint or seclusion should be discontinued. However, the decision to discontinue the intervention should be based on the determination that the need for restraint or seclusion is no longer present, or that the patient's needs can be addressed using less restrictive methods.

Hospital leadership is responsible for creating a culture that supports a patient's right to be free from restraint or seclusion. Leadership must ensure that systems and processes are developed, implemented, and evaluated that support the patients' rights addressed in this standard, and that eliminate the inappropriate use of restraint or seclusion. Through their QAPI program, hospital leadership should:

- Assess and monitor the use of restraint or seclusion in their facility;

- Implement actions to ensure that restraint or seclusion is used only to ensure the physical safety of the patient, staff and others; and

- Ensure that the hospital complies with the requirements set forth in this standard as well as those set forth by State law and hospital policy when the use of restraint or seclusion is necessary.

Patients have a right to receive safe care in a safe environment. However, the use of restraint is inherently risky. When the use of restraint is necessary, the least restrictive method must be used to ensure a patient's safety. The use of restraint for the management of patient behavior should **not** be considered a routine part of care.

The use of restraints for the prevention of falls should **not** be considered a routine part of a **falls prevention program**. Although restraints have been traditionally used as a falls prevention approach, they have major, serious drawbacks and can contribute to serious injuries. There is no evidence that the use of physical restraint, (including, but not limited to, raised side rails) will prevent or reduce falls. Additionally, falls that occur while a person is physically restrained often result in more severe injuries.[1]
In fact in some instances reducing the use of physical restraints may actually decrease the risk of falling.[2]

FOOTNOTES

[1]- *American Geriatrics Society, British Geriatrics Society, and American Academy of Orthopaedic Surgeons Panel on Falls Prevention. Guideline for the prevention of falls in older persons. Journal of the American Geriatrics Society. 49(5):664-72, 2001 May.*

- Neufeld RR, Libow LS, Foley WJ, Dunbar JM, Cohen C, Breuer B. Restraint reduction reduces serious injuries among nursing home residents. J Am Geriatr Soc 1999; 47:1202-1207.

- Si M, Neufeld RR, Dunbar J. Removal of bedrails on a short-term nursing home rehabilitation unit. Gerontologist 1999; 39:611-614.

- Hanger HC, Ball MC, Wood LA. An analysis of falls in the hospital: can we do without bedrails? J Am Geriatr Soc 1999; 47:529-531.

- Tinetti ME, Liu YB, Ginter S. Mechanical restraint use and fall related injuries among residents of skilled nursing facilities. Ann Intern Med 1992; 116:369-374.

- Capezuti E, Evans L, Strumpf N, Maislin G. Physical restraint use and falls in nursing home residents. J Am Geriatr Soc 1996; 44:627-633.

- Capezuti E, Strumpf NE, Evans LK, Grisso JA, Maislin G. The relationship between physical restraint removal and falls and injuries among nursing home residents. J Gerontol A Biol Sci Med Sci 1998; 53:M47-M52.

[2]*University of California at San Francisco (UCSF)-Stanford University Evidence-based Practice Center Subchapter 26.2. Interventions that Decrease the Use of Physical Restraints" of the Evidence Report/Technology Assessment, No. 43 entitled, "Making*

Consider, for example, a patient who is displaying symptoms of Sundowner's Syndrome, a syndrome in which a patient's dementia becomes more apparent at the end of the day than at the beginning of the day. The patient is not acting out or behaving in a violent or self-destructive manner. However, the patient has an unsteady gait and continues to get out of bed even after staff has tried alternatives to keep the patient from getting out of bed. There is nothing inherently dangerous about a patient being able to walk or wander, even at night. Under the provisions of this regulation, the rationale that the patient should be restrained because he "might" fall does **not** constitute an adequate basis for using a restraint for the purposes of this regulation. When assessing a patient's risk for falls and planning care for the patient, staff should consider whether the patient has a medical condition or symptom that indicates a current need for a protective intervention to prevent the patient from walking or getting out of bed. A history of falling without a current clinical basis for a restraint intervention is inadequate to demonstrate the need for restraint. It is important to note that the regulation specifically states that convenience is not an acceptable reason to restrain a patient. In addition, a restraint must not serve as a substitute for the adequate staffing needed to monitor patients.

An individualized patient assessment is critical. In this example, an assessment should minimally address the following questions:

- Are there safety interventions or precautions (other than restraint) that can be taken to reduce the risk of the patient slipping, tripping, or falling if the patient gets out of bed?

- Is there a way to enable the patient to safely ambulate?

- Is there some assistive device that will improve the patient's ability to self ambulate?

- Is a medication or a reversible condition causing the unsteady gait?

- Would the patient be content to walk with a staff person?

- Could the patient be brought closer to the nurse's station where he or she could be supervised?

If an assessment reveals a medical condition or symptom that indicates the need for an intervention to protect the patient from harm, the regulation requires the hospital to use the least restrictive intervention that will effectively protect the patient from harm. Upon making this determination, the hospital may consider the use of a restraint; however, that

Health Care Safer: A Critical Analysis of Patient Safety Practices." The full report can be accessed at: http://www.ahrq.gov/qual/errorsix.htm

consideration should weigh the risks of using a restraint (which are widely documented in research) against the risks presented by the patient's behavior. If the hospital chooses to use the restraint, it must meet the requirements contained in this standard.

In addition, a request from a patient or family member for the application of a restraint, which they would consider to be beneficial, is not a sufficient basis for the use of a restraint intervention. A patient or family member request for a restraint intervention, such as a vest restraint or raising all four side rails, to keep the patient from getting out of bed or falling should prompt a patient and situational assessment to determine whether such a restraint intervention is needed. If a need for restraint is confirmed, the practitioner must then determine the type of restraint intervention that will meet the patient's needs with the least risk and most benefit to the patient. If restraint (as defined by the regulation) is used, then the requirements of the regulation must be met.

Patient care staff must demonstrate through their documentation in the patient's medical record that the restraint intervention used is the least restrictive intervention that protects the patient's safety, and that the use of restraint is based on individual assessments of the patient. The assessments and documentation of those assessments must be ongoing in order to demonstrate a continued need for restraint. Documentation by the physician or other staff once a day may not be adequate to support that the restraint intervention needs to continue and may not comply with the requirement to end the restraint as soon as possible. A patient's clinical needs often change over time.

CMS does not consider **the use of weapons** in the application of restraint or seclusion as a safe, appropriate health care intervention. For the purposes of this regulation, the term "weapon" includes, but is not limited to, pepper spray, mace, nightsticks, tazers, cattle prods, stun guns, and pistols. Security staff may carry weapons as allowed by hospital policy, and State and Federal law. However, the use of weapons by security staff is considered a law enforcement action, not a health care intervention. CMS does not support the use of weapons by any hospital staff as a means of subduing a patient in order to place that patient in restraint or seclusion. If a weapon is used by security or law enforcement personnel on a person in a hospital (patient, staff, or visitor) to protect people or hospital property from harm, we would expect the situation to be handled as a criminal activity and the perpetrator be placed in the custody of local law enforcement.

The use of handcuffs, manacles, shackles, other chain-type restraint devices, or other restrictive devices applied by non-hospital employed or contracted law enforcement officials for custody, detention, and public safety reasons are not governed by this rule. **The use of such devices are considered law enforcement restraint devices and would not be considered safe, appropriate health care restraint interventions for use by hospital staff to restrain patients.** The law enforcement officers who maintain custody and direct supervision of their prisoner (the hospital's patient) are responsible for the use, application, and monitoring of these restrictive devices in accordance with Federal and State law. However, the hospital is still responsible for an appropriate patient assessment and the provision of safe, appropriate care to its patient (the law enforcement officer's prisoner).

Survey Procedures §482.13(e)

- Review hospital restraint and seclusion policies and procedures to determine if they address, at a minimum:

  - o Who has the authority to discontinue the use of restraint or seclusion (based on State law and hospital policies); and

  - o Circumstances under which restraint or seclusion should be discontinued. (Also see §482.13(e)(3)).

- Review a sample of medical records of patients for whom restraints were used to manage non-violent, non-self-destructive behavior, as well as a sample of medical records of patients for whom restraint or seclusion was used to manage violent or self-destructive behavior;

- Include in the review patients who are currently in restraint or seclusion, as well as those who have been in restraint or seclusion during their hospital stay (include both violent or self-destructive patients as well as non-violent, non-self-destructive patients).

- What evidence is there that hospital staff identified the reason for the restraint or seclusion, and determined that other less restrictive measures would not be effective before applying the restraint?

- Interview staff who work directly with patients to determine their understanding of the restraint and seclusion policies. If any patients are currently in restraint or seclusion, ascertain the rationale for use and when the patient was last monitored and assessed.

- Is the actual use of restraints or seclusion consistent with hospital restraint and seclusion policies and procedures, as well as CMS requirements?

- Review incident and accident reports to determine whether patient injuries occurred proximal to or during a restraint or seclusion intervention. Are incidents and accidents occurring more frequently with restrained or secluded patients?

- If record review indicates that restrained or secluded patients sustained injuries, determine what the hospital did to prevent additional injury. Determine if the hospital investigated possible changes to its restraint or seclusion policies.

- Obtain data on the use of restraint and seclusion for a specified time period (e.g., 3 months) to determine any patterns in their use for specific units, shifts, days of the week, etc.

- Does the number of patients who are restrained or secluded increase on weekends, on holidays, at night, on certain shifts; where contract nurses are used; in one unit more than other units? Such patterns of restraint or seclusion use may suggest that the intervention is not based on the patient's need, but on issues such as convenience, inadequate staffing or lack of staff training. Obtain nursing staffing schedules during time periods in question to determine if staffing levels impact the use of restraint or seclusion.

- Interview a random sample of patients who were restrained to manage non-violent, non-self-destructive behavior. Were the reasons for the use of a restraint to manage non-violent, non-self-destructive behavior explained to the patient in understandable terms? Could the patient articulate his/her understanding?

A-0159
(Rev. 37, Issued: 10-17-08; Effective/Implementation Date: 10-17-08)

§482.13(e) (1) Definitions. (i) A restraint is—

(A) Any manual method, physical or mechanical device, material, or equipment that immobilizes or reduces the ability of a patient to move his or her arms, legs, body, or head freely; or

Interpretive Guidelines §482.13(e)(1)(i)(A)

This restraint definition applies to **all** uses of restraint in **all** hospital care settings. Under this definition, commonly used hospital devices and other practices could meet the definition of a restraint, such as:

- Tucking a patient's sheets in so tightly that the patient cannot move;

- Use of a "net bed" or an "enclosed bed" that prevents the patient from freely exiting the bed. **EXCEPTION**: Placement of a toddler in an "enclosed" or "domed" crib;

- Use of "Freedom" splints that immobilize a patient's limb;

- Using side rails to prevent a patient from voluntarily getting out of bed; or

- Geri chairs or recliners, **only** if the patient cannot easily remove the restraint appliance and get out of the chair on his or her own.

NOTE: Generally, if a patient can easily remove a device, the device would not be considered a restraint. In this context, **"easily remove"** means that the manual method, device, material, or equipment can be removed intentionally by the patient in the same manner as it was applied by the staff (e.g., side rails are put down, not climbed over; buckles are intentionally unbuckled; ties or knots are intentionally untied; etc.) considering the patient's physical condition and ability to accomplish objective (e.g., transfer to a chair, get to the bathroom in time).

Survey Procedures §482.13(e)(1)(i)(A)

- Determine whether the hospital's policy and procedures employ a definition or description of what constitutes a restraint that is consistent with the regulation.

- While touring hospital units look for restraints in use. Where a restraint is in use, check the medical record for appropriate documentation.

- Interview hospital staff to determine whether they know the definition of a restraint.

A-0160
(Rev. 37, Issued: 10-17-08; Effective/Implementation Date: 10-17-08)

§482.13(e)(1)(i)(B) [A restraint is -] A drug or medication when it is used as a restriction to manage the patient's behavior or restrict the patient's freedom of movement and is not a standard treatment or dosage for the patient's condition.

Interpretive Guidelines §482.13(e)(1)(i)(B)

Drugs or medications that are used as part of a patient's standard medical or psychiatric treatment, and are administered within the standard dosage for the patient's condition, would not be subject to the requirements of standard (e). These regulations are not intended to interfere with the clinical treatment of patients who are suffering from serious mental illness and who need therapeutic doses of medication to improve their level of functioning so that they can more actively participate in their treatment. Similarly, these regulations are not intended to interfere with appropriate doses of sleeping medication prescribed for patients with insomnia, anti-anxiety medication prescribed to calm a patient who is anxious, or analgesics prescribed for pain management. The regulatory language is intended to provide flexibility and recognize the variations in patient conditions.

Whether or not an order for a drug or medication is PRN (Latin abbreviation for pro re nata - as needed; as circumstances require) or a standing-order does not determine whether or not the use of that drug or medication is considered a restraint. The use of PRN or standing-order drugs or medications is only prohibited if the drug or medication meets the definition of a drug or medication used as a restraint.

Criteria used to determine whether the use of a drug or medication, or combination of drugs or medications is a standard treatment or dosage for the patient's condition includes all of the following:

- The drug or medication is used within the pharmaceutical parameters approved by the Food and Drug Administration (FDA) and the manufacturer for the indications that it is manufactured and labeled to address, including listed dosage parameters;

- The use of the drug or medication follows national practice standards established or recognized by the medical community, or professional medical associations or organizations; and,

- The use of the drug or medication to treat a specific patient's clinical condition is based on that patient's symptoms, overall clinical situation, and on the physician's or other licensed independent practitioner's (LIP) knowledge of that patient's expected and actual response to the medication.

Another component of "standard treatment or dosage" for a drug or medication is the expectation that the standard use of a drug or medication to treat the patient's condition enables the patient to more effectively or appropriately function in the world around them than would be possible without the use of the drug or medication. If the overall effect of a drug or medication, or combination of drugs or medications, is to reduce the patient's ability to effectively or appropriately interact with the world around the patient, then the drug or medication is **not** being used as a standard treatment or dosage for the patient's condition.

As with any use of restraint or seclusion, staff must conduct a comprehensive patient assessment to determine the need for other types of interventions before using a drug or medication as a restraint. For example, a patient may be agitated due to pain, an adverse reaction to an existing drug or medication, or other unmet care need or concern.

There are situations where the use of a drug or medication is clearly outside the standard for a patient or a situation, or a medication is not medically necessary but is used for patient discipline or staff convenience (neither of which is permitted by the regulation).

- **EXAMPLE 1:** A patient has Sundowner's Syndrome, a syndrome in which a patient's dementia becomes more apparent at the end of the day rather than at the beginning of the day. The patient may become agitated, angry, or anxious at sundown. This may lead to wandering, pacing the floors, or other nervous behaviors. The staff finds the patient's behavior bothersome, and asks the physician to order a high dose of a sedative to "knock out" the patient and keep him in bed. The patient has no medical symptoms or condition that indicates the need for a sedative. In this case, for this patient, the sedative is being used inappropriately as a restraint for staff convenience. Such use is not permitted by the regulation.

A drug or medication that is not being used as a standard treatment for the patient's medical or psychiatric condition, and that results in restricting the patient's freedom of movement would be a drug used as a restraint.

In addition, the regulation does not permit a drug or medication to be used to restrain the patient for staff convenience, to coerce or discipline the patient, or as a method of retaliation. While drugs or medications can be a beneficial part of a carefully constructed, individualized treatment plan for the patient, drug and medication use should be based on the assessed needs of the individual patient, and the effects of drugs and medications on the patient should be carefully monitored.

- **EXAMPLE 2:** A patient is in a detoxification program. The patient becomes violent and aggressive. Staff administers a PRN medication ordered by the patient's physician or other LIP to address these types of outbursts. The use of the medication enables the patient to better interact with others or function more effectively. In this case, the medication used for this patient is not considered a "drug used as a restraint." The availability of a PRN medication to manage outbursts of specific behaviors, such as aggressive, violent behavior is standard for this patient's medical condition (i.e., drug or alcohol withdrawal). Therefore, this patient's medication does not meet the definition of "drug used as a restraint" since it is a standard treatment or dosage for the patient's medical or psychiatric condition. The use of this medication for this patient is not affected by standard (e).

  If a drug or medication is used as a standard treatment (as previously defined) to address the assessed symptoms and needs of a patient with a particular medical or psychiatric condition, its use is **not** subject to the requirements of this regulation. However, the patient would still need to receive assessments, monitoring, interventions, and care that are appropriate for that patient's needs.

The regulation supports existing State laws that provide more vigorous promotion of the patient's choice and rights. Therefore, when a State's law prohibits the administration of drugs against the wishes of the patient without a court order, the State law applies.

Survey Procedures §482.13(e)(1)(i)(B)

- Determine whether the hospital's policies and procedures employ a definition or description of what constitutes the use of drugs or medications as a restraint that is consistent with the regulation.

- Interview hospital staff to determine whether they can identify when the use of a drug or medication is considered a chemical restraint.

A-0161
(Rev. 37, Issued: 10-17-08; Effective/Implementation Date: 10-17-08)

§482.13(e)(1)(i)(C) - A restraint does not include devices, such as orthopedically prescribed devices, surgical dressings or bandages, protective helmets, or other methods that involve the physical holding of a patient for the purpose of conducting routine physical examinations or tests, or to protect the patient from falling out of bed, or to permit the patient to participate in activities without the risk of physical harm (this does not include a physical escort).

Interpretive Guidelines §482.13(e)(1)(i)(C)

The devices and methods listed here would not be considered restraints, and, therefore, not subject to these requirements. These devices and methods are typically used in medical-surgical care.

Use of an **IV arm board** to stabilize an IV line is generally not considered a restraint. However, if the arm board is tied down (or otherwise attached to the bed), or the entire limb is immobilized such that the patient cannot access his or her body, the use of the arm board would be considered a restraint.

A **mechanical support** used to achieve proper body position, balance, or alignment so as to allow greater freedom of mobility than would be possible without the use of such a mechanical support is not considered a restraint. For example, some patients lack the ability to walk without the use of leg braces, or to sit upright without neck, head, or back braces.

A medically necessary **positioning or securing device** used to maintain the position, limit mobility, or temporarily immobilize the patient during medical, dental, diagnostic, or surgical procedures is not considered a restraint.

Recovery from anesthesia that occurs when the patient is in a critical care or postanesthesia care unit is considered part of the surgical procedure; therefore, medically necessary restraint use in this setting would not need to meet the requirements of the regulation. However, if the intervention is maintained when the patient is transferred to another unit, or recovers from the effects of the anesthesia (whichever occurs first), a restraint order would be necessary and the requirements of standard (e) would apply.

Many types of **hand mitts** would not be considered restraint. However, pinning or otherwise attaching those same mitts to bedding or using a wrist restraint in conjunction with the hand mitts would meet the definition of restraint and the requirements would apply. In addition, if the mitts are applied so tightly that the patient's hand or fingers are immobilized, this would be considered restraint and the requirements would apply. Likewise, if the mitts are so bulky that the patient's ability to use their hands is significantly reduced, this would be considered restraint and the requirements would apply.

NOTE: Because this definition of physical restraint does not name each device and situation that can be used to immobilize or reduce the ability of the patient to move his or her arms, legs, body or head freely, it promotes looking at each patient situation on a case-by-case basis.

In addition, if a patient can easily remove a device, the device would not be considered a restraint. In this context, **"easily remove"** means that the manual method, device, material, or equipment can be removed intentionally by the patient in the same manner as it was applied by the staff (e.g., side rails are put down, not climbed over; buckles are intentionally unbuckled; ties or knots are intentionally untied; etc.) considering the patient's physical condition and ability to accomplish the objective (e.g., transfer to a chair, get to the bathroom in time).

Age or developmentally appropriate protective safety interventions (such as stroller safety belts, swing safety belts, high chair lap belts, raised crib rails, and crib covers) that a safety-conscious child care provider outside a health care setting would utilize to protect an infant, toddler, or preschool-aged child would not be considered restraint or seclusion for the purposes of this regulation. The use of these safety interventions needs to be addressed in the hospital's policies or procedures.

Physical Escort

A physical escort would include a "light" grasp to escort the patient to a desired location. If the patient can easily remove or escape the grasp, this would not be considered physical restraint. However, if the patient cannot easily remove or escape the grasp, this would be considered physical restraint and all the requirements would apply.

Physical holding

The regulation permits the physical holding of a patient for the purpose of conducting routine physical examinations or tests. However, patients do have the right to refuse treatment. See §482.13(b)(2). This includes the right to refuse physical examinations or tests. Holding a patient in a manner that restricts the patient's movement against the patient's will is considered restraint. This includes holds that some member of the medical community may term **"therapeutic holds."** Many deaths have occurred while employing these practices. Physically holding a patient can be just as restrictive, and just as dangerous, as restraining methods that involve devices. Physically holding a patient during a forced psychotropic medication procedure is considered a restraint and is **not** included in this exception.

For the purposes of this regulation, a staff member picking up, redirecting, or holding an infant, toddler, or preschool-aged child to comfort the patient is not considered restraint.

Physical Holding for Forced Medications

The application of force to physically hold a patient, in order to administer a medication against the patient's wishes, is considered restraint. The patient has a right to be free of restraint and, in accordance with §482.13(b)(2), also has a right to refuse medications, unless a court has ordered medication treatment. A court order for medication treatment only removes the patient's right to refuse the medication. Additionally, in accordance with State law, some patients may be medicated against their will in certain emergency circumstances. However, in both of these circumstances, health care staff is expected to use the least restrictive method of administering the medication to avoid or reduce the use of force, when possible. The use of force in order to medicate a patient, as with other restraint, must have a physician's order prior to the application of the restraint (use of force). If physical holding for forced medication is necessary with a violent patient, the 1-hour face-to-face evaluation requirement would also apply.

In certain circumstances, a patient may consent to an injection or procedure, but may not be able to hold still for an injection, or cooperate with a procedure. In such circumstances, and at the patient's request, staff may "hold" the patient in order to safely administer an injection (or obtain a blood sample, or insert an intravenous line, if applicable) or to conduct a procedure. This is **not** considered restraint.

Side rails

A restraint does not include methods that protect the patient from falling out of bed. Examples include raising the side rails when a patient is: on a stretcher, recovering from anesthesia, sedated, experiencing involuntary movement, or on certain types of therapeutic beds to prevent the patient from falling out of the bed. The use of side rails in these situations protects the patient from falling out of bed and, therefore, would not be subject to the requirements of standard (e).

However, side rails are frequently not used as a method to prevent the patient from falling out of bed, but instead, used to restrict the patient's freedom to exit the bed. The use of side rails to prevent the patient from exiting the bed would be considered a restraint and would be subject to the requirements of standard (e). The use of side rails is inherently risky, particularly if the patient is elderly or disoriented. Frail elderly patients may be at risk for entrapment between the mattress or bed frame and the side rail. Disoriented patients may view a raised side rail as a barrier to climb over, may slide between raised, segmented side rails, or may scoot to the end of the bed to get around a raised side rail and exit the bed. When attempting to leave the bed by any of these routes, the patient is at risk for entrapment, entanglement, or falling from a greater height posed by the raised side rail, with a possibility for sustaining greater injury or death than if the patient had fallen from the height of a lowered bed without raised side rails. In short, the patient may have an increased risk for a fall or other injury by attempting to exit the bed with the side rails raised. The risk presented by side rail use should be weighed against the risk presented by the patient's behavior as ascertained through individualized assessment.

When the clinician raises all four side rails in order to restrain a patient, defined in this regulation as immobilizing or reducing the ability of a patient to move his or her arms, legs, body, or head freely to ensure the immediate physical safety of the patient, then the requirements of this rule apply. Raising fewer than four side rails when the bed has segmented side rails would not necessarily immobilize or reduce the ability of a patient to move freely as defined in the regulation. For example, if the side rails are segmented and all but one segment are raised to allow the patient to freely exit the bed, the side rail is not acting as a restraint and the requirements of this rule would not apply. Conversely, if a patient is not physically able to get out of bed regardless of whether the side rails are raised or not, raising all four side rails for this patient would not be considered restraint because the side rails have no impact on the patient's freedom of movement. In this example, the use of all four side rails would not be considered restraint. Therefore, the requirements of this rule would **not** apply.

When a patient is on a bed that constantly moves to improve circulation or prevents skin breakdown, raised side rails are a safety intervention to prevent the patient from falling out of bed and are not viewed as restraint.

When a patient is placed on **seizure precautions** and all side rails are raised, the use of side rails would not be considered restraint. The use of padded side rails in this situation should protect the patient from harm; including falling out of bed should the patient have a seizure.

Placement in a crib with raised rails is an age-appropriate standard safety practice for every infant or toddler. Therefore, placement of an infant or toddler in the crib with raised rails would not be considered restraint.

If the patient is on a **stretcher** (a narrow, elevated, and highly mobile cart used to transport patients and to evaluate or treat patients), there is an increased risk of falling from a stretcher without raised side rails due to its narrow width, and mobility. In addition, because stretchers are elevated platforms, the risk of patient injury due to a fall is significant. Therefore, the use of raised side rails on stretchers is not considered restraint but a prudent safety intervention. Likewise, the use of a seat belt when transporting a patient in a wheelchair is not considered restraint.

Survey Procedures §482.13(e)(1)(i)(C)

- Determine whether the hospital's policies and procedures employ a definition or description of what constitutes a restraint that is consistent with the regulation.

- While touring hospital units look for bed side rail use to determine whether it is consistent with the definition of a restraint. Where bed side rails are being used as a restraint, check the medical record for appropriate documentation.

- Interview hospital staff to determine whether they know the definition of a restraint, particularly with respect to use of bed side rails.

A-0162
(Rev. 37, Issued: 10-17-08; Effective/Implementation Date: 10-17-08)

§482.13(e)(1)(ii) - Seclusion is the involuntary confinement of a patient alone in a room or area from which the patient is physically prevented from leaving. Seclusion may only be used for the management of violent or self-destructive behavior.

Interpretive Guidelines §482.13(e)(1)(ii)

Seclusion may **only** be used for the management of violent or self-destructive behavior that jeopardizes the immediate physical safety of the patient, a staff member, or others.

Seclusion is not just confining a patient to an area, but involuntarily confining the patient alone in a room or area where the patient is physically prevented from leaving. If a patient is restricted to a room alone and staff are physically intervening to prevent the patient from leaving the room or giving the perception that threatens the patient with physical intervention if the patient attempts to leave the room, the room is considered locked, whether the door is actually locked or not. In this situation, the patient is being secluded.

A patient physically restrained alone in an unlocked room does not constitute seclusion.

Confinement on a locked unit or ward where the patient is with others does not constitute seclusion.

Timeout is not considered seclusion. Timeout is an intervention in which the patient consents to being alone in a designated area for an agreed upon timeframe from which the patient is not physically prevented from leaving. Therefore, the patient can leave the designated area when the patient chooses.

Survey Procedures §482.13(e)(1)(ii)

- Determine whether the hospital's policy and procedures employ a definition or description of what constitutes seclusion that is consistent with the regulation.

- While touring hospital units look for cases where a patient is in seclusion.

- Interview hospital staff to determine whether they know the definition of seclusion.

A-0164
(Rev. 37, Issued: 10-17-08; Effective/Implementation Date: 10-17-08)

§482.13(e)(2) - Restraint or seclusion may only be used when less restrictive interventions have been determined to be ineffective to protect the patient, a staff member, or others from harm.

Interpretive Guidelines §482.13(e)(2)

A comprehensive assessment of the patient must determine that the risks associated with the use of the restraint or seclusion is outweighed by the risk of not using the restraint or seclusion. Less restrictive interventions do not always need to be tried, but less restrictive interventions must be determined by staff to be ineffective to protect the patient or others from harm prior to the introduction of more restrictive measures. Alternatives attempted or the rationale for not using alternatives must be documented.

The underpinning of this regulation is the concept that safe patient care hinges on looking at the patient as an individual and assessing the patient's condition, needs, strengths, weaknesses, and preferences. Such an approach relies on caregivers who are skilled in individualized assessment and in tailoring interventions to the individual patient's needs after weighing factors such as the patient's condition, behaviors, history, and environmental factors.

Resources are available to assist clinicians in identifying less restrictive interventions. For example, the American Psychiatric Association (APA), American Psychiatric Nurses Association (APNA), and the National Association of Psychiatric Health Systems (NAPHS), with support from the American Hospital Association (AHA), have sponsored the publication of a document entitled, "Learning from Each Other—Success Stories and Ideas for Reducing Restraint/Seclusion in Behavioral Health." This document, published in 2003, was developed through dialogue with clinicians in the field and included extensive input from behavioral healthcare providers throughout the country who have been working to reduce the use of restraint and seclusion and to improve care within their facilities. To access this document and other useful resources, visit the web sites of the sponsoring organizations: http://www.naphs.org; http://www.psych.org; http://www.apna.org; http://www.aha.org.

Survey Procedures §482.13(e)(2)

- Do physician's or other LIP's orders specify the reason for restraint or seclusion, the type of restraint, and the duration of restraint or seclusion?

- Does the severity of the behavior justify seclusion or restraint usage by identifying an immediate and serious danger to the physical safety of the patient or others?

- Is there evidence that the hospital considers factors other than the individual patient in determining causes for the need for restraints or seclusion (i.e., environmental factors)?

- Does the medical record include documentation of an individual patient assessment and a revision of the plan of care?

- Does the medical record reflect changes in behavior and staff concerns regarding safety risks to the patient, staff, or others prompting use of seclusion or restraints?

- Did the patient's behavior place the patient or others at risk for harm? Was the patient's behavior violent or self-destructive?

- Were other, less restrictive interventions tried and documented, or is there evidence that alternatives were considered and determined to be insufficient?

A-0165
(Rev. 37, Issued: 10-17-08; Effective/Implementation Date: 10-17-08)

§482.13(e)(3) - The type or technique of restraint or seclusion used must be the least restrictive intervention that will be effective to protect the patient, a staff member, or others from harm.

Interpretive Guidelines §482.13(e)(3)

Resources are available to assist clinicians in identifying less restrictive restraint or seclusion interventions. For example, the American Psychiatric Association (APA), American Psychiatric Nurses Association (APNA), and the National Association of Psychiatric Health Systems (NAPHS), with support from the American Hospital Association (AHA), have sponsored the publication of a document entitled, "Learning from Each Other—Success Stories and Ideas for Reducing Restraint/Seclusion in

Behavioral Health." This document, published in 2003, was developed through dialogue with the field and extensive input from behavioral healthcare providers throughout the country who have been working to reduce the use of restraint and seclusion and to improve care within their facilities. To access this document and other useful resources, visit the web sites of the sponsoring organizations: http://www.naphs.org; http://www.psych.org; http://www.apna.org; http://www.aha.org

Survey Procedures §482.13(e)(3)

- Is there clear documentation in the patient's medical record describing the steps or interventions used prior to the use of the needed restraint or seclusion? That is, what documentation is in the medical record to explain the rationale for the use of restraint or seclusion?

- Is there documentation that less restrictive measures were tried or considered?

  - Is the restraint or seclusion intervention the least restrictive intervention that meets the patient's clinical needs and protects the safety of the patient, staff, or others?

  - Did the staff determine that less restrictive alternatives would not meet the patient's clinical needs, or protect the patient's safety or the safety of others?

  - Do ongoing documented assessments demonstrate that the restraint or seclusion intervention is needed at this time (or at a time in the past) and that the restraint or seclusion intervention remains the least restrictive way to protect the patient's safety?

  - If the time of restraint or seclusion use is lengthy, look for evidence that the symptoms necessitating the use of restraint or seclusion have persisted. Is there evidence to indicate that the staff have evaluated whether or not the restraint or seclusion can be safely discontinued?

A-0166
§482.13(e)(4) - The use of restraint or seclusion must be --

(i) in accordance with a written modification to the patient's plan of care.

Interpretive Guidelines §482.13(e)(4)(i)

The use of restraint or seclusion (including drugs or medications used as restraint as well as physical restraint) must be documented in the patient's plan of care or treatment plan. The use of restraint or seclusion constitutes a change in a patient's plan of care.

The regulation does not require that a modification to the patient's plan of care be made before initiating or obtaining an order for the use of restraint or seclusion. The use of a restraint or seclusion intervention should be reflected in the patient's plan of care or treatment plan based on an assessment and evaluation of the patient. The plan of care or treatment plan should be reviewed and updated in writing within a timeframe specified by hospital policy.

Survey Procedures §482.13(e)(4)(i)

- Determine whether the hospital's procedures are consistent with the requirements of this regulation. Does the plan of care or treatment reflect a process of assessment, intervention, and evaluation when restraint or seclusion is used?

- Is there evidence of assessment of the identified problem or of an individual patient assessment?

- Does the patient's plan of care reflect that assessment?

- What was the goal of the intervention?

- What was the described intervention?

- Who is responsible for implementation?

- Was the patient informed of the changes in his or her treatment plan or plan of care?

- Did the physician or other LIP write orders that included a time limit? Were these orders incorporated into the plan of care?

- After the discontinuation of the restraint or seclusion intervention, was this information documented in an update of the plan of care or treatment plan?

A-0167
(Rev. 37, Issued: 10-17-08; Effective/Implementation Date: 10-17-08)

[The use of restraint or seclusion must be --]

§482.13(e)(4)(ii) - implemented in accordance with safe and appropriate restraint and seclusion techniques as determined by hospital policy in accordance with State law.

Interpretive Guidelines §482.13(e)(4)(ii)

Restraint or seclusion must be implemented appropriately and safely, and reflect hospital policy in accordance with State law.

The use of restraint or seclusion must never act as a barrier to the provision of other interventions to meet the patient's needs.

Survey Procedures §482.13(e)(4)(ii)

- Review the hospital's policies and procedures to determine if they reflect current standards of practice regarding safe and appropriate restraint and seclusion techniques. Are there any references to State law statutes or any indication State laws were reviewed and incorporated?

- Review a sample of patient medical records that include patients who required the use of restraint or seclusion for the management of both violent, self-destructive behaviors, and non-violent, non-self-destructive behaviors.
- After restraints were applied, was an assessment immediately made to ensure that restraints were properly and safely applied?

- Were the hospital policies and procedures followed?

- Was the use of restraint or seclusion effective in achieving the purpose for which it was ordered? If not, were timely changes made?

- Was there any evidence of injury to the patient?

A-0168
(Rev. 37, Issued: 10-17-08; Effective/Implementation Date: 10-17-08)

§482.13(e)(5) - The use of restraint or seclusion must be in accordance with the order of a physician or other licensed independent practitioner who is responsible for the care of the patient as specified under §481.12(c) and authorized to order restraint or seclusion by hospital policy in accordance with State law.

Interpretive Guidelines §482.13(e)(5)

Hospitals must have policies and procedures for the initiation of restraint or seclusion that identify the categories of LIPs that are permitted to order restraint or seclusion in that hospital, consistent with State law.

The regulation requires that a physician or other LIP responsible for the care of the patient to order restraint or seclusion prior to the application of restraint or seclusion. In some situations, however, the need for a restraint or seclusion intervention may occur so quickly that an order cannot be obtained prior to the application of restraint or seclusion. In these **emergency application situations,** the order must be obtained either during the emergency application of the restraint or seclusion, or immediately (within a few minutes) after the restraint or seclusion has been applied. The failure to immediately obtain an order is viewed as the application of restraint or seclusion without an order. The hospital should address this process in its restraint and seclusion policies and procedures. The policies and procedures should specify who can initiate the emergency application of restraint or seclusion prior to obtaining an order from a physician or other LIP.

Licensed Independent Practitioner (LIP)

For the purpose of ordering restraint or seclusion, an LIP is any practitioner permitted by State law and hospital policy as having the authority to independently order restraints or seclusion for patients.

A resident who is authorized by State law and the hospital's residency program to practice as a physician can carry out functions reserved for a physician or LIP by the regulation. A medical school student holds no license, and his/her work is reviewed and must be countersigned by the attending physician; therefore, he or she is not licensed or independent. A medical school student is not an LIP.

Protocols

A protocol cannot serve as a substitute for obtaining a physician's or other LIP's order prior to initiating each episode of restraint or seclusion use. If a hospital uses protocols that include the use of restraint or seclusion, a specific physician or LIP order is still required for each episode of restraint or seclusion use. The philosophy that serves as a foundation for the regulation is that restraint or seclusion use is an exceptional event, not a routine response to a certain patient condition or behavior. Each patient must be assessed, and interventions should be tailored to meet the individual patient's needs. The creation of a protocol can run counter to this philosophy if it sets up the expectation that restraint or seclusion will be used as a routine part of care. The use of restraint or seclusion is a last resort when less restrictive measures have been determined ineffective to ensure the safety of the patient, staff or others, should not be a standard response to a behavior or patient need.

Survey Procedures §482.13(e)(5)

- Review hospital policies and medical staff by-laws to ascertain clinical practice guidelines that describe the responsibilities of medical staff and clinicians who are privileged to order restraint and seclusion.

- Do the hospital's written policies identify what categories of practitioners the State recognizes as an LIP or as having the authority to order restraint and seclusion?

- Does the hospital have written policies indicating which practitioners are permitted to order restraint or seclusion in the facility?

- Do the hospital's written policies conform to State law?

- Does the hospital have established policies for who can initiate restraint or seclusion?

- Does the hospital utilize protocols for the use of restraint or seclusion? If so, is the use of protocols consistent with the requirements of the regulation?

- Do the medical records reviewed identify the physician or LIP who ordered each use of restraint or seclusion?

- During the medical record review, verify that a physician or LIP order was obtained prior to the initiation of restraint or seclusion. When emergency application of restraint or seclusion was necessary, verify that a physician or LIP order was obtained immediately (within a few minutes) after application of the restraint or seclusion.

A-0169
(Rev. 37, Issued: 10-17-08; Effective/Implementation Date: 10-17-08)

§482.13(e)(6) - Orders for the use of restraint or seclusion must never be written as a standing order or on an as needed basis (PRN).

Interpretive Guidelines §482.13(e)(6)
This regulation prohibits the use of standing or PRN (Latin abbreviation for pro re nata - as needed; as circumstances require) orders for the use of restraint or seclusion. The ongoing authorization of restraint or seclusion is not permitted. Each episode of restraint or seclusion must be initiated in accordance with the order of a physician or other LIP. If a patient was recently released from restraint or seclusion, and exhibits behavior that can only be handled through the reapplication of restraint or seclusion, a new order would be required. Staff cannot discontinue a restraint or seclusion intervention, and then re-start it under the same order. This would constitute a PRN order. A "trial release" constitutes a PRN use of restraint or seclusion, and, therefore, is not permitted by this regulation.

When a staff member ends an ordered restraint or seclusion intervention, the staff member has no authority to reinstitute the intervention without a new order. For example, a patient is released from restraint or seclusion based on the staff's assessment of the patient's condition. If this patient later exhibits behavior that jeopardizes the immediate physical safety of the patient, a staff member, or others that can only be handled through the use of restraint or seclusion, a new order would be required.

NOTE: A temporary, directly-supervised release, however, that occurs for the purpose of caring for a patient's needs (e.g., toileting, feeding, or range of motion exercises) is **not** considered a discontinuation of the restraint or seclusion intervention. As long as the patient remains under direct staff supervision, the restraint is not considered to be discontinued because the staff member is present and is serving the same purpose as the restraint or seclusion.

The use of PRN orders for drugs or medications is only prohibited when a drug or medication is being used as a restraint. A drug or medication is deemed to be a restraint only if it is not a standard treatment or dosage for the patient's condition, and the drug or medication is a restriction to manage the patient's behavior or restricts the patient's freedom of movement Using a drug to restrain the patient for staff convenience is expressly prohibited.

EXCEPTIONS

- **Geri chair**. If a patient requires the use of a Geri chair with the tray locked in place in order for the patient to safely be out of bed, a standing or PRN order is permitted. Given that a patient may be out of bed in a Geri chair several times a day, it is not necessary to obtain a new order each time.

- **Raised side rails.** If a patient's status requires that all bedrails be raised (restraint) while the patient is in bed, a standing or PRN order is permitted. It is not necessary to obtain a new order each time the patient is returned to bed after being out of bed.

- **Repetitive self-mutilating behavior**. If a patient is diagnosed with a chronic medical or psychiatric condition, such as Lesch-Nyham Syndrome, and the patient engages in repetitive self-mutilating behavior, a standing or PRN order for restraint to be applied in accordance with specific parameters established in the treatment plan would be permitted. Since the use of restraints to prevent self-injury is needed for these types of rare, severe, medical and psychiatric conditions, the specific requirements (1-hour face-to-face evaluation, time-limited orders, and evaluation every 24 hours before renewal of the order) for the management of violent or self- destructive behavior do not apply.

Survey Procedures §482.13(e)(6)

Review a random sample of medical records for patients that have been restrained or secluded. Review orders, progress notes, flow sheets, and nursing notes to:

- Verify that there is a physician or other LIP order for each episode of restraint or seclusion;

- Evaluate patterns of use and verify that orders were obtained when necessary;

- Verify that the documentation specifically addresses the patients' behaviors or symptoms; and,

- Determine if restraint or seclusion is being improperly implemented on a PRN basis.

A-0170
(Rev. 37, Issued: 10-17-08; Effective/Implementation Date: 10-17-08)

§482.13(e)(7) - The attending physician must be consulted as soon as possible if the attending physician did not order the restraint or seclusion.

Interpretive Guidelines §482.13(e)(7)

The attending physician is the MD/DO who is responsible for the management and care of the patient. Hospital medical staff policies determine who is considered the attending physician. The intent of this requirement is to ensure that the physician who has overall responsibility and authority for the management and care of the patient is aware of the patient's condition and is aware of the restraint or seclusion intervention. It is important to consult with the attending physician to promote continuity of care, to ensure patient safety, and to elicit information that might be relevant in choosing the most appropriate intervention for the patient. The attending physician may have information regarding the patient's history that may have a significant impact on the selection of a restraint or seclusion intervention or an alternative intervention, and the subsequent course of treatment. Therefore, consultation should occur as soon as possible. Hospital policies and procedures should address the definition of "as soon as possible" based on the needs of their particular patient population(s). However, any established time frames must be consistent with "as soon as possible."

The hospital CoPs do permit the patient to be under the care of a treating LIP other than a physician. Section 482.12(c)(1) requires every Medicare patient to be under the care of a doctor of medicine or osteopathy; or, within the scope of their respective licenses, a doctor of dental surgery or dental medicine, a doctor of podiatry, chiropractor, or clinical psychologist. The individual overseeing the patient's care may be the attending physician or a health professional practicing with the delegated authority or supervision of a doctor of medicine or osteopathy as permitted by State law and hospital policy.

When the attending physician of record is unavailable, responsibility for the patient must be delegated to another physician, who would then be considered the attending physician.

This provision does not specify that consultation with the attending physician be face-to-face. The consultation can occur via telephone.

Survey Procedures §482.13(e)(7)

- Review the patient's medical record for documentation that the attending physician was notified immediately if the attending physician did not order the restraint or seclusion. Was the attending physician notified "as soon as possible?"

- Review the hospital's policies and procedures regarding consultation with the attending physician if the attending physician did not order the restraint or seclusion.

- Interview staff to determine if actual practice is consistent with written hospital policies and procedures.

A-0171
(Rev. 37, Issued: 10-17-08; Effective/Implementation Date: 10-17-08)

§482.13(e)(8) - Unless superseded by State law that is more restrictive --

(i) Each order for restraint or seclusion used for the management of violent or self-destructive behavior that jeopardizes the immediate physical safety of the patient, a staff member, or others may only be renewed in accordance with the following limits for up to a total of 24 hours:

(A) 4 hours for adults 18 years of age or older;
(B) 2 hours for children and adolescents 9 to 17 years of age; or
(C) 1 hour for children under 9 years of age; and

Interpretive Guidelines §482.13(e)(8)(i)

Patients of all ages are vulnerable and at risk when restrained or secluded to manage violent or self-destructive behavior. Therefore, time limits have been established for each order for restraint or seclusion used to manage violent or self-destructive behavior. State law may require more restrictive time limits. These time limits **do not** apply to orders for restraint used to manage non-violent or non-self-destructive behavior. However, the requirement that restraint use be ended at the earliest possible time applies to all uses of restraint.

In the final rule on the use of restraint or seclusion, CMS did not include specific criteria for differentiating between emergency situations where the patient's behavior is violent or self-destructive and jeopardizes the immediate physical safety of the patient, a staff member, or others, and non-emergency use of restraint. Clinicians are adept at identifying various behaviors and symptoms, and can readily recognize violent and self-destructive behavior that jeopardizes the immediate physical safety of the patient, a staff member, or others. Asking clinicians to act based on an evaluation of the patient's behavior is no different than relying on the clinical judgment that they use daily in assessing the needs of each patient and taking actions to meet those individual needs.

The regulation identifies **maximum** time limits on the length of each order for restraint or seclusion based on age. The physician or other LIP has the discretion to write the order for a shorter length of time. The length-of-order requirement identifies critical points at which there is mandatory contact with a physician or other LIP responsible for the care of the patient. In addition, the time limits do not dictate how long a patient should remain in restraint or seclusion. Staff is expected to continually assess and monitor the patient to ensure that the patient is released from restraint or seclusion at the earliest possible time. Restraint or seclusion may only be employed while the unsafe situation continues. Once the unsafe situation ends, the use of restraint or seclusion should be discontinued. The regulation explicitly states that the intervention must be discontinued at the earliest possible time, regardless of the length of time identified in the order. For example, if a patient's behavior is no longer violent or self-destructive 20 minutes after the intervention is initiated, then the restraint or seclusion should be discontinued, even if the order was given for up to 4 hours. If restraint or seclusion is discontinued prior to the expiration of the original order, **a new order** must be obtained prior to reinitiating the use of restraint or seclusion.

At the end of the time frame, if the continued use of restraint or seclusion to manage violent or self-destructive behavior is deemed necessary based on an individualized patient assessment, another order is required. When the original order is about to expire, an RN must contact the physician or other LIP, report the results of his or her most recent assessment and request that the original order be renewed (not to exceed the time limits established in the regulation). Whether or not an onsite assessment is necessary prior to renewing the order is left to the discretion of the physician or other LIP in conjunction with a discussion with the RN who is over-seeing the care of the patient. Another 1-hour face-to-face patient evaluation (see §482.13(e)(12) and the related interpretive guidance) is not required when the original order is renewed.

The original restraint or seclusion order may only be renewed within the required time limits for up to a total of 24 hours. After the original order expires, a physician or other LIP must see and assess the patient before issuing a new order.

EXCEPTION: Repetitive self-mutilating behaviors – see interpretive guidance for §482.13(e)(6).

Survey Procedures §482.13(e)(8)(i)

- When restraint or seclusion is used to manage violent or self-destructive behavior, do orders contain the appropriate time frames based on the patient's age? Does the total number of hours covered by an order or its renewal exceed 24 hours?

  - If more restrictive State laws apply, are they being followed?

- Is the renewal order for restraint or seclusion based on a comprehensive individual patient assessment?

- Is there evidence in the patient's medical record that the symptoms necessitating the continued use of restraint or seclusion have persisted?

A-0172
(Rev. 37, Issued: 10-17-08; Effective/Implementation Date: 10-17-08)

[Unless superseded by State law that is more restrictive --]

§482.13(e)(8)(ii) - After 24 hours, before writing a new order for the use of restraint or seclusion for the management of violent or self-destructive behavior, a physician or other licensed independent practitioner who is responsible for the care of the patient as specified under §482.12(c) of this part and authorized to order restraint or seclusion by hospital policy in accordance with State law must see and assess the patient.

Interpretive Guidelines §482.13(e)(8)(ii)

At a minimum, if a patient remains in restraint or seclusion for the management of violent or self-destructive behavior 24 hours after the original order, the physician or other LIP must see the patient and conduct a face-to-face re-evaluation before writing a new order for the continued use of restraint or seclusion. Twenty-four hours of restraint or seclusion for the management of violent or self-destructive behavior is an extreme measure with the potential for serious harm to the patient.

State laws may be more restrictive and require the physician or other LIP to conduct a face-to-face re-evaluation within a shorter timeframe.

When the physician or other LIP renews an order or writes a new order authorizing the continued use of restraint or seclusion, there must be documentation in the patient's medical record that describes the findings of the physician's or other LIP's re-evaluation supporting the continued use of restraint or seclusion.

EXCEPTION: Repetitive self-mutilating behaviors – see interpretive guidance for §482.13(e)(6).

Survey Procedures §482.13(e)(8)((ii)

- If restraint or seclusion is used to manage violent or self-destructive behavior for longer than 24 hours, is there documentation of a new written order, patient assessments, and a re-evaluation by a physician or other LIP in the medical record? Does the documentation provide sufficient evidence to support the need to continue the use of restraint or seclusion? Is there evidence in the medical record that the symptoms necessitating the continued use of restraint or seclusion have persisted?

- Does the patient's plan of care or treatment plan address the use of restraint or seclusion?

- What is the patient's documented clinical response to the continued need for restraint or seclusion?

A-0173
(Rev. 37, Issued: 10-17-08; Effective/Implementation Date: 10-17-08)

[Unless superseded by State law that is more restrictive --]

§482.13(e)(8)(iii) - Each order for restraint used to ensure the physical safety of the non-violent or non-self-destructive patient may be renewed as authorized by hospital policy.

Interpretive Guidelines §482.13(e)(8)(iii)

Hospitals have the flexibility to determine time frames for the renewal of orders for restraint of the non-violent, non-self-destructive patient. These time frames should be addressed in hospital policies and procedures.

Survey Procedures §482.13(e)(8)(iii)

- Review the hospital policy on renewal of restraint orders for the management of non-violent, non-self-destructive patient behavior.

- Interview staff and review the medical record documentation to ensure that practice is consistent with the hospital policy.

A-0174
(Rev. 37, Issued: 10-17-08; Effective/Implementation Date: 10-17-08)

§482.13(e)(9) - Restraint or seclusion must be discontinued at the earliest possible time, regardless of the length of time identified in the order.

Interpretive Guidelines §482.13(e)(9)

Restraint or seclusion may only be employed while the unsafe situation continues. Once the unsafe situation ends, the use of restraint or seclusion must be discontinued.

Staff members are expected to assess and monitor the patient's condition on an ongoing basis to determine whether restraint or seclusion can safely be discontinued. The regulation requires that these interventions be ended as quickly as possible. However, the decision to discontinue the intervention should be based on the determination that the patient's behavior is no longer a threat to self, staff members, or others. When the physician or LIP renews an order or writes a new order authorizing the continued use of restraint or seclusion, there must be documentation in the medical record that describes the patient's clinical needs and supports the continued use of restraint or seclusion.

The hospital policies and procedures should address, at a minimum:

- Categories of staff that the hospital authorizes to discontinue restraint or seclusion in accordance with State law; and

- The circumstances under which restraint or seclusion is to be discontinued.

Survey Procedures §482.13(e)(9)

- Does the hospital have policies and procedures for ending restraint or seclusion? Do the policies include a requirement to end the restraint or seclusion as soon as is safely possible?

- Does the medical record contain evidence that the decision to continue or discontinue the use of restraint or seclusion was based on an assessment and re-evaluation of the patient's condition?

- Interview staff to determine whether they are aware that use of a restraint or seclusion must be discontinued as soon as is safely possible.

A-0175
(Rev. 37, Issued: 10-17-08; Effective/Implementation Date: 10-17-08)

§482.13(e)(10) - The condition of the patient who is restrained or secluded must be monitored by a physician, other licensed independent practitioner or trained staff that have completed the training criteria specified in paragraph (f) of this section at an interval determined by hospital policy.

Interpretive Guidelines §482.13(e)(10)

Ongoing assessment and monitoring of the patient's condition by a physician, other LIP or trained staff is crucial for prevention of patient injury or death, as well as ensuring that the use of restraint or seclusion is discontinued at the earliest possible time. Hospital policies are expected to guide staff in determining appropriate intervals for assessment and monitoring based on the individual needs of the patient, the patient's condition, and the type of restraint or seclusion used. The selection of an intervention and determination of the necessary frequency of assessment and monitoring should be individualized, taking into consideration variables such as the patient's condition, cognitive status, risks associated with the use of the chosen intervention, and other relevant factors. In some cases, checks every 15 minutes or vital signs taken every 2 hours may not be sufficient to ensure the patient's safety. In others, it may be excessive or disruptive to patient care (e.g., it may be unnecessary to mandate that a patient with wrist restraints, and who is asleep, be checked every 15 minutes and awakened every 2 hours to take the patient's vital signs). Similarly, depending on the patient's needs and situational factors, the use of restraint or seclusion may require either periodic (e.g., every 15 minutes, every 30 minutes, etc.) or continual (i.e., moment to moment) monitoring and assessment.

Hospital policies should address: frequencies of monitoring and assessment; assessment content (e.g., vital signs, circulation, hydration needs, elimination needs, level of distress and agitation, mental status, cognitive functioning, skin integrity, etc.); providing for nutritional needs, range of motion exercises, and elimination needs; and mental status and neurological evaluations.

With the exception of the simultaneous use of restraint and seclusion, one-to-one observation with a staff member in constant attendance is not required by this regulation unless deemed necessary based on a practitioner's clinical judgment. For example, placing staff at the bedside of a patient with wrist restraints may be unnecessary. However, for a more restrictive or risky intervention and/or a patient who is suicidal, self injurious, or combative, staff may determine that continual face-to-face monitoring is needed. The hospital is responsible for providing the level of monitoring and frequency of reassessment that will protect the patient's safety.

Hospitals have flexibility in determining which staff performs the patient assessment and monitoring. This determination must be in accordance with the practitioner's scope of clinical practice and State law. For example, assessment and monitoring are activities within a registered nurse's scope of practice. However, some trained, unlicensed staff may perform components of monitoring (e.g., checking the patient's vital signs, hydration and circulation; the patient's level of distress and agitation; or skin integrity), and may also provide for general care needs (e.g., eating, hydration, toileting, and range of motion exercises). Section 482.13(f) requires that before applying restraints, implementing seclusion, or performing associated monitoring and care tasks, staff must be trained and able to demonstrate competency in the performance of these actions.

Survey Procedures §482.13(e)(10)

- Review hospital policies regarding assessment and monitoring of a patient in restraint or seclusion.

  o What evidence do you find that the hospital's monitoring policies are put into practice for all restrained or secluded patients?

  o Do hospital policies identify which categories of staff are responsible for assessing and monitoring the patient?

  o Do hospital policies include time frames for offering fluids and nourishment, toileting/elimination, range of motion, exercise of limbs and systematic release of restrained limbs? Is this documented in the patient's medical record?

- Review patient medical records:

  o Was there a valid rationale for the decision regarding the frequency of patient assessment and monitoring documented in the medical record?

  o Was documentation consistent, relevant, and reflective of the patient's condition?

  o Are time frames described for how often a patient is monitored for vital signs, respiratory and cardiac status, and skin integrity checks?

  o Is there documentation of ongoing patient monitoring and assessment (e.g., skin integrity, circulation, respiration, intake and output, hygiene, injury, etc)?

  o Is the patient's mental status assessed? Is this documented in the medical record?

  o Is the patient assessed regarding continued need for the use of seclusion or restraint?

  o Is there adequate justification for continued use and is this documented?

  o Is the level of supervision appropriate to meet the safety needs of the patient who is at a higher risk for injury (e.g., self-injurious, suicidal)?

A-00176
(Rev. 37, Issued: 10-17-08; Effective/Implementation Date: 10-17-08)

§482.13(e)(11) - Physician and other licensed independent practitioner training requirements must be specified in hospital policy. At a minimum, physicians and other licensed independent practitioners authorized to order restraint or seclusion by hospital policy in accordance with State law must have a working knowledge of hospital policy regarding the use of restraint or seclusion.

Interpretive Guidelines §482.13(e)(11)

At a minimum, physicians and other LIPs authorized to order restraint and seclusion must have a working knowledge of hospital policy regarding the use of restraint and seclusion.

Hospitals have the flexibility to identify training requirements above this minimum requirement based on the competency level of their physicians and other LIPs, and the needs of the patient population(s) that they serve. Physicians receive training in the assessment, monitoring, and evaluation of a patient's condition as part of their medical school education. However, physicians generally do not receive training regarding application of restraint or implementation of seclusion as part of their basic education. Depending on the level and frequency of involvement that a physician or other LIP has in the performance of these activities, additional training may or may not be necessary to ensure the competency of these individuals in this area. The hospital is in the best position to determine if additional physician or other LIP training is necessary based on the model of care, level of physician competency, and the needs of the patient population(s) that the hospital serves.

Survey Procedures §482.13(e)(11)

- Review the hospital policy regarding restraint and seclusion training requirements for physicians and other LIPs. Are the minimum training requirements addressed?

- Review medical staff credentialing and privileging files to determine if physicians or other LIPs involved in restraint and seclusion activities have completed the required training.

A-0178
(Rev. 37, Issued: 10-17-08; Effective/Implementation Date: 10-17-08)

§482.13(e)(12) - When restraint or seclusion is used for the management of violent or self-destructive behavior that jeopardizes the immediate physical safety of the patient, a staff member, or others, the patient must be seen face-to-face within 1 hour after the initiation of the intervention --

(i) By a –

    (A) **Physician or other licensed independent practitioner; or**

    (B) **Registered nurse or physician assistant who has been trained in accordance with the requirements specified in paragraph (f) of this section.**

Interpretive Guidelines §482.13(e)(12)(i)

When restraint or seclusion is used to manage violent or self-destructive behavior, a physician or other LIP, or a registered nurse (RN) or physician assistant (PA) trained in accordance with the requirements specified under §482.13(f), must see the patient face-to-face within 1-hour after the initiation of the intervention. This requirement also applies when a drug or medication is used as a restraint to manage violent or self-destructive behavior.

The 1-hour face-to-face patient evaluation must be conducted in person by a physician or other LIP, or trained RN or PA. A telephone call or telemedicine methodology is not permitted.

If a patient's violent or self-destructive behavior resolves and the restraint or seclusion intervention is discontinued before the practitioner arrives to perform the 1-hour face-to-face evaluation, the practitioner is still required to see the patient face-to-face and conduct the evaluation within 1 hour after the initiation of this intervention. The fact that the patient's behavior warranted the use of a restraint or seclusion indicates a serious medical or psychological need for prompt evaluation of the patient behavior that led to the intervention. The evaluation would also determine whether there is a continued need for the intervention, factors that may have contributed to the violent or self-destructive behavior, and whether the intervention was appropriate to address the violent or self-destructive behavior.

EXCEPTION: Repetitive self-mutilating behaviors – see interpretive guidance for §482.13(e)(6).

Survey Procedures §482.13(e)(12)(i)

- Review the hospital policy regarding the 1-hour face-to-face evaluation.

- What categories of practitioners does the hospital policy authorize to conduct the 1-hour face-to-face evaluation?

- Interview staff to determine if practice is consistent with hospital policy.

A-0179
(Rev. 37, Issued: 10-17-08; Effective/Implementation Date: 10-17-08)

[the patient must be seen face-to-face within 1 hour after the initiation of the intervention --]

§482.13(e)(12)(ii)To evaluate –

    (A)   **The patient's immediate situation;**
    (B)   **The patient's reaction to the intervention;**
    (C)   **The patient's medical and behavioral condition; and**
    (D)   **The need to continue or terminate the restraint or seclusion.**

Interpretive Guidelines §482.13(e)(12)(ii)

The 1-hour face-to-face evaluation includes both a physical and behavioral assessment of the patient that must be conducted by a qualified practitioner within the scope of their practice. An evaluation of the patient's medical condition would include a complete review of systems assessment, behavioral assessment, as well as review and assessment of the patient's history, drugs and medications, most recent lab results, etc. The purpose is to complete a comprehensive review of the patient's condition to determine if other factors, such as drug or medication interactions, electrolyte imbalances, hypoxia, sepsis, etc., are contributing to the patient's violent or self-destructive behavior.

Training for an RN or PA to conduct the 1-hour face-to-face evaluation would include all of the training requirements at §482.13(f) as well as content to evaluate the patient's immediate situation, the patient's reaction to the intervention, the patient's medical and behavioral condition (documented training in conducting physical and behavioral assessment); and the need to continue or terminate the restraint or seclusion.

Survey Procedures §482.13(e)(12)(ii):

- Was the 1-hour face-to-face evaluation conducted by a practitioner authorized by hospital policy in accordance with State law to conduct this evaluation?

- If the 1-hour face-to-face evaluations are conducted by RNs who are not advanced practice nurses (APN), verify that those RNs have documented training that demonstrates they are qualified to conduct a physical and behavioral assessment of the patient that addresses: the patient's immediate situation, the patient's reaction to the intervention, the patient's medical and behavioral condition, and the need to continue or terminate the restraint or seclusion.

- Does documentation of the 1-hour face-to-face evaluation in the patient's medical record include all the listed elements of this requirement?

- Did the evaluation indicate whether changes in the patient's care were required, and, if so, were the changes made?

- Is practice consistent with hospital policy and State law?

A-0180
(Rev. 37, Issued: 10-17-08; Effective/Implementation Date: 10-17-08)

§482.13(e)(13) - States are free to have requirements by statute or regulation that are more restrictive than those contained in paragraph (e)(12)(i) of this section.

Interpretive Guidelines §482.13(e)(13)

States are free to have requirements that are more restrictive regarding the types of practitioners who may conduct the 1-hour face-to-face evaluation. Generally, States may have more restrictive requirements as long as they do not conflict with Federal requirements.

Survey Procedures §482.13(e)(13):

- When preparing for the hospital survey, determine whether there are State provisions governing the use of restraint or seclusion that are more restrictive than those found in this section.

- When State requirements are more restrictive, apply those requirements instead of those found in this section.

A-0182
(Rev. 37, Issued: 10-17-08; Effective/Implementation Date: 10-17-08)

§482.13(e)(14) - If the face-to-face evaluation specified in paragraph (e)(12) of this section is conducted by a trained registered nurse or physician assistant, the trained registered nurse or physician assistant must consult the attending physician or other licensed independent practitioner who is responsible for the care of the patient as specified under §482.12(c) as soon as possible after the completion of the 1 hour face-to-face evaluation.

Interpretive Guidelines §482.13(e)(14)

When a trained RN or PA conducts the required face-to-face evaluation, he or she must consult the attending physician or other LIP responsible for the patient's care as soon as possible after the completion of the evaluation. Hospital policy should address the expected time frame for and the components of the consultation with the attending physician or other LIP consistent with "as soon as possible." This consultation should include, at a minimum, a discussion of the findings of the 1-hour face-to-face evaluation, the need for other interventions or treatments, and the need to continue or discontinue the use of restraint or seclusion. A consultation that is not conducted prior to a renewal of the order would not be consistent with the requirement, "as soon as possible."

Survey Procedures §482.13(e)(14):

- Review the relevant hospital restraint and seclusion policy.

- Does the hospital policy clarify expectations regarding the requirement, "as soon as possible"?

- Does documentation in the patient's medical record indicate consultation with the attending physician or other LIP when the 1-hour face-to-face evaluation was conducted by a trained RN or PA?

- Is practice consistent with hospital policy?

A-0183
(Rev. 37, Issued: 10-17-08; Effective/Implementation Date: 10-17-08)

§482.13(e)(15) - All requirements specified under this paragraph are applicable to the simultaneous use of restraint and seclusion. Simultaneous restraint and seclusion use is only permitted if the patient is continually monitored –

- (i) **Face-to-face by an assigned, trained staff member; or**
- (ii) **By trained staff using both video and audio equipment. This monitoring must be in close proximity to the patient.**

Interpretive Guidelines §482.13(e)(15)

When the simultaneous use of restraint and seclusion is employed, there must be adequate documentation that justifies the decision for simultaneous use as well as vigilance in continuously monitoring the patient so that the patient's care needs are met.

All requirements specified under standard (e) apply to the simultaneous use of restraint and seclusion. The simultaneous use of restraint and seclusion is not permitted unless the patient is continually monitored by trained staff, either through face-to-face observation or through the use of both video and audio equipment. Monitoring with video and audio equipment further requires that staff perform the monitoring in close proximity to the patient. For the purposes of this requirement, "continually" means ongoing without interruption. The use of video and audio equipment does not eliminate the need for frequent monitoring and assessment of the patient.

An individual who is physically restrained alone in his or her room is not necessarily being simultaneously secluded. The individual's privacy and dignity should be protected to the extent possible during any intervention. In fact, the purpose of restraining a patient alone in his or her room may be to promote privacy and dignity versus simultaneously using seclusion and restraint. While this distinction may be difficult to make, it is helpful to consider whether the patient would, in the absence of the physical restraint, be able to voluntarily leave the room. If so, then the patient is not also being secluded. However, if the physical restraint was removed and the patient was still unable to leave the room because the door was locked or staff were otherwise physically preventing the patient from doing so, then the patient is also being secluded.

Staff must take extra care to protect the safety of the patient when interventions that are more restrictive are used. Monitoring must be appropriate to the intervention chosen, so that the patient is protected from possible abuse, assault, or self injury during the intervention.

Survey Procedures §482.13(e)(15):

- Review the hospital's policy regarding simultaneous use of restraint and seclusion to determine whether it provides for continual monitoring and otherwise complies with all requirements of §482.13.

- Conduct document review and staff interviews to determine if practice is consistent with the hospital policy and required uninterrupted audio and visual monitoring is provided as required.

- Is the staff member monitoring the patient with video and audio equipment trained and in close proximity to ensure prompt emergency intervention if a problem arises?

- Does the video equipment cover all areas of the room or location where the patient is restrained or secluded?

- Is the audio and video equipment located in an area that assures patient privacy?

- Is the equipment appropriately maintained and in working condition?

A-0184
(Rev. 37, Issued: 10-17-08; Effective/Implementation Date: 10-17-08)

§482.13(e)(16) - When restraint or seclusion is used, there must be documentation in the patient's medical record of the following:

(i) **The 1-hour face-to-face medical and behavioral evaluation if restraint or seclusion is used to manage violent or self-destructive behavior;**

Interpretive Guidelines §482.13(e)(16)(i)

When restraint or seclusion is used to manage violent or self-destructive behavior, the 1 hour face-to-face medical and behavioral evaluation must be documented in the patient's medical record.

Survey Procedures §482.13(e)(16)(i)

Does the patient's medical record include documentation of the1 hour face-to-face medical and behavioral evaluation when restraint or seclusion is used to manage violent or self-destructive behavior?

A-0185
(Rev. 37, Issued: 10-17-08; Effective/Implementation Date: 10-17-08)

[When restraint or seclusion is used, there must be documentation in the patient's medical record of the following:]

§482.13(e)(16)(ii) - A description of the patient's behavior and the intervention used.

Interpretive Guidelines §482.13(e)(16)(ii)

Documentation that must be included in the patient's medical record when the patient is restrained or secluded includes a description of the patient's behavior and the intervention used. The patient's behavior should be documented in descriptive terms to evaluate the appropriateness of the interventions used. The documentation should include a detailed description of the patient's physical and mental status assessments, and of any environmental factors (e.g., physical, milieu, activities, etc.) that may have contributed to the situation at the time of the intervention.

Survey Procedures §482.13(e)(16(ii)

- Does the patient's medical record include a clear description of the patient's behavior that warranted the use of restraint or seclusion?

- Was the intervention employed appropriate for the identified behavior?

- What was the patient's clinical response to the intervention(s)?

A-0186

(Rev. 37, Issued: 10-17-08; Effective/Implementation Date: 10-17-08)

[When restraint or seclusion is used, there must be documentation in the patient's medical record of the following:]

§482.13(e)(16)(iii) - Alternatives or other less restrictive interventions attempted (as applicable).

Interpretive Guidelines §482.13(e)(16)(iii)

The use of restraint or seclusion must be selected only when less restrictive measures have been judged to be ineffective to protect the patient or others from harm. It is not always appropriate for less restrictive alternatives to be attempted prior to the use of restraint or seclusion. When a patient's behavior presents an immediate and serious danger to his- or herself, or others, immediate action is needed. For example, when a patient physically attacks someone, immediate action is needed. While staff should be mindful of using the least intrusive intervention, it is critical that the intervention selected be effective in protecting the patient or others from harm.

Survey Procedures §482.13(e)(16)(iii):

- Does the patient's medical record document any alternatives or less restrictive interventions attempted by staff, if appropriate?

- What was the effect of less restrictive interventions, if attempted by staff?

- Were the interventions selected appropriate to the targeted patient behaviors?

- When an immediate and serious danger to the patient or others occurred, was the more restrictive intervention(s) effective? Could a less restrictive intervention have been used to ensure the safety of the patient, staff or others?

A-0187

(Rev. 37, Issued: 10-17-08; Effective/Implementation Date: 10-17-08)

[When restraint or seclusion is used, there must be documentation in the patient's medical record of the following:]

§482.13(e)(16)(iv) - The patient's condition or symptom(s) that warranted the use of the restraint or seclusion.

Interpretive Guidelines §482.13(e)(16)(iv)

A comprehensive, individualized patient assessment is necessary to identify the most appropriate intervention to effectively manage a patient's condition or symptom(s). When using a restraint or seclusion intervention, the patient's condition or symptom(s) must be identified and documented in the patient's medical record.

Survey Procedures §482.13(e)(16)(iv):

Does the patient's medical record include descriptions of the patient's condition or symptom(s) that warranted the use of restraint or seclusion?

A-0188
(Rev. 37, Issued: 10-17-08; Effective/Implementation Date: 10-17-08)

[When restraint or seclusion is used, there must be documentation in the patient's medical record of the following:]

§482.13(e)(16)(v) - The patient's response to the intervention(s) used, including the rationale for continued use of the intervention.

Survey Procedures §482.13(e)(16)(v):

- Does the patient's medical record include descriptions of the impact of the intervention on the patient behavior that resulted in the use of restraint or seclusion?

- Does the patient's medical record include a detailed assessment of the patient's response to the intervention and a well-reasoned plan for the continued use of restraint or seclusion?

A-0194
(Rev. 37, Issued: 10-17-08; Effective/Implementation Date: 10-17-08)

§482.13(f) Standard: Restraint or seclusion: Staff training requirements. The patient has the right to safe implementation of restraint or seclusion by trained staff.

Interpretive Guidelines §482.13(f)

Without adequate staff training and competency, the direct care staff, patients, and others are placed at risk. Patients have a right to the safe application of restraint or seclusion by trained and competent staff. Staff training and education play a critical role in the reduction of restraint and seclusion use in a hospital.

Survey Procedures §482.13(f)

- Determine whether the hospital has staff training and education program that protects the patient's right to safe implementation of restraint or seclusion.

- Observe patients in restraint or seclusion to verify safe application of the restraint or seclusion.

A-0196
(Rev. 37, Issued: 10-17-08; Effective/Implementation Date: 10-17-08)

§482.13(f)(1) Training Intervals - Staff must be trained and able to demonstrate competency in the application of restraints, implementation of seclusion, monitoring, assessment, and providing care for a patient in restraint or seclusion –

  (i)   **Before performing any of the actions specified in this paragraph;**
  (ii)   **As part of orientation; and**
  (iii) **Subsequently on a periodic basis consistent with hospital policy.**

Interpretive Guidelines §482.13(f)(1)(i) - (iii)

All staff designated by the hospital as having direct patient care responsibilities, including contract or agency personnel, must demonstrate the competencies specified in standard (f) prior to participating in the application of restraints, implementation of seclusion, monitoring, assessment, or care of a patient in restraint or seclusion. These competencies must be demonstrated initially as part of orientation and subsequently on a periodic basis consistent with hospital policy. Hospitals have the flexibility to identify a time frame for ongoing training based on the level of staff competency, and the needs of the patient population(s) served.

Training for an RN or PA to conduct the 1-hour face-to-face evaluation would include all of the training requirements at §482.13(f) as well as content to evaluate the patient's immediate situation, the patient's reaction to the intervention, the patient's medical and behavioral condition, and the need to continue or terminate the restraint or seclusion. An evaluation of the patient's medical condition would include a complete review of systems assessment, behavioral assessment, as well as review and assessment of the patient's history, medications, most recent lab results, etc. The purpose of the 1-hour face-to-face evaluation is to complete a comprehensive review of the patient's condition and determine if other factors, such as drug or medication interactions, electrolyte imbalances, hypoxia, sepsis, etc., are contributing to the patient's violent or self-destructive behavior.

Once initial training takes place, training must be provided frequently enough to ensure that staff possesses the requisite knowledge and skills to safely care for restrained or secluded patients in accordance with the regulations. The results of skills and knowledge assessments, new equipment, or QAPI data may indicate a need for targeted training or more frequent or revised training.

Hospitals are required to have appropriately trained staff for the proper and safe use of seclusion and restraint interventions. It would not be appropriate for a hospital to routinely call upon a law enforcement agency or agencies as a means of applying restraint or initiating seclusion. If hospital security guards, or other non-healthcare staff, as part of hospital policy, may assist direct care staff, when requested, in the application of restraint or seclusion, the security guards, or other non-healthcare staff, are also expected to be trained and able to demonstrate competency in the safe application of restraint and seclusion (in accordance with §482.13(f))

Survey Procedures §482.13(f)(1)(i) - (iii)

- Does the hospital have a documented training program for the use of restraint and seclusion interventions employed by the hospital?

- Does the hospital have documented evidence that all levels of staff, including agency or contract staff, that have direct patient care responsibilities and any other individuals who may be involved in the application of restraints (e.g., security guards) have been trained and are able to demonstrate competency in the safe use of seclusion and the safe application and use of restraints?

- Review and verify restraint and seclusion education staff training documentation for all new employees and contract staff.

- Does the training include demonstration of required competencies?

- What areas were included in this training program?

A-0199

§482.13(f)(2) Training Content. - The hospital must require appropriate staff to have education, training, and demonstrated knowledge based on the specific needs of the patient population in at least the following:

   (i) **Techniques to identify staff and patient behaviors, events, and environmental factors that may trigger circumstances that require the use of a restraint or seclusion.**

Interpretive Guidelines §482.13(f)(2)(i)

The term "appropriate staff" includes all staff that apply restraint or seclusion, monitor, assess, or otherwise provide care for patients in restraint or seclusion.

All staff, including contract or agency personnel, designated by the hospital as having direct patient care responsibilities are required to receive training in the areas of clinical techniques used to identify patient and staff behaviors, events and environmental factors that may trigger circumstances that require the use of restraint or seclusion. This training should be targeted to the specific needs of the patient populations being served, and to the competency level of staff.

Staff needs to be able to employ a broad range of clinical interventions to maintain the safety of the patient and others. The hospital is expected to provide education and training at the appropriate level to the appropriate staff based upon the specific needs of the patient population being served. For example, staff routinely providing care for patients who exhibit violent or self-destructive behavior that jeopardizes the immediate physical safety of the patient, a staff member, or others (such as in an emergency department or on a psychiatric unit) generally require more in-depth training in the areas included in the regulation than staff routinely providing medical/surgical care. Hospitals may develop and implement their own training programs or use an outside training program. However, standard (f) specifies that individuals providing staff training must be qualified as evidenced by education, training, and experience.

Hospitals have the flexibility to develop their own training program to meet the staff training requirements at §482.13(f) or purchase a training program from the outside. CMS does not specify that any particular outside vendor must be used to provide the required training. Each hospital must assess the learning needs and competency of their staff to determine how extensive periodic training and staff competency demonstration must be subsequent to initial training. The training program must be provided to all appropriate staff. Any person monitoring or providing care to a restrained patient must demonstrate the knowledge and abilities required by the regulations.

At a minimum, physicians and other LIPs authorized to order restraint or seclusion by hospital policy in accordance with State law must have a working knowledge of hospital policy regarding the use of restraint and seclusion. Hospitals have the flexibility to identify training requirements above this minimum based on the competency level of their physicians and other LIPs and the needs of the patient population that they serve.

Survey Procedures §482.13(f)(2)(i):

- Does the hospital educational program include techniques related to the specific patient populations being served?

- Does the hospital educational program include techniques to identify staff and patient behaviors, events, and environmental factors that may trigger circumstances that require the use of restraint or seclusion?

- Does the hospital educational program provide more in-depth training in the areas included in the regulation for staff members who routinely provide care to patients who exhibit violent or self-destructive behavior (e.g., staff who work in the emergency department or psychiatric unit)?

- Interview staff to assess their knowledge of the restraint and seclusion techniques addressed in this requirement.

A-0200
(Rev. 37, Issued: 10-17-08; Effective/Implementation Date: 10-17-08)

[The hospital must require appropriate staff to have education, training, and demonstrated knowledge based on the specific needs of the patient population in at least the following:]

§482.13(f)(2)(ii) - The use of nonphysical intervention skills.

Interpretive Guidelines §482.13(f)(2)(ii)

Although we recognize that there may be circumstances in which the use of restraint or seclusion may be necessary to prevent a patient situation from escalating, staff often skillfully intervene with alternative techniques to redirect a patient, engage the patient in constructive discussion or activity, or otherwise help the patient maintain self-control and avert escalation.

The use of nonphysical intervention skills does not mean attempting a complex series of interventions or a lengthy checklist of steps to initiate before restraining or secluding a patient. Rather, a whole toolbox of possible interventions can be implemented during the course of a patient's treatment based upon the assessment of an individual patient's responses.

Survey Procedures §482.13(f)(2)(ii)

- Does the hospital educational program address the use of nonphysical intervention skills?

- Does the hospital's training program comply with the regulatory requirements?

- Interview staff to assess their non-physical intervention skills.

A-0201

(Rev. 37, Issued: 10-17-08; Effective/Implementation Date: 10-17-08)

[The hospital must require appropriate staff to have education, training, and demonstrated knowledge based on the specific needs of the patient population in at least the following:]

§482.13(f)(2)(iii) - Choosing the least restrictive intervention based on an individualized assessment of the patient's medical, or behavioral status or condition.

Interpretive Guidelines §482.13(f)(2)(iii)

The underpinning of this regulation is the concept that safe patient care hinges on looking at the patient as an individual and assessing the patient's condition, needs, strengths, weaknesses, and preferences. Such an approach relies on caregivers who are skilled in individualized assessment and in tailoring interventions to individual patient's needs after weighing factors such as the patient's condition, behaviors, history, and environmental factors.

Resources are available to assist clinicians in identifying less restrictive interventions. For example, the American Psychiatric Association (APA), American Psychiatric Nurses Association (APNA), and the National Association of Psychiatric Health Systems (NAPHS), with support from the American Hospital Association (AHA), have sponsored the publication of a document entitled, "Learning from Each Other—Success Stories and Ideas for Reducing Restraint/Seclusion in Behavioral Health." This document, published in 2003, was developed through dialogue with the field and extensive input from behavioral healthcare providers throughout the country who have been working to reduce the use of restraint and seclusion, and to improve care within their facilities. To access this document and other useful resources, visit the web sites of the sponsoring organizations: http://www.naphs.org; http://www.psych.org; http://www.apna.org; http://www.aha.org

Survey Procedures §482.13(f)(2)(iii)

- Does the hospital educational program address choosing the least restrictive intervention based on an individualized assessment of the patient's medical or behavioral status or condition?

- Does the hospital educational program address how to conduct an assessment of a patient's medical and behavioral conditions?

- Does the hospital educational program address types of interventions appropriate to the specific needs of the patient population(s) served and ranging from less to more restrictive?

- Interview staff to determine if they are able to demonstrate the abilities addressed in this requirement.

A-0202
(Rev. 37, Issued: 10-17-08; Effective/Implementation Date: 10-17-08)

[The hospital must require appropriate staff to have education, training, and demonstrated knowledge based on the specific needs of the patient population in at least the following:]

§482.13(f)(2)(iv) - The safe application and use of all types of restraint or seclusion used in the hospital, including training in how to recognize and respond to signs of physical and psychological distress (for example, positional asphyxia).

Interpretive Guidelines §482.13(f)(2)(iv)

Patients have a right to the safe application of restraint or seclusion by trained and competent staff.

Survey Procedures §482.13(f)(2)(iv)

- Is all staff, including contract or agency personnel, identified by the hospital as direct caregivers trained and able to demonstrate competency in the safe use of all types of restraints or seclusion used in the hospital?

- Does the hospital educational program address recognition and response to patient signs of physical and psychological distress?

- Is staff able to identify signs of physical and psychological distress in a timely manner?

- Is staff able to respond to and appropriately treat signs of physical and psychological distress?

- Review hospital data (i.e., incident reports, patient injury or death reports, etc.) to identify any patterns of patient injuries or death that may indicate that staff are not adequately trained to recognize and respond to patient signs of physical and psychological distress.

A-0204

(Rev. 37, Issued: 10-17-08; Effective/Implementation Date: 10-17-08)

[The hospital must require appropriate staff to have education, training, and demonstrated knowledge based on the specific needs of the patient population in at least the following:]

§482.13(f)(2)(v) - Clinical identification of specific behavioral changes that indicate that restraint or seclusion is no longer necessary.

Interpretive Guidelines §482.13(f)(2)(v)

The use of restraint or seclusion must be ended at the earliest possible time regardless of the length of time identified in the order. Staff must be trained and demonstrate competency in their ability to identify specific patient behavioral changes that may indicate that restraint or seclusion is no longer necessary and can be safely discontinued.

Survey Procedures §482.13(f)(2)(v)

Does the hospital educational program address identification of specific behavioral changes that may indicate that restraint or seclusion is no longer necessary?

Interview staff to determine if they are able to demonstrate the abilities addressed in this requirement.

A-0205

(Rev. 37, Issued: 10-17-08; Effective/Implementation Date: 10-17-08)

[The hospital must require appropriate staff to have education, training, and demonstrated knowledge based on the specific needs of the patient population in at least the following:]

§482.13(f)(2)(vi) - Monitoring the physical and psychological well-being of the patient who is restrained or secluded, including but not limited to, respiratory and circulatory status, skin integrity, vital signs, and any special requirements specified by hospital policy associated with the 1-hour face-to-face evaluation.

Interpretive Guidelines §482.13(f)(2)(vi)

Staff must be trained and demonstrate competency in monitoring the physical and psychological well-being of a patient who is restrained or secluded, including but not limited to, respiratory and circulatory status, skin integrity, vital signs, and as well as any special requirements specified by hospital policy associated with the 1-hour face-to-face evaluation.

Survey Procedures §482.13(f)(2)(vi)

- Does the hospital educational program address monitoring the physical and psychological needs of patients who are restrained or secluded, including but not limited to, respiratory and circulatory status, skin integrity, vital signs, and any special requirements specified by hospital policy associated with the 1-hour face-to-face evaluation?

- Does the hospital educational program address the specific requirements for the training of RNs and PAs that the hospital authorizes to conduct the 1-hour face-to-face evaluation?

- Interview staff to determine if they are able to demonstrate the competencies addressed in this regulation.

A-0206
(Rev. 37, Issued: 10-17-08; Effective/Implementation Date: 10-17-08)

[The hospital must require appropriate staff to have education, training, and demonstrated knowledge based on the specific needs of the patient population in at least the following:]

§482.13(f)(2)(vii) - The use of first aid techniques and certification in the use of cardiopulmonary resuscitation, including required periodic recertification.

Interpretive Guidelines §482.13(f)(2)(vii)

Hospitals are required to provide a safe environment for the patients in their care. When restraint or seclusion techniques are used, patients are placed at a higher risk for injuries or even death. Hospitals must require appropriate staff (all staff who apply restraint or seclusion, monitor, access or provide care for a patient in restraint or seclusion) to receive education and training in the use of first aid techniques as well as training and certification in the use of cardiopulmonary resuscitation.

Hospitals are not required to use any particular recognized first aid course. Additionally, such courses may not adequately address the immediate interventions, the "first aid", that needs to be rendered to a restrained or secluded patient who is in distress or injured. The goal is for staff to be able to render the appropriate "first aid" required if a restrained or secluded patient is in distress or injured. For example, a patient is found hanging in a vest restraint, a restrained patient is choking on food, a secluded suicidal patient is found hanging, a secluded suicidal patient has cut himself, etc. Hospital staff need to assess their patient population and identify likely scenarios, develop a first aid training that addresses those scenarios, and provide that "first aid" training to all staff that care for restrained or secluded patients.

Survey Procedures §482.13(f)(2)(vii)

- Does the hospital educational program address first aid techniques?

- Is appropriate staff certified in cardiopulmonary resuscitation?

- Does the hospital educational program include, or provide for, staff training and certification in cardiopulmonary resuscitation (including provisions for recertification)?

A-0207
(Rev. 37, Issued: 10-17-08; Effective/Implementation Date: 10-17-08)

§482.13(f)(3) Trainer Requirements. - Individuals providing staff training must be qualified as evidenced by education, training, and experience in techniques used to address patients' behaviors.

Interpretive Guidelines §482.13(f)(3)

There is no requirement that training be obtained from Federally-specified programs. Hospitals may develop and implement their own training programs or use an outside training program. However, individuals providing the training must be qualified as evidenced by education, training and experience in techniques used to address patients' behaviors for the patient populations being served. Trainers should demonstrate a high level of knowledge regarding all the requirements of these regulations as well as the hospital's policies and procedures that address these requirements.

Survey Procedures §482.13(f)(3)

Review personnel files of individuals responsible for providing staff education and training.

Do the individuals providing the education and training possess education, training, and experience to qualify them to teach the staff? Are they qualified to identify and meet the needs of the patient population(s) being served?
Does the hospital have a system for documenting and ensuring that the individuals providing education and training have the appropriate qualifications required by this regulation?

A-0208
(Rev. 37, Issued: 10-17-08; Effective/Implementation Date: 10-17-08)

§482.13(f)(4) Training Documentation. - The hospital must document in the staff personnel records that the training and demonstration of competency were successfully completed.

Interpretive Guidelines §482.13(f)(4)

Staff personnel records must contain documentation that the training and demonstration of competency were successfully completed initially during orientation and on a periodic basis consistent with hospital policy.

Survey Procedure §482.13(f)(4)

- Review a sample of staff personnel records, including contract or agency staff, to determine if the training and demonstration of competency have been completed during orientation and on a periodic basis consistent with hospital policy.

A-0213
(Rev. 84, Issued: 06-07-13, Effective: 06-07-13, Implementation: 06-07-13)

§482.13(g) Standard: Death Reporting Requirements: - Hospitals must report deaths associated with the use of seclusion or restraint.

(1)   With the exception of deaths described under paragraph (g)(2) of this section, the hospital must report the following information to CMS by telephone, facsimile, or electronically, as determined by CMS, no later than the close of business on the next business day following knowledge of the patient's death:

(i)   Each death that occurs while a patient is in restraint or seclusion.

(ii)   Each death that occurs within 24 hours after the patient has been removed from restraint or seclusion.

(iii)   Each death known to the hospital that occurs within 1 week after restraint or seclusion where it is reasonable to assume that use of restraint or placement in seclusion contributed directly or indirectly to a patient's death, regardless of the type(s) of restraint used on the patient during this time. "Reasonable to assume" in this context includes, but is not limited to, deaths related to restrictions of movement for prolonged periods of time, or death related to chest compression, restriction of breathing or asphyxiation....

(3) The staff must document in the patient's medical record the date and time the death was:

(i) Reported to CMS for deaths described in paragraph (g)(1) of this section; or....

Interpretive Guidelines §482.13(g)(1) & (3)(i)

The hospital must report to its CMS Regional Office each death that occurs:

- While a patient is in restraint or in seclusion, except when no seclusion has been used and the only restraint used was a soft, cloth-like two-point wrist restraints;

- Within 24 hours after the patient has been removed from restraint or seclusion, except when no seclusion has been used and the only restraint used was a soft, two-point wrist restraint; or,

- Within 1 week after use of restraint or seclusion where the death is known to the hospital and it is reasonable to assume that the use of restraint or seclusion contributed directly or indirectly to the patient's death, regardless of the type(s) of restraint used on the patient during this time.

  o "Reasonable to assume" applies only to those deaths that occur on days 2-7 after restraint or seclusion has been discontinued.

  o This criterion applies regardless of the type of restraint that was used on the patient. In other words, it applies to all uses of restraint or seclusion where the patient has died on days 2-7 after the restraint or seclusion was discontinued, and it is reasonable to assume the use of the restraint or seclusion contributed to the patient's death. In a case where only two-point soft wrist restraints were used and there was no seclusion, it may reasonably be presumed that the patient's death was not caused by the use of restraints.

  o In cases involving death within one week after use of restraint or seclusion where the intervention may have contributed to the patient's death, it is possible that the patient's death might occur outside the hospital and that the hospital might not learn of the patient's death, or that there might be a delay in the hospital's learning of the patient's death.

See the guidance for §482.13(g)(2) for handling of deaths while a patient was in, or within 24 hours after removal of a soft, two-point wrist restraint, when no other restraint or seclusion was used.

The reports required under §482.13(g)(1) must be submitted to the CMS Regional Office by telephone, facsimile, or electronically, as determined by the Regional Office no later than close of the next business day following the day in which the hospital knows of the patient's death. The report must include basic identifying information related to the hospital, the patient's name, date of birth, date of death, name of attending physician/practitioner, primary diagnosis(es), cause of death (preliminary, in case a final, official cause of death is not yet available), and type(s) of restraint or seclusion used. CMS makes a standard form available for hospitals to use in submitting the required reports.

Hospitals must document in the patient's medical record the date and time each reportable death associated with the use of restraint or seclusion was reported to the CMS Regional Office.

After reviewing the submitted information, the Regional Office will determine whether an on-site investigation of the circumstances surrounding the patient's death is warranted and will direct the State Survey Agency to conduct a survey if applicable.

Survey Procedures §482.13(g)(1) & (3)(i):

- Does the hospital have restraint/seclusion death reporting policies and procedures that address responsibilities and systems for identifying restraint/seclusion-associated deaths reportable to CMS and for implementing the reporting and recordkeeping requirements?

- Can the hospital provide examples of restraint/seclusion-associated deaths that were reported to CMS?

    o If yes, review the report and medical records to determine whether:

        - the reports met the criteria for reporting to CMS;
        - were submitted timely to CMS;
        - were complete; and
        - the date and time the death reported to CMS was entered into the patient's medical record.

    o If no:

        - Ask the hospital how it ensures that there were no reportable restraint/seclusion-associated deaths.

        - If the hospital's system relies upon staff identification of reportable deaths, interview several applicable staff members to determine whether they are aware of the hospital's policy and know when and where to report internally a restraint/seclusion-associated death. Ask if there have been any patient deaths that meet the reporting requirements.

- Interview staff in various types of inpatient units, including a psychiatric unit if applicable, to determine whether they are aware of any patients who died while in restraints or seclusion or within one day of restraint or seclusion discontinuation, excluding cases involving only the use of two-point soft wrist restraints and no seclusion. If yes, check whether the hospital has any evidence that these cases were reported to CMS.

A-0214
(Rev. 84, Issued: 06-07-13, Effective: 06-07-13, Implementation: 06-07-13)

§482.13(g) Standard: Death Reporting Requirements: [- Hospitals must report deaths associated with the use of seclusion or restraint.]

(2)   When no seclusion has been used and when the only restraints used on the patient are those applied exclusively to the patient's wrist(s), and which are composed solely of soft, non-rigid, cloth-like materials, the hospital staff must record in an internal log or other system, the following information:

(i)   Any death that occurs while a patient is in such restraints.

(ii)   Any death that occurs within 24 hours after a patient has been removed from such restraints.

(3) [The staff must document in the patient's medical record the date and time the death was:]

(ii)   Recorded in the internal log or other system for deaths described in paragraph (g)(2) of this section.

(4) For deaths described in paragraph (g)(2) of this section, entries into the log or other system must be documented as follows:

(i)   Each entry must be made not later than seven days after the date of death of the patient.

(ii)   Each entry must document the patient's name, date of birth, date of death, name of attending physician or other licensed independent practitioner who is responsible for the care of the patient as specified under §482.12(c), medical record number, and primary diagnosis(es).

(iii)   The information must be made available in either written or electronic form to CMS immediately upon request.

Interpretive Guidelines §482.13(g)(2), (3)(ii), & (4)

Hospitals must maintain an internal log or other type of tracking system for recording information on each death that occurs:

- While a patient is in only 2-point soft, cloth-like non-rigid wrist restraints and there is no use of seclusion; and

- Within 24 hours of the patient being removed from 2-point soft, cloth-like non-rigid wrist restraints where there was no use of any other type of restraint or seclusion.

Use of the log or tracking system is limited only to patient deaths meeting one of these two criteria. Examples of patient deaths associated with restraints that must still be reported to CMS include:

- Deaths occurring during or within 24 hours of discontinuation of 2-point soft, cloth-like non-rigid wrist restraints used in combination with any other restraint device or with seclusion; or

- Deaths associated with the use of other types of wrist restraints, such as 2-point rigid or leather wrist restraints.

These cases would not be included in this internal log or tracking system and would require reporting the death to CMS using telephone, fax, or electronically.

The two-point soft wrist restraint death report must be entered into the internal log or tracking system within 7 days of the patient's death.

The death report log or tracking system entry must include:

- The patient's name;
- Patient's date of birth;
- Patient's date of death;
- Name of the attending physician or other licensed independent practitioner who is responsible for the care or the patient;
- Patient's medical record number; and
- Primary diagnosis(es).

Depending on the size and nature of the patient population the hospital serves and the types of services it provides, there will likely be variations in the frequency of restraint use as well as in the incidence of patient deaths. Surveyors should adjust their expectations for the volume of log or tracking system entries accordingly. For example, hospitals with intensive care units might be more likely to use both soft, 2-point wrist restraints and to have seriously ill patients who die as a result of their disease while such restraints are being used or within 24 hours after their discontinuance. On the other hand, a rehabilitation hospital would be expected to use such restraints less frequently, and to have patients who die less frequently while hospitalized.

The log or tracking system must be available in written, i.e., hard copy, or electronic form immediately upon CMS's request. CMS will specify the form in which the information is to be provided. Generally CMS would request access to the log or tracking system during an on-site survey by CMS staff or State surveyors acting on CMS's behalf when assessing compliance with restraint/seclusion requirements. However, CMS may also request that a copy of portions or the entire log or tracking system be provided, even though no survey is in progress. Accreditation organizations conducting hospital inspections in accordance with a CMS-approved Medicare hospital accreditation program are also entitled to immediate access to the log or tracking system.

The hospital is not required to make the contents of the log or tracking system available to any other outside parties, unless required to do so under other Federal or State law.

The hospital must document in the patient's medical record the date and time the death report entry was made into the log or tracking system.

Survey Procedures §482.13(g)(2), (3)(ii), & (4)

- Does the hospital have restraint/seclusion death reporting policies and procedures that address responsibilities and systems for identifying restraint/seclusion-associated deaths that must be recorded in an internal hospital log/tracking system, and for implementing the reporting and recordkeeping requirements?

- Ask the hospital how it ensures that each death that must be captured in the log/tracking system is identified and entered.

- Interview inpatient unit staff to determine whether they have had patients who die while 2-point soft wrist restraints are being used without seclusion or within 24 hours of their discontinuance. If yes, ask the hospital to demonstrate that it has recorded such deaths.

- If the hospital's log or tracking system relies upon staff identification of reportable deaths, interview several applicable staff members to determine whether they are aware of the hospital's policy and know when and where to report internally a restraint/seclusion-associated death.
- Review the log/tracking system for patient deaths associated with use of only 2-point soft wrist restraints to determine if:

  - Each entry was made within 7 days of the patient's death; and

  - Each entry contains all the information required under the regulation.

- Is the hospital able to make the log or tracking system available immediately on request?

- Review a sample of medical records of patients whose deaths were entered in the log or tracking system.

  - Does the medical record indicate that only soft, 2-point wrist restraints were used?

- Is there documentation in the medical record of the entry into the log or tracking system?

A-0215
(Rev. 75, Issued: 12-02-11, Effective: 12-02-11, Implementation: 12-02-11)

§482.13(h) Standard: Patient visitation rights. A hospital must have written policies and procedures regarding the visitation rights of patients, including those setting forth any clinically necessary or reasonable restriction or limitation that the hospital may need to place on such rights and the reasons for the clinical restriction or limitation

Interpretive Guidelines, §482.13(h)

Visitation plays an important role in the care of hospital patients. An article published in 2004 in the Journal of the American Medical Association (Berwick, D.M., and Kotagal, M.: "Restricted visiting hours in ICUs: time to change." JAMA. 2004; Vol. 292, pp. 736-737) discusses the health and safety benefits of open visitation for patients, families, and intensive care unit (ICU) staff and debunks some of the myths surrounding the issue (physiologic stress for the patient; barriers to provision of care; exhaustion of family and friends). The article ultimately concluded that "available evidence indicates that hazards and problems regarding open visitation are generally overstated and manageable," and that such visitation policies "do not harm patients but rather may help them by providing a support system and shaping a more familiar environment" as they "engender trust in families, creating a better working relationship between hospital staff and family members." Hospitals that unnecessarily restrict patient visitation often miss an opportunity to gain valuable patient information from those who may know the patient best with respect to the patient's medical history, conditions, medications, and allergies, particularly if the patient has difficulties with recall or articulation, or is totally unable to recall or articulate this vital personal information. Many times visitors who may know the patient best act as an intermediary for the patient, helping to communicate the patient's needs to hospital staff.

Although visitation policies are generally considered to relate to visitors of inpatients, "visitors" also play a role for outpatients who wish to have a support person present during their outpatient visit. For example, a same-day surgery patient may wish to have a support person present during the pre-operative patient preparation or post-operative recovery. Or an outpatient clinic patient may wish to have a support person present during his or her examination by a physician. Accordingly, hospital visitation policies must address both the inpatient and outpatient settings.

Hospitals are required to develop and implement written policies and procedures that address the patient's right to have visitors. If the hospital's policy establishes restrictions or limitations on visitation, such restrictions/limitations must be clinically necessary or reasonable. Furthermore, the hospital's policy must include the reasons for any restrictions/limitations. The right of a patient to have visitors may be limited or restricted when visitation would interfere with the care of the patient and/or the care of other patients. The regulation permits hospitals some flexibility, so that health care professionals may exercise their best clinical judgment when determining when visitation is, and is not, appropriate. Best clinical judgment takes into account all aspects of patient health and safety, including the benefits of visitation on a patient's care as well as potential negative impacts that visitors may have on other patients in the hospital.

Broad examples of circumstances reasonably related to the care of the patient and/or the care of other patients that could provide a basis for a hospital to impose restrictions or limitations on visitors might include (but are not limited to) when:

- there may be infection control issues;
- visitation may interfere with the care of other patients;
- the hospital is aware that there is an existing court order restricting contact;
- visitors engage in disruptive, threatening, or violent behavior of any kind;
- the patient or patient's roommate(s) need rest or privacy;
- in the case of an inpatient substance abuse treatment program, there are protocols limiting visitation; and
- the patient is undergoing care interventions. However, while there may be valid reasons for limiting visitation during a care intervention, we encourage hospitals to try to accommodate the needs of any patient who requests that at least one visitor be allowed to remain in the room to provide support and comfort at such times.

It may also be reasonable to limit the number of visitors for any one patient during a specific period of time, as well as to establish minimum age requirements for child visitors. However, when a hospital adopts policies that limit or restrict patients' visitation rights, the burden of proof is upon the hospital to demonstrate that the visitation restriction is reasonably necessary to provide safe care.

Hospitals are expected to provide a clear explanation in their written policy of the clinical rationale for any visitation restrictions or limitations reflected in that policy. Hospitals are not required, however, to delineate each specific clinical reason for policies limiting or restricting visitation, given that it is not possible to anticipate every instance that may give rise to a clinically appropriate rationale for a restriction or limitation. If visitation policies differ by type of unit, e.g., separate policies for intensive care units, or for newborn nurseries, the hospital policy must address the clinical rationale for this differentiation explicitly.

The hospital's policies and procedures are expected to address how hospital staff who play a role in facilitating or controlling visitor access to patients will be trained to assure appropriate implementation of the visitation policies and procedures and avoidance of unnecessary restrictions or limitations on patients' visitation rights.

Survey Procedures §482.13(h)

- Verify that the hospital has written policies and procedures that address the right of patients to have visitors.

- Review the policy to determine if there are limitations or restrictions on visitation. If there are, does the policy explain the clinical rationale for the restrictions or limitations? Is the rationale clear and reasonably related to clinical concerns?

- Is there documentation of how the hospital identifies and trains staff who play a role in facilitating or controlling access of visitors to patients?

- Are hospital staff aware of the visitation policies and procedures? Can staff on a given unit correctly describe the hospital's visitation policies for that unit?

A-0216
(Rev. 75, Issued: 12-02-11, Effective: 12-02-11, Implementation: 12-02-11)

§482.13(h) Standard: Patient visitation rights. A hospital must have written policies and procedures regarding the visitation rights of patients, including those setting forth any clinically necessary or reasonable restriction or limitation that the hospital may need to place on such rights and the reasons for the clinical restriction or limitation. A hospital must meet the following requirements:

(1) Inform each patient (or support person, where appropriate) of his or her visitation rights, including any clinical restriction or limitation on such rights, when he or she is informed of his or her other rights under this section.

(2) Inform each patient (or support person, where appropriate) of the right, subject to his or her consent, to receive the visitors whom he or she designates, including, but not limited to, a spouse, a domestic partner (including a same-sex domestic partner), another family member, or a friend, and his or her right to withdraw or deny such consent at any time.

Interpretive Guidelines §482.13(h)(1)&(2)

Hospitals are required to inform each patient (or the patient's support person, where appropriate) of his/her visitation rights. A patient's "support person" does not necessarily have to be the same person as the patient's representative who is legally responsible for making medical decisions on the patient's behalf. A support person could be a family member, friend, or other individual who supports the patient during the course of the hospital stay. Not only may the support person visit the patient, but he or she may also exercise a patient's visitation rights on behalf of the patient with respect to other visitors when the patient is unable to do so. Hospitals must accept a patient's designation, orally or in writing, of an individual as the patient's support person.

When a patient is incapacitated or otherwise unable to communicate his or her wishes and an individual provides an advance directive designating an individual as the patient's support person (it is not necessary for the document to use this exact term), the hospital must accept this designation, provide the required notice of the patient's visitation rights, and allow the individual to exercise the patient's visitation rights on the patient's behalf.

When a patient is incapacitated or otherwise unable to communicate his or her wishes, there is no advance directive designating a representative on file, and no one has presented an advance directive designating himself or herself as the patient's representative, but an individual asserts that he or she, as the patient's spouse, domestic partner (including a same-sex domestic partner), parent or other family member, friend, or otherwise, is the patient's support person, the hospital is expected to accept this assertion, without demanding supporting documentation, provide the required notice of the patient's visitation rights, and allow the individual to exercise the patient's visitation rights on the patient's behalf. However, if more than one individual claims to be the patient's support person, it would not be inappropriate for the hospital to ask each individual for documentation supporting his/her claim to be the patient's support person.

- Hospitals are expected to adopt policies and procedures that facilitate expeditious and non-discriminatory resolution of disputes about whether an individual is the patient's support person, given the critical role of the support person in exercising the patient's visitation rights.

- A refusal by the hospital of an individual's request to be treated as the patient's support person with respect to visitation rights must be documented in the patient's medical record, along with the specific basis for the refusal.

Consistent with the patients' rights notice requirements under the regulation at §482.13(a)(1), the required notice of the patient's visitation rights must be provided, whenever possible, before the hospital provides or stops care. The notice to the patient, or to the patient's support person, where appropriate, must be in writing. If the patient also has a representative who is different from the support person, the representative must also be provided information on the patient's visitation rights, in addition to the support person, if applicable. In the event that a patient has both a representative and a support person who are not the same individual, and they disagree on who should be allowed to visit the patient, the hospital must defer to the decisions of the patient's representative. As the individual responsible for making decisions on the patient's behalf, the patient's representative has the authority to exercise a patient's right to designate and deny visitors just as the patient would if he or she were capable of doing so. The designation of, and exercise of authority by, the patient's representative is governed by State law, including statutory and case law. Many State courts have addressed the concept of substituted judgment, whereby the patient's representative is expected to make medical decisions based on the patient's values and interests, rather than the representative's own values and interests. State courts have also developed a body of closely related law around the matter of a representative acting in the patient's best interest. Such case law regarding substituted judgment and best interest may be a resource for hospitals on how to address such conflict situations as they establish visitation policies and procedures. Hospitals may also choose to utilize their own social work and pastoral counseling resources to resolve such conflicts to assure the patient's well-being.

The required visitation rights notice must address any clinically necessary or reasonable limitations or restrictions imposed by hospital policy on visitation rights, providing the clinical reasons for such limitations/restrictions, including how they are aimed at protecting the health and safety of all patients. The information must be sufficiently detailed to allow a patient (or the patient's support person) to determine what the visitation hours are and what restrictions, if any, apply to that patient's visitation rights.

The notice must also inform the patient (or the patient's support person, where appropriate) of the patient's right to:

- Consent to receive visitors he or she has designated, either orally or in writing, including but not limited to, a spouse, a domestic partner (including a same-sex domestic partner), another family member, or a friend;

- Receive the visitors he or she has designated, including but not limited to, a spouse, a domestic partner (including a same-sex domestic partner), another family member, or a friend; and

- Withdraw or deny his/her consent to receive specific visitors, either orally or in writing.

The medical record must contain documentation that the required notice was provided to the patient or, if appropriate, the patient's support person.

Survey Procedures §482.13(h)(1)&(2)

- Determine whether the hospital's visitation policies and procedures require providing notice of the patient's visitation rights to each patient or, if appropriate, to a patient's support person and/or, as applicable, the patient's representative.

- Review the hospital's standard notice of visitation rights. Does it clearly explain the:

  - hospital's visitation policy, including any limitations or restrictions, such as visiting hours, numbers of visitors, unit-specific restrictions, etc., and the clinical rationale for such limitations or restrictions?

  - right of the patient to have designated visitors, including but not limited to, a spouse, a domestic partner (including a same-sex domestic partner), another family member, or a friend, and the right to withdraw or deny consent to visitation?

- Review a sample of medical records to determine if there is documentation that the required notice was provided.

- Ask the hospital to identify how the required notice is provided. Ask staff responsible for providing the notice how they accomplish this. Ask the staff if they are familiar with the concept of a patient's "support person" and what it means.

- Ask a sample of current hospital patients or patients' support persons (where appropriate) whether they were provided notice of their right to have visitors. Ask if they were able to have visitors when they wanted to. If not, verify whether the restriction/limitation on visitors was addressed in the hospital's visitation policies and notice, and does not violate the regulations at §482.13(h)(3)&(4). (See interpretive guidelines for the latter provisions.)

- Ask a sample of current hospital patients or patients' support persons (where appropriate) whether the hospital did not limit some or all visitors, contrary to the patient's wishes.

A-0217
(Rev. 75, Issued: 12-02-11, Effective: 12-02-11, Implementation: 12-02-11)

§482.13(h) Standard: Patient visitation rights. A hospital must have written policies and procedures regarding the visitation rights of patients, including those setting forth any clinically necessary or reasonable restriction or limitation that the hospital may need to place on such rights and the reasons for the clinical restriction or limitation. A hospital must meet the following requirements:

(3) Not restrict, limit, or otherwise deny visitation privileges on the basis of race, color, national origin, religion, sex, gender identity, sexual orientation, or disability.

(4) Ensure that all visitors enjoy full and equal visitation privileges consistent with patient preferences.

Interpretive Guidelines §482.13(h)(3)&(4)

The hospital's visitation policies and procedures may not use the race, color, national origin, religion, sex, gender identity, sexual orientation, or disability of either the patient (or the patient's support person ore representative, where appropriate) or the patient's visitors (including individuals seeking to visit the patient) as a basis for limiting, restricting, or otherwise denying visitation privileges.

The hospital's policies and procedures must ensure that all visitors (including individuals seeking to visit the patient) enjoy full and equal visitation privileges, consistent with the preferences the patient (or, where appropriate, the patient's support person) has expressed concerning visitors. In other words, it is permissible for the patient (or the patient's support person, where appropriate) to limit the visiting privileges of his/her visitors, including providing for more limited visiting privileges for some visitors than those for others. But it is not permissible for the hospital, on its own, to differentiate among visitors without any clinically necessary or reasonable basis. This includes visitors designated by the patient who have characteristics not addressed specifically in §482.13(h)(3), when those characteristics do not reasonably relate to a clinically reasonable basis for limiting or denying visitation. For example, it would not be appropriate to prohibit a designated visitor based on that individual's style of dress, unless there was a clinically reasonable basis for doing so.

The hospital is responsible for ensuring that hospital staff treat all individuals seeking to visit patients equally, consistent with the preferences of the patient (or, where appropriate, the patient's support person) and do not use the race, color, national origin, religion, sex, gender identity, sexual orientation, or disability of either the patient(or the patient's support person or representative, where appropriate) or the patient's visitors (including individuals seeking to visit the patient) as a basis for limiting, restricting, or otherwise denying visitation privileges. Hospitals are expected to educate all staff who play a role in facilitating or controlling visitors on the hospital's visitation policies and procedures, and are responsible for ensuring that staff implement the hospital's policies correctly. Hospitals are urged to develop culturally competent training programs designed to address the range of patients served by the hospital.

Survey Procedures §482.13(h)(3)&(4)

- Review the hospital's visitation policies and procedures to determine whether they restrict, limit, or otherwise deny visitation to individuals on a prohibited basis.

- Ask the hospital how it educates staff to assure that visitation policies are implemented in a non-discriminatory manner.

- Ask hospital staff who play a role in facilitating or controlling visitors to discuss their understanding of the circumstances under which visitors may be subject to restrictions/limitations. Are the restrictions/limitations appropriately based on the hospital's clinically-based policies?

- Ask hospital patients (or patients' support persons, where appropriate) whether the hospital has restricted or limited visitors against their wishes. If yes, verify whether the restriction/limitation on visitors was addressed in the hospital's visitation policies and in the patient notice, and whether it was appropriately based on a clinical rationale rather than impermissible discrimination.

A-0263
(Rev. 37, Issued: 10-17-08; Effective/Implementation Date: 10-17-08)

§482.21 Condition of Participation: Quality Assessment and Performance Improvement Program

The hospital must develop, implement, and maintain an effective, ongoing, hospital-wide, data-driven quality assessment and performance improvement program. The hospital's governing body must ensure that the program reflects the complexity of the hospital's organization and services; involves all hospital departments and services (including those services furnished under contract or arrangement); and focuses on indicators related to improved health outcomes and the prevention and reduction of medical errors. The hospital must maintain and demonstrate evidence of its QAPI program for review by CMS.

A-0264
(Rev. 37, Issued: 10-17-08; Effective/Implementation Date: 10-17-08)

§482.21(a) Standard: Program Scope

Interpretive Guidelines §482.21(a):

The hospital must ensure that the program scope requirements are met.

A-0265
(Rev. 37, Issued: 10-17-08; Effective/Implementation Date: 10-17-08)

§482.21(a)(1) - The program must include, but not be limited to, an ongoing program that shows measurable improvement in indicators for which there is evidence that it will improve health outcomes and...

A-0266

(Rev. 37, Issued: 10-17-08; Effective/Implementation Date: 10-17-08)

§482.21(a)(1) (Continued)

...identify and reduce medical errors.

A-0267

(Rev. 37, Issued: 10-17-08; Effective/Implementation Date: 10-17-08)

§482.21(a)(2) - The hospital must measure, analyze, and track quality indicators, including adverse patient events, and other aspects of performance that assess processes of care, hospital service and operations.

A-0273

(Rev. 37, Issued: 10-17-08; Effective/Implementation Date: 10-17-08)

§482.21(b) Standard: Program Data

Interpretive Guidelines §482.21(b):

The hospital must ensure that the program data requirements are met.

A-0274

(Rev. 37, Issued: 10-17-08; Effective/Implementation Date: 10-17-08)

§482.21(b)(1) - The program must incorporate quality indicator data including patient care data, and other relevant data, for example, information submitted to, or received from, the hospital's Quality Improvement Organization.

A-0275

(Rev. 37, Issued: 10-17-08; Effective/Implementation Date: 10-17-08)

§482.21(b)(2) - The hospital must use the data collected to--

(i) Monitor the effectiveness and safety of services and quality of care; and

A-0276

(Rev. 37, Issued: 10-17-08; Effective/Implementation Date: 10-17-08)

[The hospital must use the data collected to--]

§482.21(b)(2)(ii) - Identify opportunities for improvement and changes that will lead to improvement.

A-0277

(Rev. 37, Issued: 10-17-08; Effective/Implementation Date: 10-17-08)

§482.21(b)(3) - The frequency and detail of data collection must be specified by the hospital's governing body.

A-0283

(Rev. 37, Issued: 10-17-08; Effective/Implementation Date: 10-17-08)

§482.21(c) Standard: Program Activities

Interpretive Guidelines §482.21(c):

The hospital must ensure that the program activities requirements are met.

A-0285

(Rev. 37, Issued: 10-17-08; Effective/Implementation Date: 10-17-08)

§482.21(c)(1) - The hospital must set priorities for its performance improvement activities that--

    (i)   Focus on high-risk, high-volume, or problem-prone areas;

    (ii)   Consider the incidence, prevalence, and severity of problems in those areas; and

    (iii)   Affect health outcomes, patient safety, and quality of care.

A-0286

(Rev. 37, Issued: 10-17-08; Effective/Implementation Date: 10-17-08)

§482.21(c)(2) - Performance improvement activities must track medical errors and adverse patient events,...

A-0287

(Rev. 37, Issued: 10-17-08; Effective/Implementation Date: 10-17-08)

§482.21(c)(2) (Continued)

[Performance improvement activities must track medical errors and adverse patient events,] analyze their causes, and...

A-0288

(Rev. 37, Issued: 10-17-08; Effective/Implementation Date: 10-17-08)

§482.21(c)(2) (Ccontinued)

[Performance improvement activities must track medical errors and adverse patient events, analyze their causes, and] implement preventive actions and mechanisms that include feedback and learning throughout the hospital.

A-0289

(Rev. 37, Issued: 10-17-08; Effective/Implementation Date: 10-17-08)

§482.21(c)(3) - The hospital must take actions aimed at performance improvement and, ...

A-0290

(Rev. 37, Issued: 10-17-08; Effective/Implementation Date: 10-17-08)

§482.21(c)(3) (Continued)

[The hospital must take actions aimed at performance improvement and,] after implementing those actions, the hospital must measure its success, and...

A-0291

(Rev. 37, Issued: 10-17-08; Effective/Implementation Date: 10-17-08)

§482.21(c)(3) (Continued)

[The hospital must take actions aimed at performance improvement and, after implementing those actions, the hospital must measure its success, and] track performance to ensure that improvements are sustained.

A-0297

(Rev. 37, Issued: 10-17-08; Effective/Implementation Date: 10-17-08)

§482.21(d) Standard: Performance Improvement Projects

As part of its quality assessment and performance improvement program, the hospital must conduct performance improvement projects.

A-0298

(Rev. 37, Issued: 10-17-08; Effective/Implementation Date: 10-17-08)

§482.21(d)(1) - The number and scope of distinct improvement projects conducted annually must be proportional to the scope and complexity of the hospital's services and operations.

A-0299

(Rev. 37, Issued: 10-17-08; Effective/Implementation Date: 10-17-08)

§482.21(d)(2) - A hospital may, as one of its projects, develop and implement an information technology system explicitly designed to improve patient safety and quality of care. This project, in its initial stage of development, does not need to demonstrate measurable improvement in indicators related to health outcomes.

A-0300

(Rev. 37, Issued: 10-17-08; Effective/Implementation Date: 10-17-08)

§482.21(d)(3) - The hospital must document what quality improvement projects are being conducted,...

A-0301

(Rev. 37, Issued: 10-17-08; Effective/Implementation Date: 10-17-08)

§482.21(d)(3) - (Continued)

[The hospital must document what quality improvement projects are being conducted,] the reasons for conducting these projects, and...

A-0302

(Rev. 37, Issued: 10-17-08; Effective/Implementation Date: 10-17-08)

§482.21(d)(3) - (Continued)

[The hospital must document what quality improvement projects are being conducted, the reasons for conducting these projects, and] the measurable progress achieved on these projects.

A-0303

(Rev. 37, Issued: 10-17-08; Effective/Implementation Date: 10-17-08)

§482.21(d)(4) - A hospital is not required to participate in a QIO cooperative project, but its own projects are required to be of comparable effort.

A-0309

(Rev. 37, Issued: 10-17-08; Effective/Implementation Date: 10-17-08)

§482.21(e) Standard: Executive Responsibilities

The hospital's governing body (or organized group or individual who assumes full legal authority and responsibility for operations of the hospital), medical staff, and administrative officials are responsible and accountable for ensuring the following:

A-0310

(Rev. 37, Issued: 10-17-08; Effective/Implementation Date: 10-17-08)

§482.21(e)(1) - That an ongoing program for quality improvement ... is defined, implemented, and maintained.

A-0311

(Rev. 37, Issued: 10-17-08; Effective/Implementation Date: 10-17-08)

§482.21(e)(1) - (Continued

[That an ongoing program for ...] patient safety, including the reduction of medical errors, [is defined, implemented, and maintained.]

A-0312

(Rev. 37, Issued: 10-17-08; Effective/Implementation Date: 10-17-08)

§482.21(e)(2) - That the hospital-wide quality assessment and performance improvement efforts address priorities for improved quality of care...and that all improvement actions are evaluated.

A-0313

§482.21(e)(2) - (Continued)

[That the hospital-wide quality assessment and performance improvement efforts address priorities for improved] and patient safety [and that all improvement actions are evaluated.]

A-0314

(Rev. 37, Issued: 10-17-08; Effective/Implementation Date: 10-17-08)

§482.21(e)(3) - That clear expectations for safety are established.

A-0315

(Rev. 37, Issued: 10-17-08; Effective/Implementation Date: 10-17-08)

§482.21(e)(4) - That adequate resources are allocated for measuring, assessing, improving, and sustaining the hospital's performance and...

A-0316

(Rev. 37, Issued: 10-17-08; Effective/Implementation Date: 10-17-08)

§482.21(e)(4) - (Continued)

[That adequate resources are allocated for...] reducing risk to patients.

A-0317

§482.21(e)(5) - That the determination of the number of distinct improvement projects is conducted annually.

A-0338

(Rev. 37, Issued: 10-17-08; Effective/Implementation Date: 10-17-08)
§482.22 Condition of Participation: Medical Staff

The hospital must have an organized medical staff that operates under bylaws approved by the governing body and is responsible for the quality of medical care provided to patients by the hospital.

Interpretive Guidelines §482.22

The hospital may have only one medical staff for the entire hospital (including all campuses, provider-based locations, satellites, remote locations, etc.). The medical staff must be organized and integrated as one body that operates under one set of bylaws approved by the governing body. These medical staff bylaws must apply equally to all practitioners within each category of practitioners at all locations of the hospital and to the care provided at all locations of the hospital. The single medical staff is responsible for the quality of medical care provided to patients by the hospital.

A-0339

(Rev. 78, Issued: 12-22-11, Effective/Implementation: 12-22-11)

§482.22(a) Standard: Composition of the Medical Staff

The medical staff must be composed of doctors of medicine or osteopathy and, in accordance with State law, may also be composed of other practitioners appointed by the governing body.

Interpretive Guidelines §482.22(a):

The medical staff must at a minimum be composed of physicians who are doctors of medicine or doctors of osteopathy. In addition, the medical staff may include other healthcare professionals included in the definition in Section 1861(r) of the Social Security Act of a physician:

- Doctor of medicine or osteopathy;
- Doctor of dental surgery or of dental medicine;
- Doctor of podiatric medicine;
- Doctor of optometry; and a
- Chiropractor.

In all cases the healthcare professional included in the definition of a physician must be legally authorized to practice within the State where the hospital is located and providing services within their authorized scope of practice. In addition, in certain instances the Social Security Act and regulations attach further limitations as to the type of hospital services for which a healthcare professional may be considered to be a "physician." See §482.12(c)(1) for more detail on these limitations.

The governing body has the flexibility to determine whether healthcare professionals included in the definition of a physician other than a doctor of medical or osteopathy are eligible for appointment to the medical staff.

Furthermore, the governing body has the authority, in accordance with State law, to appoint non-physician practitioners to the medical staff.   Practitioners are defined in Section 1842(b)(18)(C) of the Act as a:

- Physician assistant;

- Nurse practitioner;

- Clinical nurse specialist (Section 1861(aa)(5) of the Act);

- Certified registered nurse anesthetist (Section 1861(bb)(2) of the Act);

- Certified nurse-midwife (Section 1861(gg)(2) of the Act);

- Clinical social worker (Section 1861(hh)(1) of the Act;

- Clinical psychologist (42 CFR 410.71 for purposes of Section 1861(ii) of the Act); or

- Registered dietician or nutrition professional.

Other types of licensed healthcare professionals have a more limited scope of practice and are generally not eligible for hospital medical staff privileges, unless their permitted scope of practice in their State makes them comparable to the above types of practitioners.

Physicians and non-physician practitioners may be granted medical staff privileges to practice at the hospital by the governing body for practice activities authorized within their State scope of practice without being appointed a member of the medical staff.

* * *

A-0340

(Rev. 37, Issued: 10-17-08; Effective/Implementation Date: 10-17-08)

§482.22(a)(1) - The medical staff must periodically conduct appraisals of its members.

Interpretive Guidelines §482.22(a)(1)

The medical staff must at regular intervals appraise the qualifications of all practitioners appointed to the medical staff/granted medical staff privileges. In the absence of a State law that establishes a timeframe for periodic reappraisal, a hospital's medical staff must conduct a periodic appraisal of each practitioner. CMS recommends that an appraisal be conducted at least every 24 months for each practitioner.

The purpose of the appraisal is for the medical staff to determine the suitability of continuing the medical staff membership or privileges of each individual practitioner, to determine if that individual practitioner's membership or privileges should be continued, discontinued, revised, or otherwise changed.

The medical staff appraisal procedures must evaluate each individual practitioner's qualifications and demonstrated competencies to perform each task or activity within the applicable scope of practice or privileges for that type of practitioner for which he/she has been granted privileges. Components of practitioner qualifications and demonstrated competencies would include at least: current work practice, special training, quality of specific work, patient outcomes, education, maintenance of continuing education, adherence to medical staff rules, certifications, appropriate licensure, and currency of compliance with licensure requirements.

In addition to the periodic appraisal of members, any procedure/task/activity/privilege requested by a practitioner that goes beyond the specified list of privileges for that particular category of practitioner requires an appraisal by the medical staff and approval by the governing body. The appraisal must consider evidence of qualifications and competencies specific to the nature of the request. It must also consider whether the activity/task/procedure is one that the hospital can support when it is conducted within the hospital. Privileges cannot be granted for tasks/procedures/activities that are not conducted within the hospital, regardless of the individual practitioner's ability to perform them.

After the medical staff conducts its reappraisal of individual members, the medical staff makes recommendations to the governing body to continue, revise, discontinue, limit, or revoke some or all of the practitioner's privileges, and the governing body takes final appropriate action.

A separate credentials file must be maintained for each medical staff member. The hospital must ensure that the practitioner and appropriate hospital patient care areas/departments are informed of the privileges granted to the practitioner, as well as of any revisions or revocations of the practitioner's privileges. Furthermore, whenever a practitioner's privileges are limited, revoked, or in any way constrained, the hospital must, in accordance with State and/or Federal laws or regulations, report those constraints to the appropriate State and Federal authorities, registries, and/or data bases, such as the National Practitioner Data Bank.

Survey Procedures §482.22(a)(1)

- Determine whether the medical staff has a system in place that is used to reappraise each of its current members and their qualifications at regular intervals, or, if applicable, as prescribed by State law.

- Determine whether the medical staff by-laws identify the process and criteria to be used for the periodic appraisal.

- Determine whether the criteria used for reevaluation comply with the requirements of this section, State law and hospital bylaws, rules, and regulations.

- Determine whether the medical staff has a system to ensure that practitioners seek approval to expand their privileges for tasks/activities/procedures that go beyond the specified list of privileges for their category of practitioner.

- Determine how the medical staff conducts the periodic appraisals of any current member of the medical staff who has not provided patient care at the hospital or who has not provided care for which he/she is privileged to patients at the hospital during the appropriate evaluation time frames. Is this method in accordance with State law and the hospital's written criteria for medical staff membership and for granting privileges?

A-0341 *Credentials*

(Rev. 37, Issued: 10-17-08; Effective/Implementation Date: 10-17-08)

§482.22(a)(2) - The medical staff must examine credentials of candidates for medical staff membership and make recommendations to the governing body on the appointment of the candidates.

Interpretive Guidelines §482.22(a)(2)

There must be a mechanism established to examine credentials of individual prospective members (new appointments or reappointments) by the medical staff. The individual's credentials to be examined must include at least:

- A request for clinical privileges;

- Evidence of current licensure;

- Evidence of training and professional education;

- Documented experience; and

- Supporting references of competence.

The medical staff may not make its recommendation solely on the basis of the presence or absence of board certification, but must consider all of the elements above. However, this does not mean that the medical staff is prohibited from requiring in its bylaws board certification when considering a MD/DO for medical staff membership or privileges; only that such certification may not be the only factor that the medical staff considers.

The medical staff makes recommendations to the governing body for each candidate for medical staff membership/privileges that are specific to type of appointment and extent of the individual practitioner's specific clinical privileges, and then the governing body takes final appropriate action.

A separate credentials file must be maintained for each individual medical staff member or applicant. The hospital must ensure that the practitioner and appropriate hospital patient care areas/departments are informed of the privileges granted to the practitioner.

Survey Procedures §482.22(a)(2)

- Determine whether the medical staff bylaws identify the process and criteria to be used for the evaluation of candidates for medical staff membership/privileges.

- Determine whether the criteria used for evaluation comply with the requirements of this section, State law, and hospital bylaws, rules, and regulations.

- Determine whether the medical staff has a system to ensure that practitioners seek approval to expand their privileges for tasks/activities/procedures that go beyond the specified list of privileges for their category of practitioner.

A-0342 *Telemedicine*

(Rev. 78, Issued: 12-22-11, Effective/Implementation: 12-22-11)

§482.22(a)(3) When telemedicine services are furnished to the hospital's patients through an agreement with a distant-site hospital, the governing body of the hospital whose patients are receiving the telemedicine services may choose, in lieu of the requirements in paragraphs (a)(1) and (a)(2) of this section, to have its medical staff rely upon the credentialing and privileging decisions made by the distant-site hospital when making recommendations on privileges for the individual distant-site physicians and practitioners providing such services, if the hospital's governing body ensures, through its written agreement with the distant-site hospital, that all of the following provisions are met:

(i) The distant-site hospital providing the telemedicine services is a Medicare-participating hospital.

(ii) The individual distant-site physician or practitioner is privileged at the distant-site hospital providing the telemedicine services, which provides a current list of the distant-site physician's or practitioner's privileges at the distant-site hospital.

(iii) The individual distant-site physician or practitioner holds a license issued or recognized by the State in which the hospital whose patients are receiving the telemedicine services is located.

(iv) With respect to a distant-site physician or practitioner, who holds current privileges at the hospital whose patients are receiving the telemedicine services, the hospital has evidence of an internal review of the distant-site physician's or practitioner's performance of these privileges and sends the distant-site hospital such performance information for use in the periodic appraisal of the distant-site physician or practitioner. At a minimum, this information must include all adverse events that result from the telemedicine services provided by the distant-site physician or practitioner to the hospital's patients and all complaints the hospital has received about the distant-site physician or practitioner.

Interpretive guidelines §482.22(a)(3)

The hospital's governing body has the option, when considering granting privileges to telemedicine physicians and practitioners, to have the hospital's medical staff rely upon the credentialing and privileging decisions of the distant-site hospital for these physicians and practitioners. This process would be in lieu of the traditional process required under §482.22(a)(1) and §482.22(a)(2), whereby the hospital's medical staff conducts its own review of each telemedicine physician's or practitioner's credentials and makes a recommendation based on that individualized review.

In order to exercise this alternative credentialing and privileging option, the hospital's governing body must ensure through its written agreement with the distant-site hospital that all of the following requirements are met:

- The distant-site hospital participates in the Medicare program. If the distant-site hospital's participation in Medicare is terminated, either voluntarily or involuntarily, at any time during the agreement, then, as of the effective date of the termination, the hospital may no longer receive telemedicine services under the agreement;

- The distant-site hospital provides to the hospital a list of all its physicians and practitioners covered by the agreement, including their privileges at the distant-site hospital. The list may not include any physician or practitioner who does not hold privileges at the distant-site hospital. The list must be current, so the agreement must address how the distant-site hospital will keep the list current;

- Each physician or practitioner who provides telemedicine services to the hospital's patients under the agreement holds a license issued or recognized by the State where the hospital (not the distant-site hospital) is located. States may have varying requirements as to whether they will recognize an out-of-state license for purposes of practicing within their State, and they may also vary as to whether they establish different standards for telemedicine services. The licensure requirements governing in the State where the hospital whose patients are receiving the telemedicine services is located must be satisfied, whatever they may be; and

- The hospital has evidence that it reviews the telemedicine services provided to its patients and provides feedback based on this review to the distant-site hospital for the latter's use in its periodic appraisal of each physician and practitioner providing telemedicine services under the agreement. At a minimum, the hospital must review and send information to the distant-site hospital on all adverse events that result from a physician or practitioner's provision of telemedicine services under the agreement and on all complaints it has received about a telemedicine physician or practitioner covered by the agreement.

Survey Procedures §482.22(a)(3)

- If the hospital provides telemedicine services to its patients under an agreement with a distant-site hospital, ask whether the hospital's governing body has exercised the option to have the medical staff rely upon the credentialing and privileging decisions of the distant-site hospital in making privileging recommendations on telemedicine physicians and practitioners. If yes, ask to see:

  - The written agreement with the distant-site hospital. Does the agreement address the required elements concerning the distant-site hospital's Medicare participation, licensure of telemedicine physicians and practitioners, current list of telemedicine physicians and practitioners with privileges, and review by the hospital of the telemedicine physicians' and practitioners' services and provision of information based on its review to the distant-site hospital?

  - The list provided by the distant-site hospital of the telemedicine physicians and practitioners, including their current privileges and pertinent licensure information.

Evidence that the hospital reviews the services provided by the telemedicine physicians and practitioners, including any adverse events and complaints, and provides feedback to the distant-site hospital.

A-0343
(Rev. 78, Issued: 12-22-11, Effective/Implementation: 12-22-11)

§482.22(a)(4) When telemedicine services are furnished to the hospital's patients through an agreement with a distant-site telemedicine entity, the governing body of the hospital whose patients are receiving the telemedicine services may choose, in lieu of the requirements in paragraphs (a)(1) and (a)(2) of this section, to have its medical staff rely upon the credentialing and privileging decisions made by the distant- site telemedicine entity when making recommendations on privileges for the individual distant-site physicians and practitioners providing such services, if the hospital's governing body ensures, through its written agreement with the distant-site telemedicine entity, that the distant-site telemedicine entity furnishes services that, in accordance with §482.12(e), permit the hospital to comply with all applicable conditions of participation for the contracted services. The hospital's governing body must also ensure, through its written agreement with the distant-site telemedicine entity, that all of the following provisions are met:

(i) The distant-site telemedicine entity's medical staff credentialing and privileging process and standards at least meet the standards at §482.12(a)(1) through (a)(7) and §482.22(a)(1) through (a)(2).

(ii) The individual distant-site physician or practitioner is privileged at the distant-site telemedicine entity providing the telemedicine services, which provides the hospital with a current list of the distant-site physician's or practitioner's privileges at the distant-site telemedicine entity.

(iii) The individual distant-site physician or practitioner holds a license issued or recognized by the State in which the hospital whose patients are receiving such telemedicine services is located.

(iv) With respect to a distant-site physician or practitioner, who holds current privileges at the hospital whose patients are receiving the telemedicine services, the hospital has evidence of an internal review of the distant-site physician's or practitioner's performance of these privileges and sends the distant-site telemedicine entity such performance information for use in the periodic appraisal of the distant-site physician or practitioner. At a minimum, this information must include all adverse events that result from the telemedicine services provided by the distant-site physician or practitioner to the hospital's patients, and all complaints the hospital has received about the distant-site physician or practitioner.

Interpretive guidelines §482.22(a)(4)

For the purposes of this rule, a distant-site telemedicine entity is defined as an entity that - - (1) provides telemedicine services; (2) is not a Medicare-participating hospital; and (3) provides contracted services in a manner that enables a hospital using its services to meet all applicable Conditions of Participation, particularly those requirements related to the credentialing and privileging of practitioners providing telemedicine services to the patients of a hospital. A distant-site telemedicine entity would include a distant-site hospital that does not participate in the Medicare program that is providing telemedicine services to a Medicare-participating hospital. (See 76 FR 25553, May 5, 2011)

The hospital's governing body has the option, when considering granting privileges to telemedicine physicians and practitioners, to have the hospital's medical staff rely upon the credentialing and privileging decisions of the distant-site telemedicine entity for these physicians and practitioners. This process would be in lieu of the traditional process required under §482.22(a)(1) and §482.22(a)(2), whereby the medical staff conducts its own review of each telemedicine physician's or practitioner's credentials and makes a recommendation based on that individualized review.

In order to exercise this alternative credentialing and privileging option, the hospital's governing body must ensure that its written agreement with the distant-site hospital enables the hospital, as required under the regulation at §482.12(e) governing services provided under arrangement, to comply with all applicable hospital Conditions of Participation. In particular, the written agreement between the hospital and the distant-site telemedicine entity must ensure that all of the following requirements are met:

- The distant-site telemedicine entity utilizes a medical staff credentialing and privileging process and standards that at least meets the standards for the medical staff of a hospital established at §482.12(a)(1) through (a)(7) and §482.22(a)(1) through (a)(2);

- The distant-site telemedicine entity provides a list to the hospital of all physicians and practitioners covered by the agreement, including their privileges at the distant-site telemedicine entity. The list may not include any physician or practitioner who does not hold privileges at the distant-site telemedicine entity. The list must be current, so the agreement must address how the distant-site telemedicine entity will keep the list current;

- Each physician or practitioner who provides telemedicine services to the hospital's patients under the agreement holds a license issued or recognized by the State where the hospital is located. States may have varying requirements as to whether they will recognize an out-of-state license for purposes of practicing within their State, and they may also vary as to whether they establish different standards for telemedicine services. The licensure requirements governing in the State where the hospital whose patients are receiving the telemedicine services is located must be satisfied, whatever they may be; and

- The hospital has evidence that it reviews the telemedicine services provided to its patients and provides a written copy of this review to the distant-site telemedicine entity for the latter's use in its periodic appraisal of the physicians and practitioners providing telemedicine services under the agreement. At a minimum, the hospital must review and send information to the distant-site telemedicine entity on all adverse events that result from a physician or practitioner's provision of telemedicine services and on all complaints it has received about a telemedicine physician or practitioner.

Survey Procedures 482.22(a)(4)

- If the hospital provides telemedicine services to its patients under an agreement with a one or more distant-site telemedicine entities, ask whether the hospital's governing body has exercised the option to have the medical staff rely upon the credentialing and privileging decisions of the distant-site telemedicine entity in making privileging recommendations on telemedicine physicians and practitioners. If yes, ask to see:

  - The written agreement(s) with the distant-site telemedicine entity(ies). Does each agreement address the required elements concerning the distant-site telemedicine entity's utilization of a medical staff credentialing and privileging process that meets the requirements of the hospital CoPs, appropriate licensure of telemedicine physicians and practitioners, current list of telemedicine physicians and practitioners specifying their privileges, and written review by the hospital of the telemedicine physicians' and practitioners' services and provision of information based on its review to the distant-site hospital?

  - The list provided by the distant-site telemedicine entity of the telemedicine physicians and practitioners covered by the agreement, including their current privileges and pertinent licensure information.

  - Evidence that the hospital reviews the services provided by the telemedicine physicians and practitioners, including any adverse events and complaints, and provides written feedback to the distant-site telemedicine entity.

  - Ask the hospital how it verifies that the telemedicine entity employs a credentialing and privileging process that meets or exceeds what is required for hospitals under the Medicare CoPs? (Surveyors do not attempt to independently verify whether or not the distant-site telemedicine entity's credentialing and privileging process fulfills the regulatory requirements. Surveyors focus only on whether the hospital takes steps to ensure that the distant-site telemedicine entity complies with the terms of the written agreement.)

A-0347
(Rev. 84, Issued: 06-07-13, Effective: 06-07-13, Implementation: 06-07-13)

§482.22(b) Standard: Medical Staff Organization and Accountability

The medical staff must be well organized and accountable to the governing body for the quality of the medical care provided to the patients.

(1) The medical staff must be organized in a manner approved by the governing body.

(2) If the medical staff has an executive committee, a majority of the members of the committee must be doctors of medicine or osteopathy.

(3) The responsibility for organization and conduct of the medical staff must be assigned only to one of the following:

   (i) An individual doctor of medicine or osteopathy.

   (ii) A doctor of dental surgery or dental medicine, when permitted by State law of the State in which the hospital is located.

   (iii) A doctor of podiatric medicine, when permitted by State law of the State in which the hospital is located.

Interpretive Guidelines §482.22(b)

The conditions of participation create a system of checks and balances within an overall framework of collaboration between the governing body and the medical staff (and, to a certain degree, also between an individual practitioner and the hospital's medical staff and governing body). Each has its own areas of authority. The medical staff has oversight of all practitioners practicing in the hospital through processes such as peer review and making recommendations concerning privileging and re-privileging. The governing body has the authority to establish the categories of healthcare professionals (regardless of the terms used to describe those categories) who are eligible for privileges and medical staff appointment. However, the governing body must rely on the medical staff to apply the criteria for privileging and appointment to those eligible candidates and to make their recommendations before the governing body makes a final decision to appoint or not appoint a practitioner to the medical staff. (77 FR 29042 May 16, 2012)

Leadership of the medical staff

The members of the hospital's medical staff must select, in accordance with the medical staff bylaws, rules or regulations approved by the governing body, a single individual to lead the medical staff and be responsible for the organization and conduct of the medical staff. This individual must be a doctor of medicine or osteopathy, or, if permitted by State law where the hospital is located, a doctor of dental surgery, dental medicine, or podiatric medicine. Removal of the leader of the medical staff may only occur in accordance with medical staff bylaws, rules or regulations.

Executive Committee

The medical staff bylaws, rules and regulations may provide for the members of the medical staff to select a smaller executive committee to which it delegates many of the functions of the medical staff, in order to increase the efficiency of its operations. If the medical staff has an executive committee, the majority of the members must be doctors of medicine (MDs) or osteopathy (DOs).

Accountability of the medical staff

The medical staff must be accountable to the hospital's governing body for the quality of medical care provided to the patients. The medical staff demonstrates its accountability through its exercise of its duties related to appointment of members of the medical staff, its conduct of reappraisals, including peer reviews, its approval of policies and procedures as required under other conditions of participation and its leadership participation in the organization and implementation of the hospital's quality assessment and performance improvement program required in accordance with §482.21.

Survey Procedures §482.22(b)

- Verify that the medical staff has a formal, organized structure reflected in the medical staff bylaws, rules and regulations and that functions and responsibilities within the medical staff and with respect to the governing body and other parts of the hospital are reflected.

- If there is a medical staff executive committee, verify that a majority of the members are doctors of medicine or osteopathy.

- Verify that an individual doctor of medicine or osteopathy, or if permitted by State law, a doctor of dental surgery, dental medicine, or podiatric medicine, selected by the medical staff, is responsible for the conduct and organization of the medical staff.

- Ask the CEO and medical staff leadership to describe the mechanisms by which the medical staff fulfills its responsibility to be accountable for the quality of medical care in the hospital.

- Interview several members of the medical staff, including both practitioners who hold leadership or executive committee positions and ones who do not. Ask them what their medical staff duties and responsibilities are and how they perform them. Ask them to describe how the medical staff is accountable for the quality of medical care provided to patients.

A-0353
(Rev. 37, Issued: 10-17-08; Effective/Implementation Date: 10-17-08)

§482.22(c) Standard: Medical Staff Bylaws

The medical staff must adopt and enforce bylaws to carry out its responsibilities. The bylaws must:

Interpretive Guidelines §482.22(c)

The medical staff must regulate itself by bylaws that are consistent with the requirements of this and other CoPs that mention medical staff bylaws, as well as State laws. The bylaws must be enforced and revised as necessary.

Survey Procedures §482.22(c)

- Verify that the medical staff have bylaws that comply with the CoPs and State law.

- Verify that the bylaws describe a mechanism for ensuring enforcement of its provisions along with rules and regulations of the hospital.

- Verify that the medical staff enforce the bylaws.

A-0354
(Rev. 37, Issued: 10-17-08; Effective/Implementation Date: 10-17-08)

[The bylaws must:]

§482.22(c)(1) - Be approved by the governing body.

Interpretive Guidelines §482.22(c)(1)

Medical staff bylaws and any revisions of those bylaws must be submitted to the governing body for approval. The governing body has the authority to approve or disapprove bylaws suggested by the medical staff. The bylaws and any revisions must be approved by the governing body before they are considered effective.

Survey Procedures §482.22(c)(1)

Verify that the medical staff bylaws have been approved by the medical staff and the governing body.

A-0355
(Rev. 37, Issued: 10-17-08; Effective/Implementation Date: 10-17-08)

[The bylaws must:]

§482.22(c)(2) - Include a statement of the duties and privileges of each category of medical staff (e.g., active, courtesy, etc.)

Interpretive Guidelines §482.22(c)(2)

The medical staff bylaws must state the duties and scope of medical staff privileges each category of practitioner may be granted. Specific privileges for each category must clearly and completely list the specific privileges or limitations for that category of practitioner. The specific privileges must reflect activities that the majority of practitioners in that category can perform competently and that the hospital can support.

Although the medical staff bylaws must address the duties and scope for each category of practitioner, this does not mean that each individual practitioner within the category may automatically be granted the full range of privileges. It cannot be assumed that every practitioner can perform every task/activity/privilege that is specified for the applicable category of practitioner. The individual practitioner's ability to perform each task/activity/privilege must be individually assessed.

Survey Procedures §482.22(c)(2)

Determine whether the bylaws specify the duties and scope of medical staff privileges for each category of practitioner eligible for medical staff membership or privileges.

A-0356
(Rev. 37, Issued: 10-17-08; Effective/Implementation Date: 10-17-08)

[The bylaws must:]

§482.22(c)(3) - Describe the organization of the medical staff.

Interpretive Guidelines §482.22(c)(3)

The medical staff bylaws must describe the organizational structure of the medical staff, and lay out the rules and regulations of the medical staff to make clear what are acceptable standards of patient care for all diagnostic, medical, surgical, and rehabilitative services.

Survey Procedures §482.22(c)(3)

- Verify that the bylaws specify the organization and structure of the medical staff, and a mechanism that delineates accountability to the governing body.

- Verify that the bylaws describe who is responsible for regularly scheduled review and evaluation of the clinical work of the members of the medical staff and describe the formation of medical staff leadership.

A-0357
(Rev. 37, Issued: 10-17-08; Effective/Implementation Date: 10-17-08)

[The bylaws must:]

§482.22(c)(4) - Describe the qualifications to be met by a candidate in order for the medical staff to recommend that the candidate be appointed by the governing body.

Interpretive Guidelines §482.22(c)(4)

The medical staff bylaws must describe the qualifications to be met by a candidate for medical staff membership/privileges in order for the medical staff to recommend the candidate be approved by the governing body. The bylaws must describe the privileging process to be used in the hospital. The process articulated in the medical staff bylaws must include criteria for determining the privileges that may be granted to individual practitioners and a procedure for applying the criteria to individual practitioners that considers:

- Individual character;

- Individual competence;

- Individual training;

- Individual experience; and

- Individual judgment.

The medical staff may not rely solely on the fact that a MD/DO is, or is not, board-certified in making a judgment on medical staff membership. This does not mean that the medical staff is prohibited from requiring board certification when considering a MD/DO for medical staff membership; only that such certification is not the only factor that the hospital considers. After analysis of all of the criteria, if all criteria are met except for board certification, the medical staff has the discretion to not recommend that individual for medical staff membership/privileges.

The bylaws must apply equally to all practitioners in each professional category of practitioners.

The medical staff then recommends individual candidates that meet those requirements to the governing body for appointment to the medical staff.

Survey Procedures §482.22(c)(4)

- Verify that there are written criteria for appointments to the medical staff and granting of medical staff privileges.

- Verify that granting of medical staff membership or privileges, is based upon an individual practitioner's meeting the medical staff's membership/privileging criteria.

- Verify that at a minimum, criteria for appointment to the medical staff/granting of medical staff privileges are individual character, competence, training, experience, and judgment.

- Verify that written criteria for appointment to the medical staff and granting of medical staff privileges are not dependent solely upon certification, fellowship, or membership in a specialty body or society.

A-0358
(Rev. 84, Issued: 06-07-13, Effective: 06-07-13, Implementation: 06-07-13)

[The bylaws must:]

482.22(c)(5) Include a requirement that --

(i) A medical history and physical examination be completed and documented for each patient no more than 30 days before or 24 hours after admission or registration, but prior to surgery or a procedure requiring anesthesia services. The medical history and physical examination must be completed and documented by a physician (as defined in section 1861(r) of the Act), an oromaxillofacial surgeon, or other qualified licensed individual in accordance with State law and hospital policy.

Interpretive Guidelines §482.22(c)(5)(i)

The purpose of a medical history and physical examination (H&P) is to determine whether there is anything in the patient's overall condition that would affect the planned course of the patient's treatment, such as a medication allergy, or a new or existing co-morbid condition that requires additional interventions to reduce risk to the patient.

The Medical Staff bylaws must include a requirement that an H&P be completed and documented for each patient no more than 30 days prior to or 24 hours after hospital admission or registration, but prior to surgery or a procedure requiring anesthesia services. The H&P may be handwritten or transcribed, but always must be placed within the patient's medical record within 24 hours of admission or registration, or prior to surgery or a procedure requiring anesthesia services, whichever comes first.

An H&P is required prior to surgery and prior to procedures requiring anesthesia services, regardless of whether care is being provided on an inpatient or outpatient basis. (71 FR 68676) An H&P that is completed within 24 hours of the patient's admission or registration, but after the surgical procedure, procedure requiring anesthesia, or other procedure requiring an H&P would not be in compliance with this requirement.

The medical history and physical examination must be completed and documented by a physician (as defined in section 1861(r) of the Act), oromaxillofacial surgeon, or other qualified licensed individual in accordance with State law and hospital policy.

Section 1861(r) defines a physician as a:

- Doctor of medicine or osteopathy;
- Doctor of dental surgery or of dental medicine;
- Doctor of podiatric medicine;
- Doctor of optometry; or a
- Chiropractor.

In all cases the practitioners included in the definition of a physician must be legally authorized to practice within the State where the hospital is located and providing services within their authorized scope of practice. In addition, in certain instances the Social Security Act attaches further limitations as to the type of hospital services for which a practitioner is considered to be a "physician." For example, a chiropractor is considered a physician only with respect to treatment by means of manual manipulation of the spine (to correct a subluxation).

Other qualified licensed individuals are those licensed practitioners who are authorized in accordance with their State scope of practice laws or regulations to perform an H&P and who are also formally authorized by the hospital to conduct an H&P. Other qualified licensed practitioners could include nurse practitioners and physician assistants.

More than one qualified practitioner can participate in performing, documenting, and authenticating an H&P for a single patient. When performance, documentation, and authentication are split among qualified practitioners, the practitioner who authenticates the H&P will be held responsible for its contents. (71 FR 68675)

A hospital may adopt a policy allowing submission of an H&P prior to the patient's hospital admission or registration by a physician who may not be a member of the hospital's medical staff or who does not have admitting privileges at that hospital, or by a qualified licensed individual who does not practice at that hospital but is acting within his/her scope of practice under State law or regulations. Generally, this occurs where the H&P is completed in advance by the patient's primary care practitioner. (71 FR 68675)

When the H&P is conducted within 30 days before admission or registration, an update must be completed and documented by a licensed practitioner who is credentialed and privileged by the hospital's medical staff to perform an H&P. (71 FR 68675) (See discussion of H&P update requirements at 42 CFR 482.22(c)(5)(ii).)

Surveyors should cite noncompliance with the requirements of 42 CFR 482.22(c)(5) for failure by the hospital to comply with any of this standard's components.

Survey Procedures §482.22(c)(5)(i)

- Review the medical staff bylaws to determine whether they require that a physical examination and medical history be done for each patient no more than 30 days before or 24 hours after admission or registration by a physician (as defined in section 1861(r) of the Act), an oromaxillofacial surgeon, or other qualified licensed individual in accordance with State law and hospital policy. Verify whether the bylaws require the H&P be completed prior to surgery or a procedure requiring anesthesia services.

- Review the hospital's policy, if any, to determine whether other qualified licensed individuals are permitted to conduct H&Ps to ensure that it is consistent with the State's scope of practice law or regulations.

- Verify that non-physicians who perform H&Ps within the hospital are qualified and have been credentialed and privileged in accordance with the hospital's policy.

- Review a sample of inpatient and outpatient medical records that include a variety of patient populations undergoing both surgical and non-surgical procedures to verify that:

    ○ There is an H&P that was completed no more than 30 days before or 24 hours after admission or registration, but, in all cases, prior to surgery or a procedure requiring anesthesia services; and

    ○ The H&P was performed by a physician, an oromaxillofacial surgeon, or other qualified licensed individual authorized in accordance with State law and hospital policy.

A-0359

(Rev. 37, Issued: 10-17-08; Effective/Implementation Date: 10-17-08)

[The bylaws must:]

482.22(c)(5) - [Include a requirement that --]

> **(ii) An updated examination of the patient, including any changes in the patient's condition, be completed and documented within 24 hours after admission or registration, but prior to surgery or a procedure requiring anesthesia services, when the medical history and physical examination are completed within 30 days before admission or registration. The updated examination of the patient, including any changes in the patient's condition, must be completed and documented by a physician (as defined in section 1861(r) of the Act), an oromaxillofacial surgeon, or other qualified licensed individual in accordance with State law and hospital policy.**

Interpretive Guidelines 482.22(c)(5)(ii)

The Medical Staff bylaws must include a requirement that when a medical history and physical examination has been completed within 30 days before admission or registration, an updated medical record entry must be completed and documented in the patient's medical record within 24 hours after admission or registration. The examination must be conducted by a licensed practitioner who is credentialed and privileged by the hospital's medical staff to perform an H&P. In all cases, the update must take place prior to surgery or a procedure requiring anesthesia services. The update note must document an examination for any changes in the patient's condition since the patient's H&P was performed that might be significant for the planned course of treatment. The physician or qualified licensed individual uses his/her clinical judgment, based upon his/her assessment of the patient's condition and co-morbidities, if any, in relation to the patient's planned course of treatment to decide the extent of the update assessment needed as well as the information to be included in the update note in the patient's medical record.

If, upon examination, the licensed practitioner finds no change in the patient's condition since the H&P was completed, he/she may indicate in the patient's medical record that the H&P was reviewed, the patient was examined, and that "no change" has occurred in the patient's condition since the H&P was completed (71 FR 68676). Any changes in the patient's condition must be documented by the practitioner in the update note and placed in the patient's medical record within 24 hours of admission or registration, but prior to surgery or a procedure requirement anesthesia services. Additionally, if the practitioner finds that the H&P done before admission is incomplete, inaccurate, or otherwise unacceptable, the practitioner reviewing the H&P, examining the patient, and completing the update may disregard the existing H&P, and conduct and document in the medical record a new H&P within 24 hours after admission or registration, but prior to surgery or a procedure requiring anesthesia.

Survey Procedures §482.22(c)(5)(ii)

- Review the medical staff bylaws to determine whether they include provisions requiring that, when the medical history and physical examination was completed within 30 days before admission or registration, an updated medical record entry documenting an examination for changes in the patient's condition was completed and documented in the patient's medical record within 24 hours after admission or registration.

- Determine whether the bylaws require that, in all cases involving surgery or a procedure requiring anesthesia services, the update to the H&P must be completed and documented prior to the surgery or procedure.

- In the sample of medical records selected for review, look for cases where the medical history and physical examination was completed within 30 days before admission or registration. Verify that an updated medical record entry documenting an examination for any changes in the patient's condition was completed and documented in the patient's medical record within 24 hours after admission or registration. Verify that in all cases involving surgery or a procedure requiring anesthesia services, the update was completed and documented prior to the surgery or procedure.

A-0363

(Rev.78, Issued: 12-22-11, Effective/Implementation: 12-22-11)

[The bylaws must:]

§482.22(c)(6) - Include criteria for determining the privileges to be granted to individual practitioners and a procedure for applying the criteria to individuals requesting privileges. For distant-site physicians and practitioners requesting privileges to furnish telemedicine services under an agreement with the hospital, the criteria for determining privileges and the procedure for applying the criteria are also subject to the requirements in §482.12(a)(8) and (a)(9), and §482.22(a)(3) and (a)(4).

Interpretive Guidelines §482.22(c)(6)

All patient care is provided by or in accordance with the orders of a physician or practitioner who meets the medical staff criteria and procedures for the privileges granted, who has been granted privileges in accordance with those criteria by the governing body, and who is working within the scope of those granted privileges.

Privileges are granted by the hospital's governing body to individual practitioners based on the medical staff's review of that individual practitioner's qualifications and the medical staff's recommendations for that individual practitioner to the governing body. However, in the case of telemedicine physicians and practitioners providing telemedicine services under an agreement, the governing body has the option of having the medical staff rely upon the credentialing and privileging decisions of the distant-site hospital or telemedicine entity with which the hospital has entered into an agreement. When the governing body has exercised this option, the medical staff's bylaws must include a provision allowing the medical staff to rely upon the credentialing and privileging decisions of a distant-site hospital or telemedicine entity when that distant-site hospital or entity is required under the terms of its agreement with the hospital to employ a credentialing and privileging process that conforms to the provisions of §482.12(a)(8) and (a)(9), and §482.22(a)(3) and (a)(4).

Survey Procedures §482.22(c)(6)

- Verify that the medical staff bylaws contain criteria for granting, withdrawing, and modifying clinical privileges to individual physicians and practitioners of the medical staff and that a procedure exists for applying these criteria.

- In the case of telemedicine physicians and practitioners providing telemedicine services under an agreement with the hospital where the hospital's governing body has opted to have the medical staff rely upon the credentialing and privileging decisions of the distant-site hospital or telemedicine entity, verify that the bylaws include a provision permitting such reliance.

- Verify that physicians and practitioners who provide care to patients are working within the scope of the privileges granted by the governing body.

A-0364

(Rev. 37, Issued: 10-17-08; Effective/Implementation Date: 10-17-08)

§482.22(d) Standard: Autopsies

The medical staff should attempt to secure autopsies in all cases of unusual deaths and of medical-legal and educational interest. The mechanism for documenting permission to perform an autopsy must be defined. There must be a system for

notifying the medical staff, and specifically the attending practitioner, when an autopsy is being performed.

Survey Procedures §482.22(d)

Verify that the medical staff has policies requiring the practitioners to attempt to secure permission to perform autopsies, that the mechanism for documenting permission to perform an autopsy is defined, and that there is a system for notifying the medical staff, specifically the attending practitioner, when an autopsy is performed.

A-0385

(Rev. 37, Issued: 10-17-08; Effective/Implementation Date: 10-17-08)
§482.23 Condition of Participation: Nursing Services

The hospital must have an organized nursing service that provides 24-hour nursing services. The nursing services must be furnished or supervised by a registered nurse.

Interpretive Guidelines §482.23

The hospital must have an organized nursing service and must provide on premise nursing services 24 hours a day, 7 days a week with at least 1 registered nurse (RN) furnishing or supervising the service 24 hours a day, 7 days a week (Exception: small rural hospitals operating under a waiver as discussed in §482.23(b)(1)).

The Social Security Act (SSA) at §1861(b) states that nursing services must be furnished to inpatients and **furnished by the hospital**. The SSA at §1861(e) further requires that the hospital have a **RN on duty at all times** (except small rural hospitals operating under a nursing waiver).

The nursing service must be a well-organized service of the hospital and under the direction of a registered nurse.

The nursing service must be integrated into the hospital-wide QAPI program.

Survey Procedures §482.23

- Determine if the nursing service is integrated into the hospital-wide QAPI program.

- Interview the director of the service. Request the following items:

  ○ Organizational chart(s) for nursing services for all locations where the hospital provides nursing services;

  ○ Job or position descriptions for all nursing personnel including the director's position description.

- Select at least one patient from every inpatient care unit. Observe the nursing care in progress to determine the adequacy of staffing and to assess the delivery of care. Other sources of information to use in the evaluation of the nursing services are: nursing care plans, medical records, patients, family members, accident and investigative reports, staffing schedules, nursing policies and procedures, and QAPI activities and reports. Interview patients for information relative to the delivery of nursing services.

A-0386

(Rev. 37, Issued: 10-17-08; Effective/Implementation Date: 10-17-08)
§482.23(a) Standard: Organization

The hospital must have a well-organized service with a plan of administrative authority and delineation of responsibilities for patient care. The director of the nursing service must be a licensed registered nurse. He or she is responsible for the operation of the service, including determining the types and numbers of nursing personnel and staff necessary to provide nursing care for all areas of the hospital.

Interpretive Guidelines §482.23(a)

The hospital may have only one nursing service hospital-wide and the single nursing service must be under the direction of one RN.

The director of the nursing service must be a currently licensed RN and he/she is responsible for the operation of the nursing service. The operation of the nursing service would include the quality of the patient care provided by the nursing service.

The director of the nursing service must determine and provide the types and numbers of nursing care personnel necessary to provide nursing care to all areas of the hospital.

The organization will include various configurations of the following hospital personnel as determined necessary by the hospital and the Director of Nursing:

- Assistant/Associate Director(s);

- Supervisors/Coordinators;

- Head Nurses/Nurse Managers;

- Staff Nurses;

- Unit Secretaries/Clerks;

- Nurses Aide/Orderlies.

Survey Procedures §482.23(a)

- Review the organizational chart or plan for nursing services. Determine that the organizational chart(s) displays lines of authority that delegates responsibility within the department.

- Read the position description for the director of nursing (DON) to determine that it delegates to the DON specific duties and responsibilities for operation of the service.

- Verify that the director is currently licensed in accordance with state licensure requirements.

- Verify that the DON is involved with or approved the development of the nursing service staffing policies and procedures.

- Verify that the DON approves the nursing service patient care policies and procedures.

A-0392
(Rev. 37, Issued: 10-17-08; Effective/Implementation Date: 10-17-08)

§482.23(b) Standard: Staffing and Delivery of Care

The nursing service must have adequate numbers of licensed registered nurses, licensed practical (vocational) nurses, and other personnel to provide nursing care to all patients as needed. There must be supervisory and staff personnel for each department or nursing unit to ensure, when needed, the immediate availability of a registered nurse for bedside care of any patient.

Interpretive Guidelines §482.23(b)

The nursing service must ensure that patient needs are met by ongoing assessments of patients' needs and provides nursing staff to meet those needs. There must be sufficient numbers, types and qualifications of supervisory and staff nursing personnel to respond to the appropriate nursing needs and care of the patient population of each department or nursing unit.

There must be a RN physically present on the premises and on duty at all times. Every inpatient unit/department/location within the hospital-wide nursing service must have adequate numbers of RNs physically present at each location to ensure the immediate availability of a RN for the bedside care of any patient.

A RN would not be considered immediately available if the RN were working on more than one unit, building, floor in a building, or provider (distinct part SNF, RHC, excluded unit, etc.) at the same time.

Staffing schedules must be reviewed and revised as necessary to meet the patient care needs and to make adjustments for nursing staff absenteeism.

Survey Procedures §482.23(b)

- Determine that there are written staffing schedules which correlate to the number and acuity of patients. Verify that there is supervision of personnel performance and nursing care for each department or nursing unit. To determine if there are adequate numbers of nurses to provide nursing care to all patients as needed, take into consideration:

  o Physical layout and size of the hospital;

  o Number of patients;

  o Intensity of illness and nursing needs;

  o Availability of nurses' aides and orderlies and other resources for nurses, e.g., housekeeping services, ward clerks etc.;

  o Training and experience of personnel;

  o Do not count personnel assigned to areas other than bedside patient care.

- Review medical records to determine if patient care that is to be provided by nurses is being provided as ordered.

A-0393
(Rev. 37, Issued: 10-17-08; Effective/Implementation Date: 10-17-08)

§482.23(b)(1) - The hospital must provide 24-hour nursing services furnished or supervised by a registered nurse, and have a licensed practical nurse or registered nurse on duty at all times, except for rural hospitals that have in effect a 24-hour nursing waiver granted under §488.54(c)of this chapter.

Interpretive Guidelines §482.23(b)(1)

The hospital must provide nursing services 24 hours a day, 7 days a week. An LPN can provide nursing services if an RN, who is immediately available for the bedside care of those patients, supervises that care.

EXCEPTION: Section 488.54(c) sets forth certain conditions under which rural hospitals of 50 beds or fewer may be granted a temporary waiver of the 24-hour registered nurse requirement by the regional office.

Rural is defined as all areas not delineated as "urbanized" areas by the Census Bureau, in the most recent census. Temporary is defined as a one year period or less and the waiver cannot be renewed.

Survey Procedures §482.23(b)(1)

- Review the nurse staffing schedule for a one-week period. If there are concerns regarding insufficient RN coverage, review the staffing schedules for a second week period to determine if there is a pattern of insufficient coverage. Document daily RN coverage for every unit of the hospital. Verify that there is at least one RN for each unit on each tour of duty, 7 days a week, 24 hours a day. Additional nurses may be required for vacation or absenteeism coverage.

- **EXCEPTION:** If the hospital has a temporary waiver of the 24-hour RN requirement in effect, verify and document the following:

  o   50 or fewer inpatient beds;

  o   The character and seriousness of the deficiencies do not adversely affect the health and safety of patients

  o   The hospital meets all the other statutory requirements in §1861(e)(1-8).

  o   The hospital has made and continues to make a good faith effort to comply with the 24 hour nursing requirement. Determine the recruitment efforts and methods used by the hospitals' administration by requesting copies of advertisements in newspapers and other publications as well as evidence of contact with nursing schools and employment agencies. Document that the salary offered by the hospital is comparable to three other hospitals, located nearest to the facility.

o   The hospital's failure to comply fully with the 24 hour nursing requirement is attributable to a temporary shortage of qualified nursing personnel in the area in which the hospital is located.

o   A registered nurse is present on the premises to furnish the nursing service during at least the daytime shift, 7 days a week.

o   On all tours of duty not covered by a registered nurse, a licensed practical (vocational) nurse is in charge.

A-0394
(Rev. 37, Issued: 10-17-08; Effective/Implementation Date: 10-17-08)

§482.23(b)(2) - The nursing service must have a procedure to ensure that hospital nursing personnel for whom licensure is required have valid and current licensure.

Interpretive Guidelines §482.23(b)(2)

The hospital's procedure must ensure that all nursing personnel have valid and current licensure that complies with State licensure laws. Furthermore, the Condition of Participation (CoP) Compliance with Federal, State and local laws (42 CFR 482.11) requires the hospital to assure that personnel meet applicable standards (such as continuing education, certification or training) required by State or local law.

Survey Procedures §482.23(b)(2)

- Review hospital personnel records or records kept by the nursing service to determine that RNs, LPNs, and other nursing personnel for whom licensure is required have current valid licenses.

- Review the nursing service licensure verification policies and procedures. Is licensure verified for each individual nursing services staff person for whom licensure is required?

A-0395
(Rev. 37, Issued: 10-17-08; Effective/Implementation Date: 10-17-08)

§482.23(b)(3) - A registered nurse must supervise and evaluate the nursing care for each patient.

Interpretive Guidelines §482.23(b)(3)

A RN must supervise the nursing care for each patient. A RN must evaluate the care for each patient upon admission and when appropriate on an ongoing basis in accordance with accepted standards of nursing practice and hospital policy. Evaluation would include assessing the patient's care needs, patient's health status/conditioning, as well as the patient's response to interventions.

Survey Procedures §482.23(b)(3)

- Review staffing schedules and assignments.

- Determine that a RN is assigned to supervise and evaluate the nursing care furnished to each patient.

A-0396
(Rev. 84, Issued: 06-07-13, Effective: 06-07-13, Implementation: 06-07-13)

§482.23(b)(4) - The hospital must ensure that the nursing staff develops, and keeps current, a nursing care plan for each patient. The nursing care plan may be part of an interdisciplinary care plan.

Interpretive Guidelines §482.23(b)(4)

Nursing care planning starts upon admission. It includes planning the patient's care while in the hospital as well as planning for discharge to meet post-hospital needs. A nursing care plan is based on assessing the patient's nursing care needs (not solely those needs related to the admitting diagnosis). The assessment considers the patient's treatment goals and, as appropriate, physiological and psychosocial factors and patient discharge planning. The plan develops appropriate nursing interventions in response to the identified nursing care needs. The nursing care plan is kept current by ongoing assessments of the patient's needs and of the patient's response to interventions, and updating or revising the patient's nursing care plan in response to assessments. The nursing care plan is part of the patient's medical record and must comply with the medical records requirements at §482.24.

Hospitals have the flexibility of developing the nursing care plan as part of a larger, coordinated interdisciplinary plan of care. This method may serve to promote communication among disciplines and reinforce an integrated, multi-faceted approach to a patient's care, resulting in better patient outcomes. The interdisciplinary plan of care does not minimize or eliminate the need for a nursing care plan. It does, however, serve to promote the collaboration between members of the patient's health care team.

The required documentation for the nursing component of an interdisciplinary care plan remains the same. For other components, the hospital should follow the current documentation policies that it uses to document services provided by other disciplines, such as services provided by physical therapists, occupational therapists, speech-language pathologists, and others. Documentation should follow the standards of practice for those disciplines in addition to any specific requirements that the hospital might want to establish. The documentation must also comply with the requirements of the medical records requirement at §482.24. (77 FR 29049, May 16, 2012)

Survey Procedures §482.23(b)(4)

Select a sample of nursing or interdisciplinary care plans. Approximately 6-12 plans should be reviewed. For each plan reviewed, with respect to the nursing care component:

- Was the plan initiated as soon as possible after admission for each patient?

- Does the plan describe patient goals as part of the patient's nursing care assessment and, as appropriate, physiological and psychosocial factors and patient discharge planning?

- Is the plan consistent with the plan for medical care of the practitioner responsible for the care of the patient?

- Is there evidence of reassessment of the patient's nursing care needs and response to nursing interventions and, as applicable, revisions to the plan?

- Was the plan implemented in a timely manner?

A-0397
(Rev. 37, Issued: 10-17-08; Effective/Implementation Date: 10-17-08)

§482.23(b)(5) - A registered nurse must assign the nursing care of each patient to other nursing personnel in accordance with the patient's needs and the specialized qualifications and competence of the nursing staff available.

Interpretive Guidelines §482.23(b)(5)

A RN must make all patient care assignments. The director of the nursing service and the hospital are to ensure that nursing personnel with the appropriate education, experience, licensure, competence and specialized qualifications are assigned to provide nursing care for each patient in accordance with the individual needs of each patient.

Survey Procedures §482.23(b)(5)

- Review the nursing assignments. Did an RN make the assignments? Determine that the assignments take into consideration the complexity of patient's care needs and the competence and specialized qualifications of the nursing staff.

- Ask a charge nurse what considerations are necessary when making staff assignments. Answers should include:

  o Patient needs;

  o Complexity of patients;

  o Any special needs of individual patients;

  o Competence of nursing personnel;

  o Qualifications of nursing personnel;

  o Education of nursing personnel; and

  o Experience of nursing personnel.

A-0398
(Rev. 37, Issued: 10-17-08; Effective/Implementation Date: 10-17-08)

§482.23(b)(6) - Non-employee licensed nurses who are working in the hospital must adhere to the policies and procedures of the hospital. The director of nursing service must provide for the adequate supervision and evaluation of the clinical activities of non-employee nursing personnel which occur within the responsibility of the nursing services.

Interpretive Guidelines §482.23(b)(6)

The hospital must ensure that there are adequate numbers of clinical nursing personnel to meet its patients nursing care needs. In order to meet their patient's needs the hospital may supplement their hospital employed licensed nurses with volunteer and or contract non-employee licensed nurses.

The hospital and the director of the nursing service are responsible for the clinical activities of all nursing personnel. This would include the clinical activities of all non-employee nursing personnel (contract or volunteer).

Non-employee licensed nurses who are working at the hospital must adhere to the policies and procedures of the hospital. The hospital and the director of the nursing service are responsible for ensuring that non-employee nursing personnel know the hospital's policies and procedures in order to adhere to those policies and procedures.

The hospital and the director of the nursing service ensure that each non-employee nursing care staff person is adequately supervised and that their clinical activities are evaluated. This supervision and evaluation of the clinical activities of each non-employee nursing staff person must be conducted by an appropriately qualified hospital-employed RN.

Survey Procedures §482.23(b)(6)

- Review the method for orienting non-employee licensed nurses to hospital policies and procedures. The orientation should include at least the following:

  o The hospital and the unit;

  o Emergency procedures;

  o Nursing services policies and procedures; and

  o Safety policies and procedures.

- Determine if non-employee nursing personnel are appropriately oriented prior to providing care.

- If the hospital uses non-employee licensed nurses, are they supervised by a RN who is a regular employee of the hospital?

- Observe the care provided by non-employee nursing personnel.

  o Do they know and adhere to hospital policies?

  o Do they know appropriate emergency procedures?

  o Are they adequately supervised by an appropriately experienced hospital employed RN?

  o Are their clinical activities being evaluated adequately?

    o   Are they licensed in accordance with State law?

- Confirm with the director of nurses that a non-employee nurse's performance is evaluated by the hospital at least once a year. If the performance evaluation is not considered confidential, review two evaluations.

A-0405
(Rev. 84, Issued: 06-07-13, Effective: 06-07-13, Implementation: 06-07-13)

§482.23(c) Standard: Preparation and Administration of Drugs

(1) Drugs and biologicals must be prepared and administered in accordance with Federal and State laws, the orders of the practitioner or practitioners responsible for the patient's care as specified under §482.12(c), and accepted standards of practice.

(i) Drugs and biologicals may be prepared and administered on the orders of other practitioners not specified under §482.12(c) only if such practitioners are acting in accordance with State law, including scope of practice laws, hospital policies, and medical staff bylaws, rules, and regulations....

(2) All drugs and biologicals must be administered by, or under supervision of, nursing or other personnel in accordance with Federal and State laws and regulations, including applicable licensing requirements, and in accordance with the approved medical staff policies and procedures.

Interpretive Guidelines §§482.23(c)(1), (c)(1)(i) and (c)(2)

According to the Institute of Medicine of the National Academies, medication errors are among the most common medical errors, harming at least 1.5 million people each year.[3] It has been estimated that drug-related adverse outcomes were noted in nearly 1.9 million inpatient hospital stays (4.7 percent of all stays), and 838,000 treat-and-release ED visits (0.8 percent of all visits).[4] Although technological advances in electronic order entry, medication administration, and electronic medical records hold a great deal of promise for decreasing medication errors, there are a multitude of human and environmental factors that will impact their success. The increasing complexity of medical care and patient acuity present significant challenges that require an approach to medication administration that takes advantage of available technology while recognizing that it must

---

[3] Institute of Medicine. Preventing Medication Errors. Washington DC: The National Academies Press, 2007.

[4] Lucado, Jennifer, et al, *Medication-Related Adverse Outcomes in U.S. Hospitals and Emergency Departments.* Statistical Brief #109, April, 2011. Healthcare Cost and Utilization,Project, Agency For Healthcare Research and Quality, Rockville, MD.

be integrated into the medication administration work processes in a manner that meets the needs of patients and promotes their safety.

The regulations at §482.23(c) and §482.23(c)(1) promote safety in the preparation and administration of drugs and biologicals to hospital patients by requiring preparation and administration by or under the supervision of nursing or other personnel in accordance with:

- Federal and State law;

- Accepted standards of practice;

- Orders of the practitioner(s) responsible for the patient's care, as specified under §482.12(c) or of another practitioner as permitted under State law, hospital policy and medical staff bylaws, rules and regulations; and

- Medical staff-approved policies and procedures.

Federal and State Law

Federal law regulates the approval and classification of drugs and biologicals. Individual States establish laws and regulations which specify the scope of practice for various types of licensed healthcare professionals, including which medications they may prescribe and administer, including controlled substances.

Accepted Standards of Practice

Hospital policies and procedures for the preparation and administration of all drugs and biologicals must not only comply with all applicable Federal and State laws, but also must be consistent with accepted standards of practice based on guidelines or recommendations issued by nationally recognized organizations with expertise in medication preparation and administration. Examples of such organizations include, but are not limited to:

- National Coordinating Council for Medication Error Reporting and Prevention (www.nccmerp.org);
- Institute for Healthcare Improvement (http://www.ihi.org/ihi) ;
- U.S Pharmacopeia (www.usp.org) ;
- Institute for Safe Medication Practices, which offers guidelines specifically on timely medication administration, which can be found at: www.ismp.org/Newsletters/acutecare/articles/20110113.asp;
- Infusion Nurses Society (http://www.ins1.org).

In addition, the Centers for Disease Control and Prevention (CDC) publishes evidenced-based practice guidelines and recommendations on medication preparation and administration practices, designed to reduce the risk of infection associated with these activities.

Orders of an authorized practitioner

Drugs must be administered in response to an order from a practitioner, or on the basis of a standing order which is appropriately authenticated subsequently by a practitioner. (See §482.23(c)(1) (ii) concerning standing orders.) Generally, the ordering practitioner is the practitioner(s) responsible for the care of the patient in accordance with §482.12(c). However, other practitioners not specified under §482.12(c) may write orders for the preparation and administration of drugs and biologicals, if they are acting in accordance with State law, including scope of practice laws, hospital policies and procedures, and medical staff bylaws, rules and regulations. This includes practitioners ordering outpatient services who do not have privileges in the hospital but who are permitted under their State scope of practice and authorized by hospital and medical staff policy to order outpatient services.

In accordance with standard practice, all practitioner orders for the administration of drugs and biologicals must include at least the following:

- Name of the patient;
- Age and weight of the patients, or other dose calculation requirements, when applicable;
- Date and time of the order;
- Drug name;
- Dose, frequency, and route;
- Exact strength or concentration, when applicable;
- Quantity and/or duration, when applicable;
- Specific instructions for use, when applicable; and
- Name of the prescriber.

Medical Staff Approved Policies and Procedures

The hospital's medical staff must approve policies and procedures for medication administration, consistent with the requirements of Federal and State law and accepted standards of practice. It is recommended that the medical staff consult with nurses, pharmacists, Quality Assessment and Performance Improvement program staff, and others in developing these policies and procedures. The adopted policies and procedures must address key issues related to medication administration, which include but are not limited to:

Personnel authorized to administer medication

Policies and procedures must identify categories of licensed personnel and the types of medications they are permitted to prepare and administer, in accordance with state laws.

The policies and procedures must also address education and training for all personnel preparing and administering drugs and biologicals.

Medication preparation and administration education and training is typically included in hospital orientation or other continuing education for nursing staff and other authorized healthcare personnel. Training or continuing education topics regarding medication preparation and administration may include but are not limited to the following:

- Safe handling and preparation of authorized medications;

- Knowledge of the indications, side effects, drug interactions, compatibility, and dose limits of administered medications;

- Equipment, devices, special procedures, and/or techniques required for medication administration;

Policies and procedures must address the required components of the training and if the training provided during hospital orientation imparts sufficient education or whether ongoing in-services or continuing education will be required to demonstrate competence.

Basic safe practices for medication administration

The hospital's policies and procedures must reflect accepted standards of practice that require the following be confirmed prior to each administration of medication:

- the patient's identity— acceptable patient identifiers include, but are not limited to: the patient's full name; an identification number assigned by the hospital; or date of birth. Identifiers must be confirmed by patient wrist band, patient identification card, patient statement (when possible) or other means outlined in the hospital's policy. The patient's identification must be confirmed to be in agreement with the medication administration record and medication labeling prior to medication administration to ensure that the medication is being given to the correct patient.

- the correct medication, to ensure that the medication being given to the patient matches that prescribed for the patient;

- the correct dose, to ensure that the dosage of the medication matches the prescribed dose, and that the prescription itself does not reflect an unsafe dosage level (i.e., a dose that is too high or too low);

- the correct route, to ensure that the method of administration – orally, intramuscular, intravenous, etc., is the appropriate one for that particular medication and patient; and

- the appropriate time, to ensure adherence to the prescribed frequency and time of administration.

Hospitals are encouraged to promote a culture in which it is not only acceptable, but also strongly encouraged, for staff to bring to the attention of the prescribing practitioner questions or concerns they have regarding medication orders. Any questions about orders for drugs or biologicals are expected to be resolved promptly, whether they arise prior to the preparation, dispensing, or administration of the medication.

Timing of Medication Administration

Appropriate timing of medication administration must take into account the complex nature and variability among medications; the indications for which they are prescribed; the clinical situations in which they are administered; and the needs of the patients receiving them. The chemical properties, mechanism of action, or therapeutic goals of some medications require administration at the exact time prescribed, or within a narrow window of its prescribed scheduled time, to avoid compromising patient safety or achievement of the intended therapeutic effect. However, the therapeutic effect of many other medications is uncompromised by a much broader window of time for administration. Consequently, the application of a uniform required window of time before or after the scheduled time for the administration of all medications, without regard to their differences, could undermine the ability of nursing staff to prioritize nursing care activities appropriately. This could also result in staff work-arounds that jeopardize patient safety due to the imposition of unrealistic or unnecessary time constraints for medication administration. Instead, hospital policies and procedures must specifically address the timing of medication administration, based on the nature of the medication and its clinical application, to ensure safe and timely administration. The policies and procedures must address at least the following:

- Medications **not eligible** for scheduled dosing times;
- Medications **eligible for** scheduled dosing times;
- Administration of eligible medications outside of their scheduled dosing times and windows; and
- Evaluation of medication administration timing policies, including adherence to them.

Medications **not eligible** for scheduled dosing times

The policies and procedures must identify medications which are not eligible for scheduled dosing times, either in general or in specific clinical applications. These are medications that require exact or precise timing of administration, based on diagnosis type, treatment requirements, or therapeutic goals. The policies and procedures must reflect consideration of factors including, but not limited to, the pharmacokinetics of the prescribed medication; specific clinical applications; and patient risk factors. Examples of medications that hospitals may choose to identify as not eligible for scheduled dosing times may include, but are not limited to:

- Stat doses (immediate);
- First time or loading doses (initial large dose of a drug given to bring blood, tissue or fluid levels to an effective concentration quickly);
- One-time doses; doses specifically timed for procedures;
- Time-sequenced doses; doses timed for serum drug levels;
- Investigational drugs; or
- Drugs prescribed on an as needed basis (prn doses).

The policies and procedures must ensure timely administration of such medications. In addition they must specify if the policy for the administration of these medications will be applied hospital-wide or only for specific diagnosis types, hospital units or clinical situations.

Medications eligible for scheduled dosing times

Medications eligible for scheduled dosing times are those prescribed on a repeated cycle of frequency, such as once a day, BID (twice a day), TID (three times a day), hourly intervals (every 1, 2, 3 or more hours), etc. The goal of this scheduling is to achieve and maintain therapeutic blood levels of the prescribed medication over a period of time. Medication administration policies and procedures typically establish standardized dosing times for the administration of all 'scheduled' medications. For example, medications prescribed for BID (twice a day) administration might, under a given hospital's policies and procedures, be scheduled to be administered at 8am and 8pm. Another hospital might choose to schedule BID medications at 7:30 am and 7:30 pm. Use of these standardized times facilitates the medication administration process, e.g., by providing to the hospital's pharmacy that morning doses of all BID drugs must be dispensed and delivered to patient units in time for the scheduled administration. For the nursing staff, the scheduled administration time might prompt prioritization of additional activities that may be required, in the case of particular drugs, such as vital sign assessment or the collection and review of blood work, to ensure safe and timely medication administration.

Policies and procedures for medications eligible for scheduled dosing times must also address: first dose medications, including parameters within which nursing staff are allowed to use their own judgment regarding the timing of the first and subsequent doses, which may fall between scheduled dosing times; retiming of missed or omitted doses; medications that will not follow scheduled dosing times; and patient units that are not subject to following the scheduled dosing times.

Time-critical scheduled medications

Time-critical scheduled medications are those for which an early or late administration of greater than thirty minutes might cause harm or have significant, negative impact on the intended therapeutic or pharmacological effect. Accordingly, scheduled medications identified under the hospital's policies and procedures as time-critical must be administered within thirty minutes before or after their scheduled dosing time, for a total window of 1 hour.

It is possible for a given medication to be time- critical for some patients, due to diagnosis, clinical situation, various risk factors, or therapeutic intent, but not time-critical for other patients. Therefore, hospital policies and procedures must address the process for determining whether specific scheduled medications are always time-critical, or only under certain circumstances, and how staff involved in medication administration will know when a scheduled medication is time-critical. Examples of time-critical scheduled medications/medication types may include, but are not limited to:

- Antibiotics;
- Anticoagulants;
- Insulin;
- Anticonvulsants;
- Immunosuppressive agents;
- Pain medication;
- Medications prescribed for administration within a specified period of time of the medication order;
- Medications that must be administered apart from other medications for optimal therapeutic effect; or
- Medications prescribed more frequently than every 4 hours.

Non-time-critical scheduled medications

Non-time critical scheduled medications are those for which a longer or shorter interval of time since the prior dose does not significantly change the medication's therapeutic effect or otherwise cause harm. For such medications greater flexibility in the timing of their administration is permissible. Specifically:

- Medications prescribed for daily, weekly or monthly administration may be within 2 hours before or after the scheduled dosing time, for a total window that does not exceed 4 hours.

- Medications prescribed more frequently than daily but no more frequently than every 4 hours may be administered within 1 hour before or after the scheduled dosing time, for a total window that does not exceed 2 hours.

Missed or late administration of medications

The hospital's policies and procedures must address the actions to be taken when medications eligible for scheduled dosing times are not administered within their permitted window of time. This includes doses which may have been missed due to the patient being temporarily away from the nursing unit, for example, for tests or procedures; patient refusal; patient inability to take the medication; problems related to medication availability; or other reasons that result in missed or late dose administration. Likewise, policies and procedures must also outline guidelines for the administration and timing of new medications which are initiated between standardized dosing times.

These policies and procedures must identify parameters within which nursing staff are allowed to use their own judgment regarding the rescheduling of missed or late doses and when notification of the physician or other practitioner responsible for the care of the patient is required prior doing so. In either case, the reporting of medication errors that are the result of missed or late dose administration must be reported to the attending physician in accordance with requirements at §482.25(b)(6). See interpretive guidance at §482.25(b)(6) for more details on internal reporting requirements

Evaluation of medication administration timing policies

Hospitals must periodically evaluate their medication administration timing policies, including staff adherence to the policies, to determine whether they assure safe and effective medication administration. Consistent with the QAPI requirements at 42 CFR 482.21(c)(2), medication errors related to the timing of medication administration must be tracked and analyzed to determine their causes. Based on the results of the evaluations of the policies and the medication administration errors, the medical staff must consider whether there is a need to revise the policies and procedures governing medication administration timing.

Survey Procedures §§482.23(c)(1), (c)(1)(i), and (c)(2)

Verify that there is an effective method for the administration of drugs. Use the following indicators for assessing drug administration:

- Verify that there are policies and procedures approved by the medical staff and governing body concerning ordering of drugs and biologicals by practitioners.

- Verify that there are policies and procedures approved by the medical staff covering who is authorized to administer medications, and that the policies are followed.

  - Verify nursing staff authorized to administer drugs and biological are practicing within their State-permitted scope of practice.

  - Are personnel other than nursing personnel administering drugs or biologicals? If yes, determine if those personnel are administering drugs or biologicals in accordance with Federal and State laws and regulations, including scope of practice laws, hospital policy, and medical staff bylaws, rules and regulations. Use the above procedures to determine compliance.

- Verify that there are policies and procedures approved by medical staff addressing the timing of medication administration.

  - Verify that the hospital has, consistent with its policies, identified medications: which are:

    - not eligible for scheduled dosing times;
    - Eligible for scheduled dosing times and are time-critical; and
    - Eligible for scheduled dosing times and are not time-critical.

  - Verify the hospital has established total windows of time that do not exceed the following:

    - 1 hour for time-critical scheduled medications
    - 2 hours for medications prescribed more frequently than daily, but no more frequently than every 4 hours; and
    - 4 hours for medications prescribed for daily or longer administration intervals.

  - Verify that the hospital's policy describes requirements for the administration of identified time-critical medications. Is it clear whether time-critical medications or medication types are identified as such for the entire hospital or are unit-, patient diagnosis-, or clinical situation- specific?

- Review a sample of medical records to determine whether medication administration conformed to an authorized practitioner's order, i.e., that there is an order from an authorized practitioner, or an applicable standing order, and that the correct medication was administered to the right patient at the right dose via the correct route, and that timing of administration complied with the hospital's policies and procedures. Check that the practitioner's order was still in force at the time the drug was administered.

- Observe the preparation of drugs and their administration to patients [medication pass] in order to verify that procedures are being followed.

  - Is the patient's identity confirmed prior to medication administration?

  - Are procedures to assure the correct medication, dose, and route followed?

  - Are drugs administered in accordance with the hospital's established policies and procedures for timely medication administration?

- Does the nurse remain with the patient until medication is taken?

- Interview personnel who administer medication to verify their understanding of the policies regarding timeliness of medication administration.

  - Are they able to identify time-critical and non-time-critical scheduled medications? Medications not eligible for scheduled dosing times?

  - Are they able to describe requirements for the timing of administration of time critical and non-time critical medications in accordance with the hospital's policies?

A-0406
(Rev. 84, Issued: 06-07-13, Effective: 06-07-13, Implementation: 06-07-13)

§482.23(c)(1) (ii)– Drugs and biologicals may be prepared and administered on the orders contained within pre-printed and electronic standing orders, order sets, and protocols for patient orders only if such orders meet the requirements of §482.24(c)(3).

§482.23(c)(3) - With the exception of influenza and pneumococcal polysaccharide vaccines, which may be administered per physician-approved hospital policy after an assessment of contraindications, orders for drugs and biologicals must be documented and signed by a practitioner who is authorized to write orders in accordance with State law and hospital policy, and who is responsible for the care of the patient as specified under §482.12(c)…

§482.23(c)(3)(iii) Orders for drugs and biologicals may be documented and signed by other practitioners not specified under §482.12(c) only if such practitioners are acting in accordance with State law, including scope of practice laws, hospital policies, and medical staff bylaws, rules, and regulations.

Interpretive Guidelines §482.23(c)(1) (ii),(c)(3) and (c)(3)(iii)

All orders for drugs and biologicals, with the exception of influenza and pneumococcal vaccines, must be documented and signed by a practitioner who is responsible for the care of the patient, as specified under §482.12(c), or who is another practitioner who is authorized by hospital policy and medical staff bylaws, rules and regulations, and who is acting in accordance with State law, including scope of practice laws.

Flu and pneumonia vaccines

Influenza and pneumococcal vaccines may be administered per physician-approved hospital policy, i.e., hospital policy approved by the physician members of the medical staff. There must be an assessment of contraindications prior to administration of the vaccine(s). There is no requirement for authentication by a practitioner when influenza and pneumococcal vaccines are administered to a patient in accordance with hospital policy and State law.

Standing orders

Nurses or other personnel authorized by hospital policy and in accordance with State law may administer drugs and biologicals in accordance with pre-printed and electronic standing orders, order sets, and protocols for patient orders, collectively referred to in this guidance as "standing orders," to address well- defined clinical scenarios involving medication administration. The requirements governing the hospital's development and use of standing orders are found at the Medical Records CoP, under §482.24(c)(3). For the nursing services requirement under §482.23(c)(1) (ii), compliance assessment focuses on whether nurses comply with the hospital's established standing orders policies and procedures when administering drugs or biological in accordance with a standing order.

Survey Procedures §482.23(c)(1) (ii), (c)(3) and (c)(3)(iii)

- Review the hospital's policy for drug and biological orders. Does it require that all administration of drugs or biologicals be based on either an applicable standing order or the order of a practitioner who is responsible for the care of the patient or otherwise authorized by hospital and medical staff policy and in accordance with State law to write orders?

- Interview nursing staff to determine whether they initiate medications in accordance with standing orders. Are they familiar with the hospital's policies and procedures for using standing orders? Are they following the policies and procedures? Ask to see the protocol for a standing order used by nursing staff, and ask nursing staff to explain how their practice conforms to the protocol.

- Review a sample of open and closed patient medical records. Although the regulation applies to both inpatient and outpatient medical records, the sample should be weighted to include more inpatient records.

- Determine whether all orders for drugs and biologicals, with the exception of influenza and pneumococcal vaccines, are included in the patient's medical record and authenticated by a practitioner who is authorized to write orders by hospital and medical staff policy and in accordance with State law and who is responsible for the care of the patient.

- Determine whether all standing orders which were initiated by a nurse were authenticated by an authorized practitioner.

- Determine whether all orders for drugs and biologicals contain the required elements.

A-0407
(Rev. 84, Issued: 06-07-13, Effective: 06-07-13, Implementation: 06-07-13)

§482.23(c)(3)(i) - If verbal orders are used, they are to be used infrequently.

Interpretive Guidelines §482.23(c)(3)(i)

Verbal orders, if used, must be used infrequently. This means that the use of verbal orders must not be a common practice. Verbal orders pose an increased risk of miscommunication that could contribute to a medication or other error, resulting in a patient adverse event. Verbal orders should be used only to meet the care needs of the patient when it is impossible or impractical for the ordering practitioner to write the order or enter it into an electronic prescribing system without delaying treatment. Verbal orders are not to be used for the convenience of the ordering practitioner. (71 FR 68679)

Hospitals are expected to develop appropriate policies and procedures that govern the use of verbal orders and minimize their use, such as policies which:

- Describe situations in which verbal orders may be used as well as limitations or prohibitions on their use;

- Provide a mechanism to establish the identity and authority of the practitioner issuing a verbal order;

- List the elements required for inclusion in the verbal order process;

- Establish protocols for clear and effective communication and verification of verbal orders.

The content of verbal orders must be clearly communicated. CMS expects nationally accepted read-back verification practice to be implemented for every verbal order. (71 FR 68680) As required by §482.24(b), all verbal orders must be promptly documented in the patient's medical record by the individual receiving the order.

Survey Procedures §482.23(c)(3)(i)

- Are there policies and procedures in place to minimize the use of verbal orders?

- Interview direct care staff to determine whether actual practice is consistent with verbal order policies and procedures.

- Review both open and closed patient medical records for the use of verbal orders.

- Were the policies and procedures for the use of verbal orders followed?

- Does the number of verbal orders found in the sampled records suggest routine use, which the regulations do not permit? The number of verbal orders is not in itself evidence of noncompliance, but should result in more focused analysis. For example:

  - Is there a pattern to the use of verbal orders? Some patterns might make sense – e.g., for orders entered between midnight and 7:00 a.m., it might be plausible that it was impossible for the prescribing practitioner to write/computer-enter the order. On the other hand, if one patient care unit has a high proportion of verbal orders, while another does not, this might be a flag for inconsistent implementation of the hospital's policies and procedures for verbal orders.

  - Are verbal orders used frequently for certain types of situations, and if so, is it reasonable to assume that it is impossible or impractical for the prescribing practitioners to write/enter the orders in such situations?

  - Do certain practitioners use verbal orders frequently? From the limited number of records sampled it may be difficult to detect trends related to specific practitioners, but if a surveyor finds such evidence, further investigation is warranted to determine if it is evidence of noncompliance.

A-0408
(Rev. 84, Issued: 06-07-13, Effective: 06-07-13, Implementation: 06-07-13)

§482.23(c)(3)(ii) - When verbal orders are used, they must only be accepted by persons who are authorized to do so by hospital policy and procedures consistent with Federal and State law.

Interpretive Guidelines §482.23(c)(3)(ii)

A verbal order for drugs and biologicals may only be accepted by an individual who is permitted by Federal and State law and hospital policy to accept verbal orders. Consistent with the requirements of §482.24(b), the person who received the verbal order must promptly document it in the medical record.

Survey Procedures §482.23(c)(3)(ii)

- Determine whether the hospital has policies and procedures, consistent with Federal and State law, governing who is authorized to accept verbal orders.

- Review open and closed patient medical records containing verbal orders for drugs and biologicals. Determine whether the orders were accepted and documented by authorized hospital personnel.

- Interview several direct care staff to determine if they are permitted to take verbal orders for drugs and biologicals, and determine whether such staff have been authorized to do so in accordance with hospital policy.

A-0409
(Rev. 84, Issued: 06-07-13, Effective: 06-07-13, Implementation: 06-07-13)

§482.23(c)(4) - Blood transfusions and intravenous medications must be administered in accordance with State law and approved medical staff policies and procedures.

Interpretative Guidelines §482.23(c)(4)

Generally intravenous (IV) medications and blood transfusions are administered to patients by registered nurses (RNs), consistent with State law governing scope of practice, and approved medical staff policies and procedures. Education and training regarding these procedures are typically included in the nurse's hospital orientation. Nursing staff who receive training for intravenous medication administration and/or blood transfusion administration during hospital orientation or during other continuing education programs would meet the requirements of this regulation. Other non-physician personnel, for example, licensed practical nurses or licensed vocational nurses, with demonstrated competence may also administer IV medications and blood transfusions if they are acting in accordance with State law, including scope of practice law, and the hospital's approved medical staff policies and procedures. (77 FR 29050, May 16, 2012)

The appropriate competencies must be documented in the qualified staff person's employee record. Content of the training is based on nationally recognized standards for intravenous medication administration and blood transfusion and must address at least the following: fluid and electrolyte balance; venipuncture techniques, including both demonstration, and supervised practice; and, for blood transfusion training: blood components; blood administration procedures based on hospital policy, State law, and nationally recognized standards of practice; requirements for patient monitoring, including frequency and documentation of monitoring; the process for verification of the right blood product for the right patient; and identification and treatment of transfusion reactions.

All State law and scope of practice requirements must be met regarding the administration of intravenous medications and blood transfusions, as applicable.

Survey Procedures §482.23(c)(4)

- Review a sample of medical records.

    - Are blood transfusions and IV medications administered in accordance with State law and approved hospital and medical staff policies and procedures?

    - Determine the identity of staff who administered blood components and/or IV medications and review their employee records.

    - Are blood transfusions and IV medications administered by personnel who are working within their scope of practice in accordance with State law and hospital and medical staff policies?

        - Is there evidence that the competency of these staff was assessed with respect to:

            - Maintaining fluid and electrolyte balance;

            - Venipuncture techniques;

            - With respect to blood transfusions:

                - Blood components;

            - Blood administration procedures per hospital policy, State law, and nationally recognized standards of practice;

            - Patient monitoring requirements, including frequency and documentation of monitoring;

            - Process for verification of the right blood product for the right patient; and

            - Transfusion reactions: identification, treatment, and reporting requirements.

A-0410
(Rev. 84, Issued: 06-07-13, Effective: 06-07-13, Implementation: 06-07-13)

§482.23(c)(5) - There must be a hospital procedure for reporting transfusion reactions, adverse drug reactions, and errors in administration of drugs.

Interpretive Guidelines §482.23(c)(5)

Adverse drug reactions and drug administration errors

There is a similar but more detailed and prescriptive requirement concerning internal hospital reporting of adverse drug reactions, drug administration errors and incompatibilities under the Pharmaceutical Services CoP at §482.25(b)(6). Therefore, it is not necessary for hospitals to establish a different procedure in the case of adverse drug reactions and drug administration errors for such events when nurses administer drugs or transfusions. Consult the guidance for §482.25(b)(6) to see what must be reported, to whom, and in what timeframe. Failure to make required reports concerning adverse drug reactions and errors in administration of drugs should be cited under §482.23(c)(5) when the drug was administered by a nurse, as well as under §482.25(b)(6).

Transfusion reactions

Transfusion reactions can occur during or after a blood transfusion. A patient's immune system recognizes the foreign blood product and attempts to destroy the transfused cells. Incompatible blood products are typically the cause of transfusion reactions. Symptoms may include back pain, bloody urine, hives, chills, fainting, dizziness, fever, flank pain, and skin flushing. More serious complications may include acute kidney failure, anemia, respiratory distress, shock and even death.

Transfusion reactions are serious and can be life-threatening. The hospital must have policies and procedures in place for the internal reporting of transfusion reactions. The policies must include procedures for reporting transfusion reactions immediately to the practitioner responsible for the care of the patient. The transfusion reaction must also be reported to the hospital-wide quality assessment performance improvement program as an adverse event, in accordance with the QAPI CoP at 42 CFR 482.21(c)(2). The transfusion reaction must be documented in the patient's medical record, including the prompt notification of the responsible practitioner.

Survey Procedures §482.23(c)(5)

- For adverse drug events and medication administration errors, follow the survey procedures for §482.25(b)(6). Deficiencies are to be cited under both §482.23(c)(5)and §482.25(b)(6) when the drug or transfusion related to an adverse drug reaction, transfusion reaction or medication administration error relates to a drug or transfusion administered by a nurse.

- Request the hospital policy and procedure for internal reporting of transfusion reactions.

  - Interview nursing staff responsible for administering blood transfusions to determine whether they are familiar with and comply with the hospital's policies.

- Ask to see if there are any transfusion-related incident reports. Is there evidence that the transfusion reaction was reported immediately to the practitioner responsible for the patient's care? Was it reported to the hospital's QAPI program?

A-0412
(Rev. 84, Issued: 06-07-13, Effective: 06-07-13, Implementation: 06-07-13)

§482.23(c)(6) The hospital may allow a patient (or his or her caregiver/support person where appropriate) to self -administer both hospital-issued medications and the patient's own medications brought into the hospital, as defined and specified in the hospital's policies and procedures.

(i)   If the hospital allows a patient to self-administer specific hospital-issued medications, then the hospital must have policies and procedures in place to:

(A)   Ensure that a practitioner responsible for the care of the patient has issued an order, consistent with hospital policy, permitting self-administration.

(B)   Assess the capacity of the patient (or the patient's caregiver/support person where appropriate) to self-administer the specified medication(s).

(C)   Instruct the patient (or the patient's support person where appropriate) in the safe and accurate administration of the specified medication(s).

(D)   Address the security of the medication(s) for each patient.

(E)   Document the administration of each medication, as reported by the patient (or the patient's caregiver/support person where appropriate), in the patient's medical record.

Interpretative Guidelines §482.23(c)(6)(i)

Hospitals have the option of establishing a program for self-administration by patients, or, when applicable, patient caregivers or support persons, of hospital-issued medications. The existence of this regulatory option does not mean that a hospital must offer medication self-administration programs or that a patient has a right to self-administer their medications.

A hospital program for patient self-administration of hospital-issued medications could be beneficial for the appropriate patients if the proper precautions are taken in designing and implementing such a program. Generally such a program would apply only to inpatients, but there may be circumstances under which a hospital finds it appropriate to permit self-administration of hospital-issued medications by outpatients or their caregivers/support persons.

Among the potential benefits of medication self-administration, teaching patients or their caregivers/support persons adherence to the proper medication regimen could reduce hospital inpatient length of stay and also might have a positive effect on continued compliance with the regimen after discharge, potentially avoiding an emergency department visit or inpatient readmission secondary to post-hospital patient medication administration errors and noncompliance.

Hospitals have the discretion to establish policies providing for different levels of patient self-administration, and may make these levels across-the-board, patient-specific, or medication-specific. For example, a hospital may choose whether or not a nurse must be present to supervise the self-administration, and whether this supervision requirement could vary according to the type of medication or the capacity of the individual patient (or the patient's caregiver/support person). A hospital may also determine through its policies and procedures whether supervision requirements must be addressed in the practitioner's order or whether this may be left to the discretion of the nurse who assesses the patient. A hospital may choose to exclude certain medications from patient self-administration, for example, because they pose too great a medication security challenge, or because the manner in which they must be administered does not lend itself to safe self-administration. (77 FR 29052, May 16, 2012)   It must be clear in the hospital's policies and procedures whether it has established such a policy and what kind of limitations it has established for its program of patient self-administration of hospital-issued medications.

It is expected that the medical staff, nursing and pharmacy departments are to collaborate in developing policies and procedures governing self-administration of hospital-issued medications which are approved by the governing body.

Required elements of a self-administration program:

If the hospital chooses to develop programs for self-administration of hospital-issued medications by patients (and/or their caregiver/support persons), the following must be in place:

- **An order allowing the patient to administer hospital-issued medications**. The order must be consistent with the hospital's policy concerning self-administration of hospital-issued medications and be written by a practitioner who is responsible for the care of the patient and who is authorized to order medications, in accordance with hospital policies and procedures, State law, including scope of practice laws, and medical staff by-laws, rules, and regulations.

- **A documented assessment of the capacity of the patient (or their caregiver/support person) to successfully administer medications for which self-**

administration has been authorized. Nurses are expected to exercise their clinical judgment and to inform the practitioner responsible for the care of the patient about any reservations the nurse might have about an individual patient's (or caregiver/support person's) capacity to safely self-administer medications. The assessment must be documented and must highlight the findings that are affirmative – i.e., support patient-self-administration – and negative – i.e., call into question patient self-administration. The nurse is also expected to document any discussions with the practitioner responsible for the care of the patient regarding the nurses' concerns about patient's (or caregiver/support person's) capacity to safely self-administer medications. Hospitals may, as a matter of policy, permit a nurse to return to nurse administration for particular doses of a medication for which there is a self-administration order, without a discussion with the responsible practitioner if, based on the nurse's assessment, the patient's capacity has been temporarily diminished and there is no caregiver/support person who is assisting the patient with self-administration of medication. For example, a patient who has just had an invasive test or procedure may not be fully alert for a period thereafter, or the parent of a minor patient, who is administering medications to the patient may for whatever reasons not be available and a scheduled medication dose is close to being overdue.

* **Instruction in self-administration.** As part of the assessment of the patient's self-administration capacity, nurses are expected to identify the patient's (or the patient's caregiver/support person's) education and/or training needs. These needs may be related to type of medication, unique individual medication requirements, delivery route, dosage and scheduling, equipment (e.g. syringes, pill-cutters, measuring containers, etc.) intravenous access, potential adverse side effects and what to do if they occur, infection control measures, storage, medication disposal, among others. Education and training needs, and how they were addressed, must be documented in the medical record.

* **Security of the self-administered medications.** The security of a patient's self-administered medications is extremely important, but does not lend itself well to a one-size-fits-all regulatory requirement. There are Federal and State laws, including the Pharmaceutical Services CoP, which require a higher level of security for certain medications (for example, controlled substances). Hospitals are expected to comply with these already-established requirements and laws, and generally should not include such medications as part of a patient self-administration program.

Note that Patient-controlled Analgesia (PCA) pumps are a special variant of patient self-administration. Such pumps allow patients, within tightly controlled, pre-determined parameters with respect to dosage and minimum time intervals between doses, to release an intravenous dose of a controlled substance pain medication that has been pre-loaded into the PCA pump in a manner that prevents tampering by an unauthorized person. PCA pumps are considered secure despite their use of controlled substances.

Hospitals are also free to exclude other medications besides controlled substances from their patient self-administered medication programs when the hospital has concerns over its capacity to address the security of these other medications for patients.

A hospital may choose to have a policy where it maintains a list of medications that it excludes from self-administration entirely, due to security concerns. It may choose to have a policy that addresses the security of a particular medication on a patient-by-patient basis. Or it may establish a policy that is a combination of both of these approaches to medication security. (77 FR 29052, May 16, 2012)

- **Documentation of medication administration.** Under the regulation, a nurse must document the self-administration of a medication. In cases where the nurse directly supervised the self-administration, the nurse is expected to indicate that the medication administration was observed and confirmed. On the other hand, where direct nurse supervision is not required, the nurse is required to document only what the patient, or the patient's caregiver/support person, reports to the nurse as to the time and amount of medication administered. Nurses are expected to assess whether the reports of the patient or patient's caregiver/support person indicate, with respect to timing and dosage, that the patient is receiving the medication as ordered.

Survey Procedures §482.23(c)(6)(i)

If the hospital permits patient self-administration of hospital-issued medications:

- Ask the hospital to identify current inpatients for whom self-administration of hospital-issued medications is permitted.

  - Interview of several of these patients (or their caregivers/support persons when applicable) to verify that they received instruction on how to administer their medications

  - Interview nurses caring for the selected patients. Ask them:

    - What the applicable hospital policies and procedures are regarding supervision of self-medication.

    - How they assess a patient's (or patient's caregiver/support person's) capacity to self-administer medication. If they have concerns, how do they communicate them to the responsible practitioner? Does their hospital permit nurses to return to nurse administration of medications in response to temporary reduction in patient capacity or absence of the patient's caregiver/support person? If so, how do the nurses make this assessment?

- How they instruct a patient (or patient's caregiver/support person's) in medication self-administration.

- How self-administered medications are secured.

- How they document self-administration of medications.

- To provide a copy of the hospital's policies and procedures. Are they following the policies and procedures?

- Review the medical records for the selected patients. Is there documentation of:

  - An order for self-administration of specific medication(s).

  - A nurse assessment of the patient's (or patient's caregiver/support person's) capacity to self-administer medication.

  - Documentation of nurse instruction to the patient or (or patient's caregiver/support person) in safe and appropriate techniques for self-administration of medication.

  - Documentation of self-administration times and doses, as reported by the patient or (or patient's caregiver/support person) or directly observed by a nurse.

- Do the hospital's policies and procedures for self-administration of hospital-issued medications address:

  - Limitations on medications not eligible for self-administration or patient conditions which exclude self-administration;

  - Orders for self-administration of medication;

  - Requirements, if any, for supervision of self-administration;

  - Assessment of self-medication capacity;

  - Instruction in self-medication;

  - Security of self-administered medications; and

  - Documentation of self-administration.

A-0413
(Rev. 84, Issued: 06-07-13, Effective: 06-07-13, Implementation: 06-07-13)

[§482.23(c)(6) The hospital may allow a patient (or his or her caregiver/support person where appropriate) to self -administer both hospital-issued medications and the patient's own medications brought into the hospital, as defined and specified in the hospital's policies and procedures.]

§482.23(c)(6)(ii) If the hospital allows a patient to self-administer his or her own specific medications brought into the hospital, then the hospital must have policies and procedures in place to:

(A) Ensure that a practitioner responsible for the care of the patient has issued an order, consistent with hospital policy, permitting self-administration of medications the patient brought into the hospital.

(B) Assess the capacity of the patient (or the patient's caregiver/support person where appropriate) to self-administer the specified medication(s) and also determine if the patient (or the patient's caregiver/supplier person where appropriate) needs instruction in the safe and accurate administration of the specified medication(s).

(C) Identify the specified medication(s) and visually evaluate the medication(s) for integrity.

(D) Address the security of the medication(s) for each patient.

(E) Document the administration of each medication, as reported by the patient (or the patient's caregiver/support person where appropriate), in the patient's medical record.

Interpretative Guidelines §482.23(c)(6)(ii)

Hospitals have the option of establishing a program for self-administration by patients, or, when applicable, patient caregivers or support persons, of medications the patient brings himself or herself to the hospital. The existence of this regulatory option does not mean that a hospital must offer medication self-administration programs or that a patient has a right to retain and self-administer medications they bring with them from home.

A hospital program for patient self-administration of medications the patient brings from home could be beneficial for the appropriate patients if the proper precautions are taken in designing and implementing such a program. Generally such a program would apply only to inpatients, but there may be circumstances under which a hospital finds it appropriate to permit self-administration of medications that outpatients or their caregivers/support persons bring with them.

Among the potential benefits of permitting self-administration of medications the patient brings from home is that problems are avoided related to the hospital's formulary not including a particular medication that a patient needs to continue to take during his/her hospital stay, and the patient prefer to avoid medication substitution. The hospital also gains an opportunity to identify suboptimal patient medication administration techniques for these drugs and to provide instruction designed to ensure that the patient is administering his/her medications properly.

Hospitals have the discretion to establish policies providing for different levels of patient self-administration, and may make these levels across-the-board, patient-specific, or medication-specific. For example, a hospital may choose whether or not a nurse must be present to supervise the self-administration, and whether this supervision requirement could vary according to the type of medication or the capacity of the individual patient (or the patient's caregiver/support person). A hospital may also determine through its policies and procedures whether supervision requirements must be addressed in the practitioner's order or whether this may be left to the discretion of the nurse who assesses the patient. A hospital may choose to exclude certain medications from patient self-administration, for example, because they pose too great a medication security challenge. It must be clear in the hospital's policies and procedures whether it has established such a policy and what kind of limitations it has established for its program of patient self-administration of medications the patient brings from home.

It is expected that the medical staff, nursing and pharmacy departments are to collaborate in developing policies and procedures for self-administration of medications the patient brings from home which are approved by the governing body.

Required elements of a self-administration program:

If the hospital chooses to develop programs for self-administration of medications brought from home by patients (and/or their caregiver/support persons), the following must be in place:

- **An order allowing the patient to administer medications brought from home**. The order must be consistent with the hospital's policy concerning self-administration of medications brought from home and be written by a practitioner who is responsible for the care of the patient and who is authorized to order medications, in accordance with hospital policies and procedures, State law, including scope of practice laws, and medical staff by-laws, rules, and regulations.

- **A documented assessment of the capacity of the patient (or their caregiver/support person) to successfully administer the medication(s) specified in the order, including a determination whether the patient (or their caregiver/support person) needs instruction in the safe and accurate administration of the specified medication(s).** Nurses are expected to exercise their clinical judgment and to inform the practitioner responsible for the care of the patient about any reservations the nurse might have about an individual patient's (or caregiver/support person's) capacity to safely self-administer medications. The assessment must be documented and must highlight the findings that are affirmative – i.e., support patient-self-administration – and negative – i.e., call into question patient self-administration. The nurse is also expected to document any discussions with the practitioner responsible for the care of the patient regarding the nurses' concerns about patient's (or caregiver/support person's) capacity to safely self-administer medications. (77 FR 29052, May 16, 2012)

Hospitals may, as a matter of policy, permit a nurse to return to nurse administration for particular doses of a medication for which there is a self-administration order, without a discussion with the responsible practitioner if, based on the nurse's assessment, the patient's capacity has been temporarily diminished and there is no caregiver/support person who is assisting the patient with self-administration of medication. For example, a patient who has just had an invasive test or procedure may not be fully alert for a period thereafter, or the parent of a minor patient, who is administering medications to the patient may for whatever reasons not be available and a scheduled medication dose is close to being overdue.

As part of the assessment of the patient's self-administration capacity, nurses are expected to identify whether the patient (or the patient's caregiver/support person) needs instruction in the safe and accurate administration of the specified medication(s). Even though the patient has been taking the medication at home, the patient (or the patient's caregiver/support person) may not be using optimal administration techniques. Patient needs may be related to type of medication, unique individual medication requirements, delivery route, dosage and scheduling, equipment (e.g. syringes, pill-cutters, measuring containers, etc.) intravenous access, potential adverse side effects and what to do if they occur, infection control measures, storage, medication disposal, among others. Education and training needs identified, and how they were addressed, must be documented in the medical record.

* **Identification/visual evaluation for integrity.** Hospitals must have policies and procedures addressing how they will identify the medications the patient has brought from home. Identification is important because the label on the patient's medication container may not accurately reflect the contents. Further, the medication might have expired or have not been stored correctly in the patient's home, requiring hospitals to at least conduct a visual inspection to see if the medication appears to have retained its integrity. It is recognized that a visual inspection for integrity may not be definitive, but the regulation does not require use of more complex methods.

* **Security of the self-administered medications.** The security of a patient's self-administered medications is extremely important, but does not lend itself well to a one-size-fits-all regulatory requirement. There are Federal and State laws, including the Pharmaceutical Services CoP, which require a higher level of security for certain

medications (for example, controlled substances). Hospitals are expected to comply with these already-established requirements and laws, and generally should not include such medications as part of a patient self-administration program.

Hospitals are also free to exclude other medications besides controlled substances from their patient self-administered medication programs when the hospital has concerns over its capacity to address the security of these other medications for patients.

A hospital may choose to have a policy where it maintains a list of medications brought from home that it excludes from self-administration entirely, due to security concerns. It may choose to have a policy that addresses the security of a particular medication on a patient-by-patient basis. Or it may establish a policy that is a combination of both of these approaches to medication security.

- **Documentation of medication administration.** Under the regulation, a nurse must document the self-administration of a medication. In cases where the nurse directly supervised the self-administration, the nurse is expected to indicate that the medication administration was observed and confirmed. On the other hand, where direct nurse supervision is not required, the nurse is required to document only what the patient, or the patient's caregiver/support person, reports to the nurse as to the time and amount of medication administered. Nurses are expected to assess whether the reports of the patient or patient's caregiver/support person indicate, with respect to timing and dosage, that the patient is receiving the medication as ordered.

Survey Procedures §482.23(c)(6) and (c)(6)(i)

If the hospital permits patient self-administration of medications brought from home:

- Ask the hospital to identify current inpatients for whom self-administration of medications brought from home is permitted.

  - Interview of several of these patients (or their caregivers/support persons when applicable) to ask if that they received instruction on how to self-administer their medications consistent with hospital policy.

  - Interview nurses caring for the selected patients. Ask them:

    - What the applicable hospital policies and procedures are regarding supervision of self-medication.

    - How they assess a patient's (or patient's caregiver/support person's) capacity to self-administer medication. If they have concerns, how do they communicate them to the responsible practitioner? Does their hospital permit nurses to return to nurse administration of medications in response to temporary reduction in patient capacity or absence of the patient's caregiver/support person? If so, how do the nurses make this assessment?

- How they instruct a patient (or patient's caregiver/support person's) in safe and proper medication self-administration when educational needs have been identified.

- How self-administered medications are secured.

- How they document self-administration of medications.

- To provide a copy of the hospital's policies and procedures. Are they following the policies and procedures?

- Review the medical records for the selected patients. Is there documentation of:

  - An order for self-administration of specific medication(s).

  - A nurse assessment of the patient's (or patient's caregiver/support person's) capacity to self-administer medication and identification of whether or not there are educational needs that have been met.

  - Documentation of the identification and visual assessment of medications brought from home.

  - Documentation of self-administration times and doses, as reported by the patient or (or patient's caregiver/support person) or directly observed by a nurse.

- Do the hospital's policies and procedures for self-administration of medications brought from home address, consistent with the regulatory requirements, the following:

  - Limitations on medications eligible for self-administration or patient conditions which exclude self-administration;

  - Orders for self-administration of medications brought from home;

  - Requirements, if any, for supervision of self-administration;

  - Assessment of self-medication capacity, including identification of educational needs and how they are to be met;

  - Identification and visual inspection for integrity of self-administered medications brought from home;

- Security of self-administered medications; and

- Documentation of self-administration in the medical record?

A-0431

§482.24 Condition of Participation: Medical Record Services

The hospital must have a medical record service that has administrative responsibility for medical records. A medical record must be maintained for every individual evaluated or treated in the hospital.

Interpretive Guidelines §482.24

The term "hospital" includes all locations of the hospital.

The hospital must have one unified medical record service that has administrative responsibility for all medical records, both inpatient and out patient records. The hospital must create and maintain a medical record for every individual, both inpatient and out patient evaluated or treated in the hospital.

The term "**medical records**" includes at least written documents, computerized electronic information, radiology film and scans, laboratory reports and pathology slides, videos, audio recordings, and other forms of information regarding the condition of a patient.

Survey Procedures §482.24

- Review the organizational structure and policy statements and interview the person responsible for the medical records service to ascertain that the service is structured appropriately to meet the needs of the hospital and the patients.

- Review a sample of active and closed medical records for completeness and accuracy in accordance with Federal and State laws and regulations and hospital policy. The sample should be 10 percent of the average daily census and be no less than 30 records. Additionally, select a sample of outpatient records in order to determine compliance in outpatient departments, services, and locations.

A-0432
(Rev. 37, Issued: 10-17-08; Effective/Implementation Date: 10-17-08)

§482.24(a) Standard: Organization and Staffing

The organization of the medical record service must be appropriate to the scope and complexity of the services performed. The hospital must employ adequate personnel to ensure prompt completion, filing, and retrieval of records.

Interpretive Guidelines §482.24(a)

The medical records service must be organized, equipped, and staffed in accordance with the scope and complexity of the hospital's services and in such a manner as to comply with the requirements of this regulation and other Federal and State laws and regulations.

There must be an established medical record system that is organized and employs adequate personnel to ensure prompt:

- Completion of medical records;

- Filing of medical records; and

- Retrieval of medical records.

The term "employs adequate personnel" includes:

- That medical record personnel are employees of the hospital;

- That the hospital employs an adequate number of medical record personnel, employs adequate types of medical record personnel, and employs personnel who possess adequate education, skills, qualifications and experience to ensure the hospital complies with requirements of this regulation and other Federal and State laws and regulations.

Survey Procedures §482.24(a)

- Verify that there is an established system that addresses at least the following activities of the medical records services:

  o   Timely processing of records;

  o   Coding/indexing of records;

o   Retrieval of records;

o   Compiling and retrieval of data of quality assurance activities.

- Verify that the system is reviewed and revised as needed.

- Interview staff, if needed, review written job descriptions and staffing schedules to determine if staff is carrying out all designated responsibilities.

- Verify that the hospital employs adequate medical record personnel as previously described.

 Are medical records promptly completed in accordance with State law and hospital policy?

- Select a sample of past patients of the hospital (inpatient and/or outpatient). Request those patients' medical records. Can the hospital promptly retrieve those records?

A-0438
(Rev. 37, Issued: 10-17-08; Effective/Implementation Date: 10-17-08)

§482.24(b) Standard: Form and Retention of Record

The hospital must maintain a medical record for each inpatient and outpatient. Medical records must be accurately written, promptly completed, properly filed and retained, and accessible. The hospital must use a system of author identification and record maintenance that ensures the integrity of the authentication and protects the security of all record entries.

Interpretive Guidelines §482.24(b)

The hospital must maintain a medical record for each inpatient and outpatient evaluated or treated in any part or location of the hospital.

All medical records must be **accurately written**. The hospital must ensure that all medical records accurately and completely document all orders, test results, evaluations, care plans, treatments, interventions, care provided and the patient's response to those treatments, interventions and care.

All medical records must be **promptly completed**. Every medical record must be complete with all documentation of orders, diagnosis, evaluations, treatments, test results, care plans, discharge plans, consents, interventions, discharge summary, and care provided along with the patient's response to those treatments, interventions, and care.

The record must be completed promptly after discharge in accordance with State law and hospital policy but no later than 30 days after discharge.

The medical record must be **properly filed and retained**. The hospital must have a medical record system that ensures the prompt retrieval of any medical record, of any patient evaluated or treated at any location of the hospital within the past 5 years. [§482.24(b)(1) addresses the 5 year medical record retention requirement]

The medical record must be **accessible**. The hospital must have a medical record system that allows the medical record of any patient, inpatient or outpatient, evaluated and/or treated at any location of the hospital within the past 5 years to be accessible by appropriate staff, 24 hours a day, 7 days a week, whenever that medical record may be needed.

Medical records must be properly stored in secure locations where they are protected from fire, water damage and other threats.

Medical information such as consultations, orders, practitioner notes, x-ray interpretations, lab test results, diagnostic test results, patient assessments and other patient information must be accurately written, promptly completed and properly filed in the patients' medical record, and accessible to the physicians or other care providers when needed for use in making assessments of the patient's condition, decisions on the provision of care to the patient, and in planning the patient's care. This requirement applies to the medical records of current inpatients and outpatients of the hospital.

The hospital must have a system of author identification and record maintenance that ensures the integrity of the authentication and protects the security of **all** record entries. The medical record system must correctly identify the author of every medical record entry and must protect the security of all medical record entries. The medial record system must ensure that medical record entries are not lost, stolen, destroyed, altered, or reproduced in an unauthorized manner. Locations where medical records are stored or maintained must ensure the integrity, security and protection of the records. These requirements apply to both manual and electronic medical record systems.

Survey Procedures §482.24(b)

- Determine the location(s) where medical records are maintained.

- Verify that a medical record is maintained for each person treated or receiving care. The hospital may have a separate record for both inpatients and outpatients. However, when two different systems are used they must be appropriately cross referenced and accessible.

- Verify that procedures ensure the integrity of authentication and protect the security of patient records.

- Verify that medical records are stored and maintained in locations where the records are secure, that protects them from damage, flood, fire, etc., and limits access to only authorized individuals.

- Verify that records are accurate, completed promptly, easily retrieved and readily accessible, as needed, in all locations where medical records are maintained.

A-0439
(Rev. 37, Issued: 10-17-08; Effective/Implementation Date: 10-17-08)

§482.24(b)(1) - Medical records must be retained in their original or legally reproduced form for a period of at least 5 years.

Interpretive Guidelines §482.24(b)(1)

Medical records are retained in their original or legally reproduced form in hard copy, microfilm, computer memory, or other electronic storage media. The hospital must be able to promptly retrieve the complete medical record of every individual evaluated or treated in any part or location of the hospital within the last 5 years.

In accordance with Federal and State law and regulations, certain medical records may have retention requirements that exceed 5 years (for example: FDA, OSHA, EPA).

Survey Procedures §482.24(b)(1)

- Determine that records are retained for at least 5 years, or more if required by State or local laws.

- Select a sample of patients, both inpatient and outpatient who were patients of the hospital between the previous 48-60 months. Request their medical record. Is it promptly retrieved? Is it complete? Is it in original or in a legally reproduced form?

A-0440
(Rev. 37, Issued: 10-17-08; Effective/Implementation Date: 10-17-08)

§482.24(b)(2) - The hospital must have a system of coding and indexing medical records. The system must allow for timely retrieval by diagnosis and procedure, in order to support medical care evaluation studies.

Survey Procedures §482.24(b)(2)

Verify that the hospital uses a coding and indexing system that permits timely retrieval of patient records by diagnosis and procedures.

A-0441
(Rev. 84, Issued: 06-07-13, Effective: 06-07-13, Implementation: 06-07-13)

§482.24(b)(3) - The hospital must have a procedure for ensuring the confidentiality of patient records. Information from or copies of records may be released only to authorized individuals, and the hospital must ensure that unauthorized individuals cannot gain access to or alter patient records. Original medical records must be released by the hospital only in accordance with Federal or State laws, court orders, or subpoenas.

Interpretive Guidelines §482.24(b)(3)

Release of Information from or Copies of Records:

The hospital must have a procedure to ensure the confidentiality of each patient's medical record, whether it is in paper or electronic format, or a combination of the two, from unauthorized disclosure. Confidentiality applies wherever the record or portions thereof are stored, including but not limited to central records, patient care locations, radiology, laboratories, record storage areas, etc.

A hospital is permitted to disclose medical record information, without a patient's authorization, in order to provide patient care and perform related administrative functions, such as payment and other hospital operations.

- **Payment operations** include hospital activities to obtain payment or be reimbursed for the provision of health care to an individual.

- **Health care operations** are administrative, financial, legal, and quality improvement activities of a hospital that are necessary to conduct business and to support the core functions of treatment and payment. These activities include, but are not limited to: quality assessment and improvement activities, case management and care coordination; competency assurance activities, conducting or arranging for medical reviews, audits, or legal services, including fraud and abuse detection and compliance programs; business planning, development, management, and administration and certain hospital-specific fundraising activities.

The hospital must develop policies and procedures that reasonably limit disclosures of information contained in the patient's medical record to the minimum disclosure necessary, except when the disclosure is for treatment or payment purposes, or as otherwise required by State or Federal law.

When the minimum necessary standard is applied, a hospital may not disclose the entire medical record for a particular purpose, unless it can specifically justify that the whole record is the disclosure amount reasonably required for the purpose.

A hospital may disclose information from the medical record electronically, and may also share an electronic medical record system with other health care facilities, physicians and practitioners, so long as the system is designed and operated with safeguards that ensure that only authorized disclosures are made.

The hospital must obtain written authorization from the patient or the patient's representative for any other disclosure of medical record information.

Preventing Unauthorized Access

The hospital must ensure that unauthorized individuals cannot gain access to patient records. This applies to records in electronic as well as hard copy formats. Patient records must be secure at all times and in all locations. This includes open patient records for patients who are currently inpatients in the hospital and outpatients in outpatient clinics. For hard copy records, techniques such as locked cabinets or file rooms and limiting access to keys or pass codes may be employed. For electronic records technical safeguards, such as business rules that limit access based on need to know, passwords, or other control mechanisms must be in place. When disposing of copies of medical records, physical safeguards might include first shredding documents containing confidential information, taking appropriate steps to erase information from media used to store electronic records, etc.

Release of Original Records

The hospital must not release the original of a medical record that exists in a hard copy, paper version only, unless it is required to do so in response to a court order, a subpoena, or Federal or State laws. For electronic records, the hospital must ensure that the media or other mechanism by which the records are stored electronically is not removed in such a way that all or part of the record is deleted from the hospital's medical record system. The hospital must have policies and procedures that address how it assures that retains its "original" medical records, unless their release is mandated by law/court order/subpoena.

Survey Procedures §482.24(b)(3)

- Verify that policies are in place that limit access to, and disclosure of, medical records to permitted users and uses, and that require written authorization for other disclosures. Are the policies consistent with the regulatory requirements?

- Observe whether patient records are secured from unauthorized access at all times and in all locations.

- Ask the hospital to demonstrate what precautions are taken to prevent physical or electronic altering of content previously entered into a patient record, or to prevent unauthorized disposal of patient records.

- Verify that patient medical record information is released only as permitted under the hospital's policies and procedures.

- Conduct observations and interview staff to determine what safeguards are in place or precautions are taken to prevent unauthorized persons from gaining physical access or electronic access to information in patient records.

- If the hospital uses electronic patient records, is access to patient records controlled through standard measures, such as business rules defining permitted access, passwords, etc.?

- Do the hospital's policies and procedures provide that "original" medical records are retained, unless their release is mandated under Federal or State law, court order or subpoena? Interview staff responsible for medical records to determine if they are aware of the limitations on release of "original" medical records.

A-0442
(Rev. 37, Issued: 10-17-08; Effective/Implementation Date: 10-17-08)

§482.24(b)(3) - (Continued)

[Information from or copies of records may be released only to authorized individuals,] and the hospital must ensure that unauthorized individuals cannot gain access to or alter patient records.

Interpretive Guidelines §482.24(b)(3)

The hospital's patient record system must ensure the security of patient records. The hospital must ensure that unauthorized individuals cannot gain access to patient records and that individuals cannot alter patient records. Patient records must be secure at all times and in all locations. This includes open patient records for patients who are currently inpatients in the hospital and outpatients in outpatient clinics.

Survey Procedures §482.24(b)(3)

- Observe the hospital's security practices for patient records. Are patient records left unsecured or unattended? Are patient records unsecured or unattended in hallways, patient rooms, nurse's stations, or on counters where an unauthorized person could gain access to patient records?

- Verify that there is an established system in place that addresses protecting the confidentiality of medical information.

- If the hospital uses electronic patient records, are appropriate security safeguards in place? Is access to patient records controlled?

- Verify that adequate precautions are taken to prevent physical or electronic altering, damaging or deletion/destruction of patient records or information in patient records.

A-0443

§482.24(b)(3) - (Continued)

Original medical records must be released by the hospital only in accordance with Federal or State laws, court orders, or subpoenas.

A-0449
(Rev. 37, Issued: 10-17-08; Effective/Implementation Date: 10-17-08)

§482.24(c) Standard: Content of Record

The medical record must contain information to justify admission and continued hospitalization, support the diagnosis, and describe the patient's progress and response to medications and services.

Interpretive Guidelines §482.24(c)

The medical record must contain information such as notes, documentation, records, reports, recordings, test results, assessments etc. to:

- Justify admission;

- Justify continued hospitalization;

- Support the diagnosis;

- Describe the patient's progress;

- Describe the patient's response to medications; and

- Describe the patient's response to services such as interventions, care, treatments, etc.

The medical record must contain complete information/documentation regarding evaluations, interventions, care provided, services, care plans, discharge plans, and the patient's response to those activities.

Patient medical record information, such as, laboratory reports, test results, consults, assessments, radiology reports, dictated notes, etc. must be promptly filed in the patient's medical record in order to be available to the physician and other care providers to use in making assessments of the patient's condition, to justify continued hospitalization, to support the diagnosis, to describe the patient's progress, and to describe the patient's response to medications, interventions, and services, in planning the patient's care, and in making decisions on the provision of care to the patient.

A-0450
(Rev. 47, Issued: 06-05-09, Effective/Implementation: 06-05-09)

§482.24(c)(1) - All patient medical record entries must be legible, complete, dated, timed, and authenticated in written or electronic form by the person responsible for providing or evaluating the service provided, consistent with hospital policies and procedures.

Interpretive Guidelines §482.24(c)(1)

All entries in the medical record must be **legible**. Orders, progress notes, nursing notes, or other entries in the medical record that are not legible may be misread or misinterpreted and may lead to medical errors or other adverse patient events.

All entries in the medical record must be **complete**. A medical record is considered complete if it contains sufficient information to identify the patient; support the diagnosis/condition; justify the care, treatment, and services; document the course and results of care, treatment, and services; and promote continuity of care among providers. With these criteria in mind, an individual entry into the medical record must contain sufficient information on the matter that is the subject of the entry to permit the medical record to satisfy the completeness standard.

All entries in the medical record must be **dated, timed, and authenticated**, in written or electronic form, by the person responsible for providing or evaluating the service provided.

- The time and date of each entry (orders, reports, notes, etc.) must be accurately documented. Timing establishes when an order was given, when an activity happened or when an activity is to take place. Timing and dating entries is necessary for patient safety and quality of care. Timing and dating of entries establishes a baseline for future actions or assessments and establishes a timeline of events. Many patient interventions or assessments are based on time intervals or timelines of various signs, symptoms, or events. (71 FR 68687)

- The hospital must have a method to establish the identity of the author of each entry. This would include verification of the author of faxed orders/entries or computer entries.

- The hospital must have a method to require that each author takes a specific action to verify that the entry being authenticated is his/her entry or that he/she is responsible for the entry, and that the entry is accurate.

The requirements for dating and timing do not apply to orders or prescriptions that are generated outside of the hospital until they are presented to the hospital at the time of service. Once the hospital begins processing such an order or prescription, it is responsible for ensuring that the implementation of the order or prescription by the hospital is promptly dated, and timed in the patient's medical record.

When a practitioner is using a preprinted order set, the ordering practitioner may be in compliance with the requirement at §482.24(c)(1) to date, time, and authenticate an order if the practitioner accomplishes the following:

- **Last page:** Sign, date, and time the last page of the orders, with the last page also identifying the total number of pages in the order set.

- **Pages with Internal Selections:** Sign or initial any other (internal) pages of the order set where selections or changes have been made.

  o The practitioner should initial/sign the top or bottom of the pertinent page(s);and

  o The practitioner should also initial each place in the preprinted order set where changes, such as additions, deletions, or strike-outs of components that do not apply, have been made.

    - It is not necessary to initial every preprinted box that is checked to indicate selection of an order option, so long as there are no changes made to the option(s) selected.

In the case of a pre-established electronic order set, the same principles would apply, so that the practitioner would date, time and authenticate the final order that resulted from the electronic selection/annotation process, with the exception that pages with internal changes would not need to be initialed or signed if they are part of an integrated single electronic document.

Authentication of medical record entries may include written signatures, initials, computer key, or other code. For authentication, in written or electronic form, a method must be established to identify the author. When rubber stamps or electronic authorizations are used for authentication, the hospital must have policies and procedures to ensure that such stamps or authorizations are used only by the individuals whose signature they represent. There shall be no delegation of stamps or authentication codes to another individual. It should be noted that some insurers and other payers may have a policy prohibiting the use of rubber stamps as a means of authenticating the medical records that support a claim for payment. Medicare payment policy, for example, no longer permits such use of rubber stamps. Thus, while the use of a rubber stamp for signature authentication is not prohibited under the CoPs and analysis of the rubber stamp method per se is not an element of the survey process, hospitals may wish to eliminate their usage in order to avoid denial of claims for payment.

Where an electronic medical record is in use, the hospital must demonstrate how it prevents alterations of record entries after they have been authenticated. Information needed to review an electronic medical record, including pertinent codes and security features, must be readily available to surveyors to permit their review of sampled medical records while on-site in the hospital.

When State law and/or hospital policy requires that entries in the medical record made by residents or non-physicians be countersigned by supervisory or attending medical staff members, then the medical staff rules and regulations must address counter-signature requirements and processes.

A system of auto-authentication in which a physician or other practitioner authenticates an entry that he or she cannot review, e.g., because it has not yet been transcribed, or the electronic entry cannot be displayed, is not consistent with these requirements. There must be a method of determining that the practitioner did, in fact, authenticate the entry after it was created. In addition, failure to disapprove an entry within a specific time period is not acceptable as authentication.

The practitioner must separately date and time his/her signature authenticating an entry, even though there may already be a date and time on the document, since the latter may not reflect when the entry was authenticated. For certain electronically-generated documents, where the date and time that the physician reviewed the electronic transcription is automatically printed on the document, the requirements of this section would be satisfied. However, if the electronically-generated document only prints the date and time that an event occurred (e.g., EKG printouts, lab results, etc.) and does not print the date and time that the practitioner actually reviewed the document, then the practitioner must either authenticate, date, and time this document itself or incorporate an acknowledgment that the document was reviewed into another document (such as the

H&P, a progress note, etc.), which would then be authenticated, dated, and timed by the practitioner.

Survey Procedures §482.24(c)(1)

Review a sample of open and closed medical records.

- Determine whether all medical record entries are legible. Are they clearly written in such a way that they are not likely to be misread or misinterpreted?

- Determine whether orders, progress notes, nursing notes, or other entries in the medical record are complete. Does the medical record contain sufficient information to identify the patient; support the diagnosis/condition; justify the care, treatment, and services; document the course and results of care, treatment, and services; and promote continuity of care among providers?

- Determine whether medical record entries are dated, timed, and appropriately authenticated by the person who is responsible for ordering, providing, or evaluating the service provided.

- Determine whether all orders, including verbal orders, are written in the medical record and signed by the practitioner who is caring for the patient and who is authorized by hospital policy and in accordance with State law to write orders.

- Determine whether the hospital has a means for verifying signatures, both written and electronic, written initials, codes, and stamps when such are used for authorship identification. For electronic medical records, ask the hospital to demonstrate the security features that maintain the integrity of entries and verification of electronic signatures and authorizations. Examine the hospital's policies and procedures for using the system, and determine if documents are being authenticated after they are created.

A-0454
(Rev. 84, Issued: 06-07-13, Effective: 06-07-13, Implementation: 06-07-13)

§482.24(c)(2) - All orders, including verbal orders, must be dated, timed, and authenticated promptly by the ordering practitioner or by another practitioner who is responsible for the care of the patient only if such a practitioner is acting in accordance with State law, including scope-of-practice laws, hospital policies, and medical staff bylaws, rules, and regulations.

Interpretive Guidelines §482.24(c)(2)

The hospital must ensure that all orders, including verbal orders, are dated, timed, and authenticated promptly. The Merriam-Webster online dictionary defines "prompt" as performed readily or immediately.

Verbal orders are orders for medications, treatments, interventions or other patient care that are transmitted as oral, spoken communications between senders and receivers, delivered either face-to-face or via telephone.

The receiver of a verbal order must date, time, and sign the verbal order in accordance with hospital policy. CMS expects hospital policies and procedures for verbal orders to include a read-back and verification process.

The prescribing practitioner must verify, sign, date and time the order as soon as possible after issuing the order, in accordance with hospital policy, and State and Federal requirements.

Authentication of a verbal order may be written, electronic, or faxed. The hospital must have a method for establishing the identity of the practitioner who has given a verbal order, including verification of the author of faxed verbal orders or computer entries.

In some instances, the ordering practitioner may not be able to authenticate his or her order, including a verbal order (e.g., the ordering practitioner gives a verbal order which is written and transcribed, and then is "off duty" for the weekend or an extended period of time). In such cases it is acceptable for another practitioner who is responsible for the patient's care to authenticate the order, including a verbal order, of the ordering practitioner as long as it is permitted under State law, hospital policies and medical staff bylaws, rules, and regulations. Hospitals may choose in their policies to restrict which practitioners it would authorize to authenticate another practitioner's orders. For example, a hospital could choose to restrict authentication of orders for pediatric patients to practitioners who are privileged to provide pediatric care. (77 FR 29053, May 16, 2012)

- All practitioners responsible for the patient's care are expected to have knowledge of the patient's hospital course, medical plan of care, condition, and current status.

- When a practitioner other than the ordering practitioner authenticates an order, that practitioner assumes responsibility for the order as being complete, accurate and final.

- A qualified non-physician practitioner, such as a physician assistant (PA) or nurse practitioner (NP), who is responsible for the care of the patient may authenticate a physician's or other qualified non-physician practitioner's order only if the order is within his/her scope of practice.

If State law requires that the ordering practitioner authenticate his/her own orders, or his/her own verbal orders, then a practitioner other than the prescribing practitioner would

not be permitted to authenticate the verbal order in that State.
(71 FR 68682 and 77 FR 29053, May 16, 2012)

NOTE CONCERNING VERBAL ORDERS FOR LABORATORY TESTS:

The requirement to authenticate promptly a verbal order applies to verbal orders associated with both inpatients and outpatients. It is possible that a hospital verbal order for a laboratory test could be authenticated in compliance with the Clinical Laboratory Improvement Amendment (CLIA) regulatory standard of authentication, i.e., within 30 days, but nonetheless be out of compliance with the hospital Medical Records Services requirement for prompt authentication of all orders, including verbal orders. Because CLIA laboratories – even if physically situated in a hospital – are surveyed for compliance only with CLIA regulations, the laboratory would not be cited for a deficiency by a CLIA survey team. However, hospital surveyors conducting a survey would cite the hospital's inpatient or outpatient recordkeeping for deficiencies under the Medical Record Services CoP if the lab order originated for a patient during a hospital inpatient stay or hospital outpatient clinic visit and the order was not authenticated promptly.

Survey Procedures §482.24(c)(2)

Does the hospital have policies and procedures requiring prompt authentication of all orders, including verbal orders, by the ordering practitioner or, if permitted under State law, hospital policy and medical staff bylaws, rules and regulations, another practitioner responsible for the care of the patient?

- Do the hospital's policies and procedures for verbal orders include a "read back and verify" process where the receiver of the order reads back the order to the ordering practitioner to verify its accuracy?

Review orders, including verbal orders, in a sample of medical records. Have orders been dated, timed, and authenticated promptly by the ordering practitioner or, if permitted under State law, hospital policy and medical staff bylaws, rules and regulations, another practitioner who is responsible for the care of the patient?

- Has the receiver of a verbal order dated, timed, and signed the order according to hospital policy?

A-0457
(Rev. 84, Issued: 06-07-13, Effective: 06-07-13, Implementation: 06-07-13)

§482.24(c) (3) Hospitals may use pre-printed and electronic standing orders, order sets, and protocols for patient orders only if the hospital:

(i) Establishes that such orders and protocols have been reviewed and approved by the medical staff and the hospital's nursing and pharmacy leadership;

(ii) Demonstrates that such orders and protocols are consistent with nationally recognized and evidence-based guidelines;

(iii) Ensures that the periodic and regular review of such orders and protocols is conducted by the medical staff and the hospital's nursing and pharmacy leadership to determine the continuing usefulness and safety of the orders and protocols; and

(iv) Ensures that such orders and protocols are dated, timed, and authenticated promptly in the patient's medical record by the ordering practitioner or another practitioner responsible for the care of the patient only if such a practitioner is acting in accordance with State law, including scope-of-practice laws, hospital policies, and medical staff bylaws, rules, and regulations.

Interpretive Guidelines §482.24(c)(3)

What is covered by this regulation?

There is no standard definition of a "standing order" in the hospital community at large (77 FR 29055, May 16, 2012), but the terms "pre-printed standing orders," "electronic standing orders," "order sets," and "protocols for patient orders" are various ways in which the term "standing orders" has been applied. For purposes of brevity, in our guidance we generally use the term "standing order(s)" to refer interchangeably to pre-printed and electronic standing orders, order sets, and protocols. However, we note that the lack of a standard definition for these terms and their interchangeable and indistinct use by hospitals and health care professionals may result in confusion regarding what is or is not subject to the requirements of §482.24(c)(3), particularly with respect to "order sets."

- Not all pre-printed and electronic order sets are considered a type of "standing order" covered by this regulation. Where the order sets consist solely of menus of treatment or care options designed to facilitate the creation of a patient-specific set of orders by a physician or other qualified practitioner authorized to write orders, and none of the treatment choices and actions can be initiated by non-practitioner clinical staff before the physician or other qualified practitioner actually creates the patient-specific order(s), such menus would not be considered "standing orders" covered by this regulation. We note in such cases the menus provide a convenient and efficient method for the physician/practitioner to create an order, but the availability of such menu options does not create an "order set" that is a "standing order" subject to the requirements of this regulation. The physician/practitioner may, based on his/her professional judgment, choose to: use the available menu options to create an order; not use the menu options and instead create an order from scratch; or modify the available menu options to create the order. In each case the physician/practitioner exercises his privileges to prescribe specific diagnosis and/or treatment activities that are to be implemented for a patient.

- On the other hand, in cases where hospital policy permits treatment to be initiated, by a nurse, for example, without a prior specific order from the treating physician/practitioner, this policy and practice must meet the requirements of this regulation for review of standing orders, regardless of whether it is called a standing order, a protocol, an order set, or something else. Such treatment is typically initiated when a patient's condition meets certain pre-defined clinical criteria. For example, standing orders may be initiated as part of an emergency response or as part of an evidence-based treatment regimen where it is not practical for a nurse to obtain either a written, authenticated order or a verbal order from a physician or other qualified practitioner prior to the provision of care.

- Hybrids, where a component for non-practitioner-initiated treatment is embedded within a menu of options for the physician or other qualified practitioner, still require compliance with the requirements for a standing order for that component. For example, if an order set includes a protocol for nurse-initiated potassium replacement, that protocol must be reviewed under the requirements of this regulation before it may become part of a menu of treatment options from which a physician or other qualified practitioner would select treatments for a particular patient.

Requirements for "Standing Orders"

Hospitals have the flexibility to use standing orders to expedite the delivery of patient care in well-defined clinical scenarios for which there is evidence supporting the application of standardized treatments or interventions.

Appropriate use of standing orders can contribute to patient safety and quality of care by promoting consistency of care, based on objective evidence, when orders may be initiated as part of an emergency response or as part of an evidence-based treatment regimen where it is not practicable for a nurse or other non-practitioner to obtain a verbal or authenticated written order from a physician or other practitioner responsible for the care of the patient prior to the provision of care.

In all cases, implementation of a standing order must be medically appropriate for the patient to whom the order is applied.

Much of the evidence on the effectiveness of standing orders in hospitals has been narrowly focused on aspects of their use by Rapid Response Teams addressing inpatient emergencies. However, standing orders may also be appropriate in other clinical circumstances, including, but not limited to:

- Protocols for triaging and initiating required screening examinations and stabilizing treatment for emergency department patients presenting with symptoms suggestive of acute asthma, myocardial infarction, stroke, etc. (This does not relieve a hospital of its obligations under the Emergency Medical Treatment and Labor Act (EMTALA) to have qualified medical personnel complete required screening and, when applicable, stabilizing treatment in a timely manner.)

- Post-operative recovery areas.

- Timely provision of immunizations, such as certain immunizations for newborns, for which there are clearly established and nationally recognized guidelines.

Standing orders may not be used in clinical situations where they are specifically prohibited under Federal or State law. For example, the hospital patient's rights regulation at §482.13(e)(6) specifically prohibits the use of standing orders for restraint or seclusion of hospital patients.

When deciding whether to use standing orders, hospitals should also be aware that, although use of standing orders is permitted under the hospital Conditions of Participation, some insurers, including Medicare, may not pay for the services provided because of the use of standing orders. (77 FR 29056)

Minimum requirements for standing orders. Hospitals may employ standing orders only if the following requirements are met for each standing order for a particular well-defined clinical scenario:

- Each standing order must be reviewed and approved by the hospital's medical staff and nursing and pharmacy leadership before it may be used in the clinical setting. The regulation requires a multi-disciplinary collaborative effort in establishing the protocols associated with each standing order.

  - The hospital's policies and procedures for standing orders must address the process by which a standing order is developed; approved; monitored; initiated by authorized staff; and subsequently authenticated by physicians or other practitioners responsible for the care of the patient.

  - For each approved standing order, there must be specific criteria clearly identified in the protocol for the order for a nurse or other authorized personnel to initiate the execution of a particular standing order, for example, the specific clinical situations, patient conditions, or diagnoses by which initiation of the order would be justified. Under no circumstances may a hospital use standing orders in a manner that requires any staff not authorized to write patient orders to make clinical decisions outside of their scope of practice in order to initiate such orders.

    Since residents are physicians, this regulation does not require specific criteria for a resident to initiate the execution of a particular standing order. However, there may be State laws governing the practice of residents in hospitals that are more restrictive; if so, the hospital is expected to comply with the State law. Likewise, the hospital may choose through its policies and medical staff bylaws, rules and regulations to restrict the role of residents with respect to standing orders.

- Policies and procedures should also address the instructions that the medical, nursing, and other applicable professional staff receive on the conditions and criteria for using standing orders as well as any individual staff responsibilities associated with the initiation and execution of standing orders. An order that has been initiated for a specific patient must be added to the patient's medical record at the time of initiation, or as soon as possible thereafter.

- Likewise, standing order policies and procedures must specify the process whereby the physician or other practitioner responsible for the care of the patient acknowledges and authenticates the initiation of all standing orders after the fact, with the exception of influenza and pneumococcal vaccines, which do not require such authentication in accordance with § 482.23(c)(2).

(76 FR 65896, October 24, 2011 & 77 FR 29056, May 16, 2012)

- The hospital must be able to document that the standing order is consistent with nationally recognized and evidence-based guidelines. This does not mean that there must be a template standing order available in national guidelines which the hospital copies, but rather that the content of each standing order in the hospital must be consistent with nationally recognized, evidence-based guidelines for providing care. The burden of proof is on the hospital to show that there is a sound basis for the standing order.

- Each standing order must be subject to periodic and regular review by the medical staff and the hospital's nursing and pharmacy leadership, to determine the continuing usefulness and safety of the orders and protocols. At a minimum, an annual review of each standing order would satisfy this requirement. However, the hospital's policies and procedures must also address a process for the identification and timely completion of any requisite updates, corrections, modifications, or revisions based on changes in nationally recognized, evidence-based guidelines. The review may be prepared by the hospital's QAPI program, so long as the medical staff and nursing and pharmacy leadership read, review, and, as applicable, act upon the final report. Among other things, reviews are expected to consider:

  - Whether the standing order's protocol continues to be consistent with the latest standards of practice reflected in nationally recognized, evidence-based guidelines;

  - Whether there have been any preventable adverse patient events resulting from the use of the standing order, and if so, whether changes in the order would reduce the likelihood of future similar adverse events. Note that the review would not be expected to address adverse events that are a likely outcome of the course of patient's disease or injury, even if the order was applied to that patient, unless there is concern that use of the standing order exacerbated the patient's condition; and

- Whether a standing order has been initiated and executed in a manner consistent with the order's protocol, and if not, whether the protocol needs revision and/or staff need more training in the correct procedures.

- An order that has been initiated for a specific patient must be added to the patient's medical record at the time of initiation, or as soon as possible thereafter. The hospital must ensure each standing order that has been executed is dated, timed, and authenticated promptly in the patient's medical record by the ordering practitioner or another practitioner responsible for the care of the patient. Another practitioner who is responsible for the care of the patient may date, time and authenticate the standing order instead of the ordering practitioner, but only if the other practitioner is acting in accordance with State law, including scope of practice laws, hospital policies, and medical staff bylaws, rules and regulations.

The hospital's standing orders policies and procedures must specify the process whereby the responsible practitioner, or another authorized practitioner, acknowledges and authenticates the initiation of each standing order after the fact, with the exception of standing orders for influenza and pneumococcal vaccines, which do not require such authentication. Further, the responsible practitioner must be able to modify, cancel, void or decline to authenticate orders that were not medically necessary in a particular situation. The medical record must reflect the physician's actions to modify, cancel, void or refusal to authenticate a standing order that the physician determined was not medically necessary. (76 FR 65896, October 24, 2011)

Survey Procedures §482.24(c)(3)

- Ask the hospital's medical staff and its nursing and pharmacy leadership whether standing orders are used. If yes, ask them to describe how a standing order is developed and monitored, and their role in the process.

- Ask to see an example of one or more standing orders, including documentation on the development of the order, including:

  - Reference to the evidence-based national guidelines that support it;

  - Participation of medical staff and nursing and pharmacy leadership in the review and approval of the standing order;

- • Description of the protocol to be followed when initiating the execution of the order, including description of the roles and responsibilities of various types of staff;

- • Description of the process for authenticating the order's initiation by the practitioner responsible for the care of the patient, or another authorized practitioner;

- • Evidence of training of personnel on the order's protocol; and

- • Evidence of periodic evaluation and, if needed, modification of the standing order, including whether the order remains consistent with current evidence-based national guidelines, staff adherence to the protocol for initiation and execution, and whether there have been any preventable adverse events associated with the order.

- • Ask staff providing clinical services in areas of the hospital where standing orders might be typically used, including but not limited to, the emergency department, labor and delivery units, and inpatient units, whether standing orders are used. If they say yes, ask them:

    - o To describe a typical scenario where a standing order would be used, and what they would do in that case.

    - o For a copy of the protocol for that standing order. Does their description conform to the protocol?

- • Review a sample of medical records of patients where a nurse-initiated standing order was used and verify that the order was documented and authenticated by a practitioner responsible for the care of the patient.

A-0458
(Rev. 84, Issued: 06-07-13, Effective: 06-07-13, Implementation: 06-07-13)

482.24(c)(4) - All records must document the following, as appropriate:
    (i) Evidence of--

        (A) A medical history and physical examination completed and documented no more than 30 days before or 24 hours after admission or registration, but prior to surgery or a procedure requiring anesthesia services. The medical history and physical examination must be placed in the patient's medical record within 24 hours after admission or registration, but prior to surgery or a procedure requiring anesthesia services.

Interpretive Guidelines §482.24(c)(4)(i)(A)

The medical record must include documentation that a medical history and physical examination (H&P) was completed and documented for each patient no more than 30 days prior to hospital admission or registration, or 24 hours after hospital admission or registration, but in all cases prior to surgery or a procedure requiring anesthesia services.

The purpose of an H&P is to determine whether there is anything in the patient's overall condition that would affect the planned course of the patient's treatment, such as an allergy to a medication that must be avoided, or a co-morbidity that requires certain additional interventions to reduce risk to the patient.

The H&P documentation must be placed in the medical record within 24 hours of admission or registration, but in all cases prior to surgery or a procedure requiring anesthesia services, including all inpatient, outpatient, or same-day surgeries or procedures. (71 FR 68676) The H&P may be handwritten or transcribed. An H&P that is completed within 24 hours of the patient's admission or registration, but after surgery or a procedure requiring anesthesia would not be in compliance.

Survey Procedures §482.24(c)(4)(i)(A)

Review a sample of inpatient medical records for various types of patients and outpatient medical records for patients having same day surgery or a procedure requiring anesthesia to determine whether:

- There is an H&P that was done no more than 30 days before or 24 hours after admission or registration, but, for all cases involving surgery or a procedure requiring anesthesia services, prior to the surgery or procedure;

- The H&P documentation was placed in the medical record within 24 hours after admission or registration, but, for all cases involving surgery or a procedure requiring anesthesia services, prior to the surgery or procedure;

A-0461
(Rev. 84, Issued: 06-07-13, Effective: 06-07-13, Implementation: 06-07-13)

482.24(c)(4) - [All records must document the following, as appropriate:

(i) Evidence of --]

(B)   An updated examination of the patient, including any changes in the patient's condition, when the medical history and physical examination are completed within 30 days before admission or registration. Documentation of the updated examination must be placed in the patient's medical record within 24 hours after admission or registration, but prior to surgery or a procedure requiring anesthesia services.

Interpretive Guidelines §482.24(c)(4)(i)(B)

When an H&P is completed within the 30 days before admission or registration, the hospital must ensure that an updated medical record entry documenting an examination for any changes in the patient's condition is placed in the patient's medical record within 24 hours after admission or registration, but, in all cases involving surgery or a procedure requiring anesthesia services, prior to the surgery or procedure.

The update note must document an examination for any changes in the patient's condition since the time that the patient's H&P was performed that might be significant for the planned course of treatment. The physician, oromaxillofacial surgeon, or qualified licensed individual uses his/her clinical judgment, based upon his/her assessment of the patient's condition and co-morbidities, if any, in relation to the patient's planned course of treatment to decide the extent of the update assessment needed as well as the information to be included in the update note in the patient's medical record.

If, upon examination, the licensed practitioner finds no change in the patient's condition since the H&P was completed, he/she may indicate in the patient's medical record that the H&P was reviewed, the patient was examined, and that "no change" has occurred in the patient's condition since the H&P was completed. (71 FR 68676) Such statements in the medical record would meet the requirement for documenting the H&P update.

Any changes in the patient's condition must be documented by the practitioner in the update note and placed in the patient's medical record within 24 hours of admission or registration, but prior to surgery or a procedure requirement anesthesia services. Additionally, if the practitioner finds that the H&P done before admission is incomplete, inaccurate, or otherwise unacceptable, the practitioner reviewing the H&P, examining the patient, and completing the update may disregard the existing H&P, and conduct and document in the medical record a new H&P within 24 hours after admission or registration, but prior to surgery or a procedure requiring anesthesia.

Survey Procedures §482.24(c)(4)(i)(B)

In the sample of medical records selected for review, look for cases where the medical history and physical examination was completed within 30 days before admission or registration.

- Determine whether an updated medical record entry documenting an examination for changes in the patient's condition was completed and documented in the patient's medical record within 24 hours after admission or registration.

- Determine whether, in all cases involving surgery or a procedure requiring anesthesia services, the update was completed and documented prior to the surgery or procedure.

A-0463
(Rev. 84, Issued: 06-07-13, Effective: 06-07-13, Implementation: 06-07-13)

[All records must document the following, as appropriate:]

§482.24(c)(4)(ii) - Admitting diagnosis.

Interpretive Guidelines §482.24(c)(4)(ii)

All inpatient medical records must contain the admitting diagnosis.

Survey Procedures §482.24(c)(4)(ii)

Verify in a sample of medical records that the patient's admitting diagnosis is documented in each medical record.

A-0464
(Rev. 84, Issued: 06-07-13, Effective: 06-07-13, Implementation: 06-07-13)

[All records must document the following, as appropriate:]

§482.24(c)(4)(iii) - Results of all consultative evaluations of the patient and appropriate findings by clinical and other staff involved in the care of the patient.

Interpretive Guidelines §482.24(c)(4)(iii)

All patient records, both inpatient and outpatient, must contain the results of all consultative evaluations of the patient and appropriate findings by clinical and other staff involved in the care of the patient. This information must be promptly filed in the patient's medical record in order to be available to the physician or other care providers to use in making assessments of the patient's condition, to justify treatment or continued hospitalization, to support or revise the patient's diagnosis, to support or revise the plan of care, to describe the patient's progress and to describe the patient's response to medications, treatments, and services.

Survey Procedures §482.24(c)(4)(iii)

Review a sample of medical records of patients who have orders for consultative evaluations. Are the results/reports and other clinical findings of those consultative evaluations included in the patient's medical record?

A-0465
(Rev. 84, Issued: 06-07-13, Effective: 06-07-13, Implementation: 06-07-13)

[All records must document the following, as appropriate:]

§482.24(c)(4)(iv) - Documentation of complications, hospital acquired infections, and unfavorable reactions to drugs and anesthesia.

Interpretive Guidelines §482.24(c)(4)(iv)

All patient medical records, both inpatient and outpatient, must document:

- Complication;

- Hospital-acquired infections;

- Unfavorable reactions to drugs; and

- Unfavorable reactions to anesthesia.

Survey Procedures §482.24(c)(4)(iv)

Through observations, interviews, and reviews of hospital reports and documentation, determine if patient complications, hospital-acquired infections, unfavorable reactions to drugs/anesthesia have been documented in the applicable patient's medical record.

A-0466
(Rev. 84, Issued: 06-07-13, Effective: 06-07-13, Implementation: 06-07-13)

[All records must document the following, as appropriate:]

§482.24(c)(4)(v) - Properly executed informed consent forms for procedures and treatments specified by the medical staff, or by Federal or State law if applicable, to require written patient consent.

Interpretive Guidelines §482.24(c)(4)(v)

Informed consent is discussed in three locations in the CMS Hospital CoPs. See also the guidelines for 42 CFR 482.13(b)(2) pertaining to patients' rights, and the guidelines for 42 CFR 482.51(b)(2), pertaining to surgical services.

The medical record must contain a document recording the patient's informed consent for those procedures and treatments that have been specified as requiring informed consent. Medical staff policies should address which procedures and treatments require written informed consent. There may also be applicable Federal or State law requiring informed consent. The informed consent form contained in the medical record should provide evidence that it was properly executed.

Informed Consent Forms

A properly executed informed consent form should reflect the patient consent process. Except as specified for emergency situations in the hospital's informed consent policies, all inpatient and outpatient medical records must contain a properly executed informed consent form prior to conducting any procedure or other type of treatment that requires informed consent. An informed consent form, in order to be properly executed, must be consistent with hospital policies as well as applicable State and Federal law or regulation. A properly executed informed consent form contains the following minimum elements:

- Name of the hospital where the procedure or other type of medical treatment is to take place;

- Name of the specific procedure, or other type of medical treatment for which consent is being given;

- Name of the responsible practitioner who is performing the procedure or administering the medical treatment;

- Statement that the procedure or treatment, including the anticipated benefits, material risks, and alternative therapies, was explained to the patient or the patient's legal representative; (Material risks could include risks with a high degree of likelihood but a low degree of severity, as well as those with a very low degree of likelihood but high degree of severity. Hospitals are free to delegate to the responsible practitioner, who uses the available clinical evidence as informed by the practitioner's professional judgment, the determination of which material risks, benefits and alternatives will be discussed with the patient.)

- Signature of the patient or the patient's legal representative; and

- Date and time the informed consent form is signed by the patient or the patient's legal representative.

If there is applicable State law governing the content of the informed consent form, then the hospital's form must comply with those requirements.

A well-designed informed consent form might also include the following additional information:

- Name of the practitioner who conducted the informed consent discussion with the patient or the patient's representative.

- Date, time, and signature of the person witnessing the patient or the patient's legal representative signing the consent form.

- Indication or listing of the material risks of the procedure or treatment that were discussed with the patient or the patient's representative;

- Statement, if applicable, that physicians other than the operating practitioner, including but not limited to residents, will be performing important tasks related to the surgery, in accordance with the hospital's policies and, in the case of residents, based on their skill set and under the supervision of the responsible practitioner.

- Statement, if applicable, that qualified medical practitioners who are not physicians who will perform important parts of the surgery or administration of anesthesia will be performing only tasks that are within their scope of practice, as determined under State law and regulation, and for which they have been granted privileges by the hospital.

Survey Procedures §482.24(c)(4)(v)

- Verify that the hospital has assured that the medical staff has specified which procedures and treatments require written patient consent.

- Verify that the hospital's standard informed consent form contains the elements listed above as the minimum elements of a properly executed informed consent.

- Compare the hospital's standard informed consent form to the hospital's policies on informed consent, to verify that the form is consistent with the policies. If there is applicable State law, verify that the form is consistent with the requirements of that law.

- Review a minimum of six random medical records of patients who have, are undergoing, or are about to under a procedure or treatment that requires informed consent. Verify that each medical record contains informed consent forms.

- Verify that each completed informed consent form contains the information for each of the elements listed above as the minimum elements of a properly executed informed consent, as well as any additional elements required by State law and/or the hospital's policy.

A-0467
(Rev. 84, Issued: 06-07-13, Effective: 06-07-13, Implementation: 06-07-13)

[All records must document the following, as appropriate:]

§482.24(c)(4)(vi) - All practitioners' orders, nursing notes, reports of treatment, medication records, radiology, and laboratory reports, and vital signs and other information necessary to monitor the patient's condition.

Interpretive Guidelines §482.24(c)(4)(vi)

The requirement means that the stated information is necessary to monitor the patient's condition and that this and other necessary information must be in the patient's medical record. In order for necessary information to be used it must be promptly filed in the medical record so that health care staff involved in the patient's care can access/retrieve this information in order to monitor the patient's condition and provide appropriate care.

The medical record must contain:

- All practitioner's orders (properly authenticated);

- All nursing notes (including nursing care plans);

- All reports of treatment (including complications and hospital-acquired infections);

- All medication records (including unfavorable reactions to drugs);

- All radiology reports;

- All laboratory reports;
- All vital signs; and

- All other information necessary to monitor the patient's condition.

Survey Procedures §482.24(c)(4)(vi)

- Verify that the patient records contain appropriate documentation of practitioners' orders, interventions, findings, assessments, records, notes, reports and other information necessary to monitor the patient's condition.

- Is this information included in patient records in a prompt manner so that health care staff involved in the care of the patient have access to the information necessary to monitor the patient's condition?

A-0468
(Rev. 84, Issued: 06-07-13, Effective: 06-07-13, Implementation: 06-07-13)

[All records must document the following, as appropriate:]

§482.24(c)(4)(vii) - Discharge summary with outcome of hospitalization, disposition of case, and provisions for follow-up care.

Interpretive Guidelines §482.24(c)(4)(vii)

All patient medical records must contain a discharge summary. A discharge summary discusses the outcome of the hospitalization, the disposition of the patient, and provisions for follow-up care. Follow-up care provisions include any post hospital appointments, how post hospital patient care needs are to be met, and any plans for post-hospital care by providers such as home health, hospice, nursing homes, or assisted living.

The MD/DO or other qualified practitioner with admitting privileges in accordance with State law and hospital policy, who admitted the patient is responsible for the patient during the patient's stay in the hospital. This responsibility would include developing and entering the discharge summary.

Other MD/DOs who work with the patient's MD/DO and who are covering for the patient's MD/DO and who are knowledgeable about the patient's condition, the patient's care during the hospitalization, and the patient's discharge plans may write the discharge summary at the responsible MD/DO's request.

In accordance with hospital policy, and 42 CFR Part 482.12(c)(1)(i) the MD/DO may delegate writing the discharge summary to other qualified health care personnel such as nurse practitioners and MD/DO assistants to the extent recognized under State law or a State's regulatory mechanism.

Whether delegated or non-delegated, we would expect the person who writes the discharge summary to authenticate, date, and time their entry and additionally for delegated discharge summaries we would expect the MD/DO responsible for the patient during his/her hospital stay to co-authenticate and date the discharge summary to verify its content.

The discharge summary requirement would include outpatient records. For example:

- The outcome of the treatment, procedures, or surgery;

- The disposition of the case;

- Provisions for follow-up care for an outpatient surgery patient or an emergency department patient who was not admitted or transferred to another hospital.

Survey Procedures §482.24(c)(4)(vii)

- Verify that a discharge summary is included to assure that proper continuity of care is required.

- Verify that a final diagnosis is included in the discharge summary.

A-0469
(Rev. 84, Issued: 06-07-13, Effective: 06-07-13, Implementation: 06-07-13)

[All records must document the following, as appropriate:]

§482.24(c)(4)(viii) - Final diagnosis with completion of medical records within 30 days following discharge.

Interpretive Guidelines §482.24(c)(4)(viii)

All medical records must contain a final diagnosis. All medical records must be complete within 30 days of discharge or outpatient care.

Survey Procedures §482.24(c)(4)(viii)

Select a sample of patients who have been discharged for more than 30 days. Request their medical records. Are those records complete? Does each record have the patient's final diagnosis?

A-0490

(Rev. 37, Issued: 10-17-08; Effective/Implementation Date: 10-17-08)

§482.25 Condition of Participation: Pharmaceutical Services

The hospital must have pharmaceutical services that meet the needs of the patients. The institution must have a pharmacy directed by a registered pharmacist or a drug storage area under competent supervision. The medical staff is responsible for developing policies and procedures that minimize drug errors. This function may be delegated to the hospital's organized pharmaceutical service.

Interpretive Guidelines §482.25

Provision of pharmaceutical services must meet the needs of the patients' therapeutic goal by promoting a safe medication use process that ensures optimal selection of medications, dose, dosage form, frequency, route, duration of therapy and that substantially reduces or eliminates adverse drug events and duplication of treatment.

The hospital's pharmacy must be directed by a registered pharmacist. If a drug storage area is used instead of a pharmacy at any location providing pharmacy services, that storage area must be under competent supervision in accordance with State and Federal law.

Pharmaceutical Services would include:

- The procuring, manufacturing, compounding, packaging, dispensing, ordering, distributing, disposition, use, and administering of all medications, biologicals, chemicals and the use of medication related devices.

- Provision of medication-related information to hospital health care professionals and patients necessary to optimize therapeutic outcomes.

- Provision of pharmaceutical care. Pharmaceutical care is defined as the direct, responsible provision of medication-related care for the purpose of achieving definite outcomes that improve a patient's quality of life while minimizing patient risk.

Functions of Pharmaceutical Care are the:

- Collection and organization of patient-specific information;

- Determination of the presence of medication-therapy problems both potential and actual;

- Summary of the patient's medication related health care needs;

- Identification and specification of pharmacotherapeutic goals;

- Development of a pharmacotherapeutic regimen;

- Implementation of a monitoring plan in collaboration with the patient, if applicable, and other health care professionals;

- Monitoring the effects of the pharmacotherapeutic regimen; and

- Redesigning the regimen and monitoring plan as indicated.

Medication errors are a substantial source of morbidity and mortality in the hospitalized setting. Therefore, the development of policies and procedures to minimize medication errors should be based on accepted professional principles; external alerts and proactive review of facility reported and reviewed adverse drug events. It is important to flag new types of mistakes and continually improve and refine things, based on what went wrong.

The hospital's medical staff must develop policies and procedures to minimize drug errors, but may delegate this function to the hospital's organized pharmaceutical service.

Policies and procedures to minimize drug errors should include:

- High-alert medications - dosing limits, administration guidelines, packaging, labeling and storage;

- Limiting the variety of medication-related devices and equipment. For Example limit the types of general-purpose infusion pumps to one or two;

- Availability of up-to-date medication information;

- Availability of pharmacy expertise. Pharmacist available on-call when pharmacy does not operate 24 hours a day;

- Standardization of prescribing and communication practices to include:

    o Avoidance of dangerous abbreviations;
    o All elements of the order – dose, strength, units (metric), route, frequency, and rate;

    o Alert systems for look-like and sound-alike drug names;

    o Use of facility approved pre-printed order sheets whenever possible.

- That orders to "resume previous orders" are prohibited;

- A voluntary, non-punitive, reporting system to monitor and report adverse drug events (including medication errors and adverse drug reactions);

- The preparation, distribution, administration and proper disposal of hazardous medications;

- Drug recalls;

- That patient-specific information is readily accessible to all individuals involved in provision of pharmaceutical care. The patient information must be sufficient to properly order, prepare, dispense, administer and monitor medications as appropriate;

- Identification of when weight-based dosing for pediatric populations is required; and

- Requirements for review and revision based on facility-generated reports of adverse drug events and QAPI activities.

The hospital should have policies and procedures to actively identify potential and actual adverse drug events. Proactive identification could include; direct observation of medication administration, review of patient's clinical records, identification of patient signals that would warrant immediate review of patient's medication therapy and implementation of medication use evaluation studies.

The hospital should have a means to incorporate external alerts and/or recommendations from national associations and governmental agencies for review and facility policy and procedure revision consideration. National associations could include Institute for Safe Medications Practice, National Coordination Council for Medication Error Reporting and Prevention and Joint Commission for Accreditation of Health Care Facilities, Sentinel Event Reports. Governmental agencies may include: Food and Drug Administration, Med Watch Program, and Agency for Health Care Research and Quality.

The hospital's pharmacy services must be integrated into its hospital-wide QAPI program.

Survey Procedures §482.25

- Interview the chief pharmacist or the individual delegated to fulfill the chief pharmacist's functions. Determine that either the medical staff has developed policies and procedures regarding the management of pharmaceuticals or that this function is fulfilled by the pharmacy service.

- Verify that the purpose of pharmaceutical policies and procedures is to minimize drug errors. Review the pharmaceutical policies and procedures, the hospital's formulary and, if there is a pharmacy and therapeutic committee, the minutes of the committee meetings.

- Does a multidisciplinary committee composed of representatives from nursing, pharmacy, administration and medicine develop policies and procedures?

- Are there policies and procedures to minimize drug errors?

- Are policies and procedures reviewed and amended based on:
  - Facility-generated reports of adverse drug events;

  o Facility QAPI activities pertaining to pharmaceutical care;

  o Evaluation of external alerts and/or recommendations from national associations;

  o Evaluation of literature for new technologies or successful practices that have demonstrated enhanced medication safety in other organizations.

- Is the staff familiar with the medication-related policies and procedures?

- Is there a method to periodically review and evaluate the actual implementation of pharmaceutical policies and procedures by staff?

- Upon review of patient clinical record are issues with regard to provision of pharmaceutical services identified? Is the facility aware of the issues? Was there a failure to implement a policy and procedure?

- Are pharmacists an integral component of pharmaceutical care?

- Verify that the hospital's pharmacy services is integrated into its hospital-wide QAPI program.

A-0491
(Rev. 37, Issued: 10-17-08; Effective/Implementation Date: 10-17-08)

§482.25(a) Standard: Pharmacy Management and Administration

The pharmacy or drug storage area must be administered in accordance with accepted professional principles.

Interpretive Guidelines §482.25(a)

The hospital may utilize a unit dose system, individual prescription, floor stock system or a combination of these systems, properly stored.

Pharmaceutical services must be administered in accordance with accepted professional principles. Accepted professional principles includes compliance with applicable Federal and State laws, regulations, and guidelines governing pharmaceutical services, as well as, standards or recommendations promoted by nationally recognized professional organizations. Agencies and organizations could include FDA, NIH, American Society of Health-System Pharmacists, etc.

A fundamental purpose of pharmaceutical services is to ensure the safe and appropriate use of medications and medication-related devices. The pharmacy director, with input from appropriate hospital staff and committees, develops, implements and periodically reviews and revises policies and procedures governing provision of pharmaceutical services.

Methods a hospital may use to maintain professional principles include:

- Policies and procedures have been developed and are being followed;

- Drugs and biologicals are stored in accordance with manufacturer's directions and State and Federal requirements;

- Employees provide pharmaceutical services within their scope of license and education;

- Pharmacy records have sufficient detail to follow the flow of pharmaceuticals from their entry into the hospital through dispensation/administration;

- Maintaining controls over drugs and medications including the floor stock and those of the pharmacy or drug room;
- Maintaining pharmacy and accounting records pertaining to the requisitioning and dispensing of drugs and pharmaceutical supplies;

- Ensuring that drugs are being dispensed only by a licensed pharmacist;

- Only pharmacists or pharmacy-supervised personnel compound, label and dispense drugs or biologicals.

Survey Procedures §482.25(a)

- Are the policies and procedures consistent with accepted professional principles?

- Determine that professional principles are maintained by verifying that:

  o Policies and procedures have been developed and are being followed;

  o Drugs and biologicals are stored in accordance with manufacturers directions and State and Federal requirements;

  o Records have sufficient detail to follow the flow of control from entry through dispensation; and

  o Employees provide pharmaceutical services within their scope of license and education.

- Does the hospital have a means to incorporate external alerts and/or recommendations from national associations and governmental agencies for review and facility policy and procedure revision consideration?

- Are policies developed to promote consistent application of pharmaceutical services and care throughout the hospital?

- Is the pharmacy director periodically monitoring implementation of policies and procedures?

- Are policies and procedures reviewed and revised as warranted?

- Are services provided in a manner consistent with accepted professional principles?

- Is the pharmacy responsible for the procurement, distribution and control of all medication products used in the hospital (including medication-related devices) for inpatient and outpatient care?

A-0492
(Rev. 37, Issued: 10-17-08; Effective/Implementation Date: 10-17-08)

§482.25(a)(1) - A full-time, part-time, or consulting pharmacist must be responsible for developing, supervising, and coordinating all the activities of the pharmacy services.

Interpretive Guidelines §482.25(a)(1)

Direction of pharmaceutical services may not require continuous on-premise supervision at the hospital's single pharmacy or at any pharmacy location but may be accomplished through regularly scheduled visits, and/or telemedicine in accordance with Federal and State law and regulation and accepted professional principles.

A single pharmacist must be responsible for the overall administration of the pharmacy service and must be responsible for developing, supervising, and coordinating all the activities of the hospital wide pharmacy service.

The job description or the written agreement for the responsibilities of the pharmacist should be clearly defined and include development, supervision and coordination of all the activities of pharmacy services.

A professional, competent, legally qualified pharmacist must manage the pharmacy. The Director of pharmacy service must be thoroughly knowledgeable about hospital pharmacy practice and management.

Pharmacists and pharmacy technicians must perform their duties within scope of their license and education.

The Pharmacy Director should be actively involved in those committees responsible for establishing medication-related policies and procedures.

Survey Procedures §482.25(a)(1)

- Determine whether the pharmacist is a full-time, or part-time employee or employed on a consultative basis.

- Review the implementation of the chief pharmacist's responsibilities by:

  o Reviewing written status reports;

  o Reviewing minutes of meetings (if any) with facility staff regarding pharmaceutical services;

  o Reviewing schedules, time logs, etc.;

  o Reviewing the job description or the written agreement to see that the responsibilities of the pharmacist are clearly defined and include development supervision and coordination of all the activities of pharmacy services;

  o Determining whether the Pharmacy Director routinely evaluates the performance and competency of pharmacy personnel? Do performance evaluations include high-risk activities such as the compounding of hazardous medications, pharmacy-based prescriptive activities (e.g. aminoglycoside protocols) and pharmaceutical care for high-risk patients (pediatric, ICU, geriatric etc)?

- Determine whether the pharmacy director is actively involved in those committees responsible for establishing medication-related policies and procedures?

A-0493
(Rev. 37, Issued: 10-17-08; Effective/Implementation Date: 10-17-08)

§482.25(a)(2) - The pharmaceutical service must have an adequate number of personnel to ensure quality pharmaceutical services, including emergency services.

Interpretive Guidelines §482.25(a)(2)

There must be sufficient personnel to respond to the pharmaceutical needs of the patient population being served.

The pharmaceutical services staff must be sufficient in types, numbers, and training to provide quality services, including 24 hour, 7-day emergency coverage, or there is an arrangement for emergency services, as determined by the needs of the patients and as specified by the medical staff.

The number of pharmacists and/or the number of hours of services provided by pharmacists at the hospital, or at each location of the hospital that provides pharmaceutical services, must meet and be in accordance with the needs of its patients and accepted professional principles (as previously defined), and reflect the scope and complexity of the hospital's pharmaceutical services.

There must be sufficient numbers and types of personnel to provide accurate and timely medication delivery, ensure accurate and safe medication administration and to provide appropriate clinical services as well as the participation in continuous quality improvement programs that meet the needs of the patient population being served.

Survey Procedures §482.25(a)(2)

- Determine that the pharmaceutical services staff is sufficient in number and training to provide quality services, including 24 hour, 7-day emergency coverage, or there is an arrangement for emergency services, as determined by the needs of the patients and as specified by the medical staff.
- Determine if there are sufficient personnel to provide accurate and timely medication delivery, ensure accurate and safe medication administration and to provide appropriate clinical services as well as the participation in continuous quality improvement programs that meet the needs of the patient population being served.

A-0494

(Rev. 37, Issued: 10-17-08; Effective/Implementation Date: 10-17-08)

§482.25(a)(3) - Current and accurate records must be kept of the receipt and disposition of all scheduled drugs.

Interpretive Guidelines §482.25(a)(3)

Components of a record system to maintain current and accurate records of the receipt and disposition of scheduled drugs would include:

- Accountability procedures to ensure control of the distribution, use, and disposition of all scheduled drugs.

- Records of the receipt and disposition of all scheduled drugs must be current and must be accurate.

- Records trace the movement of scheduled drugs throughout the service.

- The pharmacist is responsible for determining that all drug records are in order and that an account of all scheduled drugs is maintained and reconciled.

- The record system, delineated in policies and procedures, tracks movement of all scheduled drugs from the point of entry into the hospital to the point of departure either through administration to the patient, destruction or return to the manufacture. This system provides documentation on scheduled drugs in a readily retrievable manner to facilitate reconciliation of the receipt and disposition of all scheduled drugs.

- All drug records are in order and an account of all scheduled drugs is maintained and any discrepancies in count are reconciled promptly.
- The hospital system is capable of readily identifying loss or diversion of all controlled substances in such a manner as to minimize the time frame between the actual loss or diversion to the time of detection and determination of the extent of loss or diversion?

- Facility policies and procedures should minimize scheduled drug diversion.

Survey Procedures §482.25(a)(3)

- Determine if there is a record system in place that provides information on controlled substances in a readily retrievable manner.

- Review the records to determine that they trace the movement of scheduled drugs throughout the service.

- Determine if there is a system, delineated in policies and procedures, that tracks movement of all scheduled drugs from the point of entry into the hospital to the point of departure either through administration to the patient, destruction or return to the manufacture. Determine if this system provides documentation on scheduled drugs in a readily retrievable manner to facilitate reconciliation of the receipt and disposition of all scheduled drugs.

- Determine if the pharmacist is responsible for determining that all drug records are in order and that an account of all scheduled drugs is maintained and periodically reconciled.

- Is the hospital system capable of readily identifying loss or diversion of all controlled substances in such a manner as to minimize the time frame between the actual losses or diversion to the time of detection and determination of the extent of loss or diversion?

- Determine if facility policy and procedures minimize scheduled drug diversion.

A-0500

(Rev. 37, Issued: 10-17-08; Effective/Implementation Date: 10-17-08)
§482.25(b) Standard: Delivery of Services

In order to provide patient safety, drugs and biologicals must be controlled and distributed in accordance with applicable standards of practice, consistent with Federal and State law.

Interpretive Guidelines §482.25(b)

Drugs and biologicals must be controlled and distributed in accordance with applicable Federal and State laws and regulations, and in accordance with applicable standards of practice. Applicable standards of practice include compliance with all Federal and State laws, regulations, and guidelines, as well as, standards and recommendations promoted by nationally recognized professional organizations that apply to pharmaceutical care and the control and distribution of drugs and biologicals.

The procedures established to prevent unauthorized usage and distribution must provide for an accounting of the receipt and disposition of drugs subject to the Comprehensive Drug Abuse Prevention and Control Act of 1970.

The pharmacist, in consultation with appropriate hospital staff and committees, is to develop and implement guidelines, protocols, policies and procedures for the provision of pharmaceutical services that ensure patient safety through the appropriate control and distribution of medications, medication-related devices and biologicals.

For high risk medications and high-risk patients (pediatric, geriatric or patients with renal or hepatic impairment) there should be systems in place to minimize adverse drug events. Such systems could include but not limited to; checklists, dose limits, pre-printed orders, special packaging, special labeling, double-checks and written guidelines. **"High risk medications"** are those medications involved in a high percentage of medication errors and/or sentinel events and medications that carry a higher risk for abuse, errors, or other adverse outcomes. Lists of high-risk or high-alert drugs are available from such organizations as the Institute for Safe Medication Practices (ISMP) and the United States Pharmcopoeia (USP). Examples of high-risk drugs may include investigational drugs, controlled medications, medications not on the approved FDA list, medications with a narrow therapeutic range, psychotherapeutic medications and look-alike/sound-alike medications and those new to the market or new to the hospital.

All medication orders (except in emergency situations) should be reviewed for appropriateness by a pharmacist before the first dose is dispensed.

Review of medication orders should include:

- Therapeutic appropriateness of a patient's medication regimen;

- Therapeutic duplication in the patient's medication regimen;

- Appropriateness of the drug, dose, frequency, route and method of administration;

- Real or potential medication-medication, medication-food, medication-laboratory test and medication-disease interactions;

- Real or potential allergies or sensitivities;
- Variation from organizational criteria for use

- Other contraindications;

The effects of medication(s) on patients are monitored to assure medication therapy is appropriate and minimizes the occurrence of adverse events. That monitoring process includes:

- Clinical and laboratory data to evaluate the efficacy of medication therapy to anticipate or evaluate toxicity and adverse effects;

- Physical signs and clinical symptoms relevant to the patient's medication therapy;

- Assessing the patient's own perceptions about side effects, and, when appropriate, perceived efficacy.

Sterile products should be prepared and labeled in a suitable environment by appropriately trained and qualified personnel.

The pharmacy should participate in hospital decisions about emergency medication kits. The supply and provision of emergency medications stored in the kits must be consistent with standards of practice and appropriate for a specified age group or disease treatment as well as consistent with applicable Federal and State laws.

The pharmacy should be involved in the evaluation, use and monitoring of drug delivery systems, administration devices and automated drug-dispensing machines? The evaluation and monitoring should include the potential for medication errors.

There must be a process to report serious adverse drug reactions to the FDA in accordance with the MedWatch program?

There is a policy that addresses the use of medications brought into the hospital by patients or their families.

There is a process and policy to ensure that investigational medications are safety controlled and administered. Procedures for the use of investigational medications include the following: A written process for reviewing, approving, supervising and monitoring investigational medications specifying that when pharmacy services are provided, the pharmacy controls the storage, dispensing, labeling, and distribution of the investigational medication.

Medications dispensed by the hospital are retrieved when recalled or discontinued by the manufacturer or the Food and Drug Administration (FDA) for safety reasons.

The hospital pharmacy must ensure that medication orders are accurate and that medications are administered as ordered. The pharmacy should have a system to reconcile medications that are not administered, that remain in the patient's medication drawer, slot, etc., when the pharmacy inventories patient medications or restocks patient medications. The pharmacy should determine the reason the medications were not used. For example, did the patient refuse the medication, was there a clinical or treatment reason the medication was not used, or was the medication not used due to an error?

Survey Procedures §482.25(b)

- Are there limits on the number of possible concentrations for a medication, particularly high-alert drugs like morphine and heparin?

- Is access to concentrated solutions (e.g. potassium chloride, sodium chloride solutions greater than 0.9%) restricted?

- Are questions regarding the order resolved with the prescriber and a written notation of these discussions documented in the patient's medical record or pharmacy copy of the prescriber's order?

- Identify and assess the quality assurance procedures for the preparation of sterile products.

- Is appropriate monitoring of medication therapy being conducted?

- Is the pharmacy involved in the evaluation, use and monitoring of drug delivery systems, administration devices and automated drug dispensing machines? The evaluation and monitoring should include the potential for medication errors.

- Is there a process to report serious adverse drug reactions to the Federal MedWatch program?

- Review the procedures established to prevent unauthorized usage and distribution. These procedures must provide for an accounting of the receipt and disposition of drugs subject to the Comprehensive Drug Abuse Prevention and Control Act of 1970.

- Are medication storage areas periodically inspected to make sure medications are properly stored?

- Does the hospital retrieve and remove medications available or patient use when the hospital has been informed of a drug recall? Does the recall include notification of patients that have been impacted and those that would order, dispense or administer the medication?

A-0501
(Rev. 37, Issued: 10-17-08; Effective/Implementation Date: 10-17-08)

§482.25(b)(1) - All compounding, packaging, and dispensing of drugs and biologicals must be under the supervision of a pharmacist and performed consistent with State and Federal laws.

Interpretive Guidelines §482.25(b)(1)

All compounding, packaging, and dispensing of drugs and biologicals must be conducted by a registered pharmacist or under the supervision of a registered pharmacist and performed consistent with State and Federal laws.

Medications must be prepared safely. Safe preparation procedures could include:

- Only the pharmacy compounds or admixes all sterile medications, intravenous admixtures, or other drugs except in emergencies or when not feasible (for example, when the product's stability is short).

- Whenever medications are prepared, staff uses safety materials and equipment while preparing hazardous medications.

- Wherever medications are prepared, staff uses techniques to assure accuracy in medication preparation.

- Whenever medications are prepared, staff uses appropriate techniques to avoid contamination during medication preparation, which include but are not limited to the following:

  o Using clean or sterile technique as appropriate;

  o Maintaining clean, uncluttered, and functionally separate areas for product preparation to minimize the possibility of contamination;

  o Using a laminar airflow hood or other appropriate environment while preparing any intravenous (IV) admixture in the pharmacy, any sterile product made from non-sterile ingredients, or any sterile product that will not be used with 24 hours; and

  o Visually inspecting the integrity of the medications.

Medications should be dispensed in a manner that is safe and meets the needs of the patient:

- Quantities of medications are dispensed which minimize diversion and potential adverse events while meeting the needs of the patient;

- Medications are dispensed in a timely manner. The hospital must have a system that ensures that medication orders get to the pharmacy and medications get back to patients promptly.

- Whenever possible, medications are dispensed in the most ready to administer form available from the manufacturer or, if feasible, in unit dose that have been repackaged by the pharmacy;

- The hospital consistently uses the same dose packaging system, or, if a different system is used, provides education about the use of the dose packaging system; and

- All concerns, issues or questions are clarified with the individual prescriber before dispensing.

Survey Procedures §482.25(b)(1)

- Determine that only pharmacists or pharmacy supervised personnel compound, label and dispense drugs or biologicals in accordance with State and Federal laws and regulations and as accepted national principles by:

  o Reviewing policies and procedures;

  o Interviewing pharmacy and hospital staff to determine how drugs and biologicals are prepared and dispensed;

  o Observing on site dispensing and compounding operations (if applicable);

  o Reviewing records of drugs and biologicals removed from the pharmacy by non-pharmacy personnel; and

  o Inspecting drug storage areas.

- Verify through interviews of pharmacy and hospital staff, observation of on-site dispensing operations, inspection and review of hospital records that compounding, dispensing and packaging of drugs and biologicals are performed under the supervision of a pharmacist, in accordance with applicable laws and in a manner to promote patient safety.

A-0502
(Rev. 37, Issued: 10-17-08; Effective/Implementation Date: 10-17-08)

§482.25(b)(2)(i) - All drugs and biologicals must be kept in a secure area, and locked when appropriate.

Interpretive Guidelines §482.25(b)(2)(i)

A secure area means that drugs and biologicals are stored in a manner to prevent unmonitored access by unauthorized individuals. Drugs and biologicals must not be stored in areas that are readily accessible to unauthorized persons. For example, if medications are kept in a private office, or other area where patients and visitors are not allowed without the supervision or presence of a health care professional (for example, ambulatory infusion), they are considered secure. Areas restricted to authorized personnel only would generally be considered "secure areas." If there is evidence of tampering or diversion, or if medication security otherwise becomes a problem, the hospital is expected to evaluate its current medication control policies and procedures, and implement the necessary systems and processes to ensure that the problem is corrected, and that patient health and safety are maintained. (71 FR 68689)

All controlled substances must be locked. Hospitals are permitted flexibility in the storage of non-controlled drugs and biologicals when delivering care to patients, and in the safeguarding of drugs and biologicals to prevent tampering or diversion. An area in which staff are actively providing care to patients or preparing to receive patients, i.e., setting up for procedures before the arrival of a patient, would generally be considered a secure area. When a patient care area is not staffed, **both** controlled and non-controlled substances are expected to be locked.

Generally labor and delivery suites and critical care units are staffed and actively providing patient care around the clock, and, therefore, considered secure. However, hospital policies and procedures are expected to ensure that these areas are secure, with entry and exit limited to appropriate staff, patients and visitors.

The operating room suite is considered secure when the suite is staffed and staff are actively providing patient care. When the suite is not in use (e.g., weekends, holidays and after hours), it would not be considered secure. A hospital may choose to lock the entire suite, lock non-mobile carts containing drugs and biologicals, place mobile carts in a locked room, or otherwise lock drugs and biologicals in a secure area. If an individual operating room is not in use, the hospital is expected to lock non-mobile carts, and ensure mobile carts are in a locked room. (71FR 68689)

This regulation gives hospitals the flexibility to integrate patient self-administration of non-controlled drugs and biologicals into their practices as appropriate. When a hospital allows a patient to self-administer selected drugs and biologicals, the hospital authorizes the patient to have access to these medications. This regulation is consistent with the current practice of giving patients access at the bedside to urgently needed medications, such as nitroglycerine tablets and inhalers. It supports the current practice of placing selected nonprescription medications at the bedside for the patient's use, such as lotions and creams, and rewetting eye drops. Hospitals are expected to address patient self-administration of non-controlled drugs and biologicals in their policies and procedures. This regulation supports hospital development, in collaboration with the medical staff and the nursing and pharmacy departments, of formal patient medication self-administration programs for select populations of patients, including hospital policies and procedures necessary to ensure patient safety and security of medications. The policies and procedures are expected to include measures to ensure the security of bedside drugs and biologicals. They are also expected to address both the competence of the patient to self-administer drugs and biologicals as well as patient education regarding self-administration of drugs and biologicals. (71FR 68689)

Due to their mobility, mobile nursing medication carts, anesthesia carts, epidural carts and other medication carts containing drugs or biologicals (hereafter, all referred to as "carts") must be locked in a secure area when not in use. Hospital policies and procedures are expected to address the security and monitoring of carts, locked or unlocked, containing drugs and biologicals in all patient care areas to ensure their safe storage and to ensure patient safety. (71 FR 68689)

Medication automated distribution units with security features, such as logon and password or biometric identification, are considered to be locked, since they can only be accessed by authorized personnel who are permitted access to the medications. Such units must be stored in a secure area.

Survey Procedures §482.25(b)(2)(i)

- Review hospital policies and procedures governing the security of drugs and biologicals to determine whether they provide for securing and locking as appropriate.

- Review hospital policies and procedures governing patient self-administration of drugs and biologicals.

- Observe whether medications in various areas of the hospital are stored in a secure area, and locked when appropriate.

- Determine that security features in automated medication distribution units are implemented and actively maintained, e.g., that access authorizations are regularly updated to reflect changes in personnel, assignments, etc.

- Interview staff to determine whether policies and procedures to restrict access to authorized personnel are implemented and effective.

- Interview patients and staff to determine whether policies and procedures regarding patient self-administration of drugs and biologicals are implemented and effective.

A-0503
(Rev. 37, Issued: 10-17-08; Effective/Implementation Date: 10-17-08)

§482.25(b)(2)(ii) - Drugs listed in Schedules II, III, IV, and V of the Comprehensive Drug Abuse Prevention and Control Act of 1970 must be kept locked within a secure area.

Interpretive Guidelines §482.25(b)(2)(ii)

All Schedule II, III, IV, and V drugs must be kept locked within a secure area. A secure area means the drugs and biologicals are stored in a manner to prevent unmonitored access by unauthorized individuals. Medication automated distribution units with logon and password/biometric identification are considered to be locked, since they can only be accessed by authorized personnel who are permitted access to Schedule II – V medications.

Mobile nursing medication carts, anesthesia carts, epidural carts and other medication carts containing Schedule II, III, IV, and V drugs must be locked within a secure area.

Survey Procedures §482.25(b)(2)(ii)

- Determine whether there is a hospital policy and procedure that requires Schedule II, III, IV, and V drugs to be kept in a locked storage area.

- Observe in various parts of the hospital whether Schedule II, III, IV and V drugs are locked and stored in a secure area..

- Determine whether security features in automated medication distribution units are implemented and actively maintained, e.g., that access authorizations are regularly updated to reflect changes in personnel, assignments, etc.

- Interview staff to determine whether policies and procedures to restrict access to authorized personnel are implemented and effective.

A-0504
(Rev. 37, Issued: 10-17-08; Effective/Implementation Date: 10-17-08)

§482.25(b)(2)(iii) - Only authorized personnel may have access to locked areas.

Interpretive Guidelines §482.25(b)(2)(iii)

The hospital must assure that only authorized personnel may have access to locked areas where drugs and biologicals are stored.

A hospital has the flexibility to define which personnel have access to locked areas, based on the hospital's needs as well as State and local law. For example, a hospital could include within its definition of "authorized personnel" ancillary support personnel, such as engineering, housekeeping staff, orderlies and security personnel as necessary to perform their assigned duties. The hospital's policies and procedures must specifically address how "authorized personnel" are defined for purposes of this section. It is not necessary for the policy to name specific authorized individuals, but the policy should be clear in describing the categories of personnel who have authorized access, as well as whether there are different levels of access authorized in different areas of the hospital, or at different times of day, or for different classes of drugs and biologicals, etc.

The hospital's policies and procedures must also address how it prevents unauthorized personnel from gaining access to locked areas where drugs and biologicals are stored. Whenever unauthorized personnel have access, or could gain access, to those locked areas, the hospital is not in compliance with this requirement and is expected to re-evaluate and tighten its security measures.

Survey Procedures §482.25(b)(2)(iii)

- Determine whether there is a hospital policy and procedure defining authorized personnel that are permitted access to locked areas where drugs and biologicals are stored.

- Determine whether there is a hospital policy and procedure for limiting access to locked storage areas to authorized personnel only.

- Observe whether or not access to locked storage areas is limited to personnel authorized by the hospital's policy.

A-0505
(Rev. 37, Issued: 10-17-08; Effective/Implementation Date: 10-17-08)

§482.25(b)(3) - Outdated, mislabeled, or otherwise unusable drugs and biologicals must not be available for patient use.

Interpretive Guidelines §482.25(b)(3)

The hospital must have a pharmacy labeling, inspection, and inventory management system that ensures that outdated, mislabeled, or otherwise unusable drugs and biologicals are not available for patient use.

Survey Procedures §482.25(b)(3)

- Spot-check the labels of individual drug containers to verify that they conform to State laws, and/or contain the following minimal information:

  o Each patient's individual drug container bears his/her full name, the prescriber's name, and strength and quantity of the drug dispensed. Appropriate accessory and cautionary statements are included as well as the expiration date.

  o Each floor stock container bears the name and strength of the drug, lot and control number of equivalent, expiration date.

- If the unit dose system is utilized, verify that each single unit dose package bears name and strength of the drug, lot and control number equivalent, and expiration date.

- Inspect patient-specific and floor stock medications to identify expired, mislabeled or unusable medications.

A-0506
(Rev. 37, Issued: 10-17-08; Effective/Implementation Date: 10-17-08)

§482.25(b)(4) - When a pharmacist is not available, drugs and biologicals must be removed from the pharmacy or storage area only by personnel designated in the policies of the medical staff and pharmaceutical service, in accordance with Federal and State law.

Interpretive Guidelines §482.25(b)(4)

Routine after-hours access to the pharmacy by non-pharmacists for access to medication should be minimized and eliminated as much as possible. The use of well-designed night cabinets, after-hours medication carts, and other methods may preclude the need for non-pharmacist to enter the pharmacy. Policies and procedures should be consistent with Federal and State Law.

If an urgent or emergent patient need occurs, the hospital must be able to provide medications to the patients in its facility.

The hospital must have a process for providing medications to meet patient needs when the pharmacy is closed.

When non-pharmacist health care professionals are allowed by law and regulation to obtain medications after the pharmacy is closed, the following safeguards are applied:

- Access is limited to a set of medications that has been approved by the hospital. These medications can be stored in a night cabinet, automated storage and distribution device, or a limited section of the pharmacy.

- Only trained, designated prescribers and nurses are permitted access to medications.

- Quality control procedures (such as an independent second check by another individual or a secondary verification built into the system, such as bar coding) are in place to prevent medication retrieval errors.

- The hospital arranges for a qualified pharmacist to be available either on-call or at another location (for example, at another organization that has 24-hour pharmacy service) to answer questions or provides medications beyond those accessible to non-pharmacy staff.

- This process is evaluated on an on-going basis to determine the medications accessed routinely and the causes of accessing the pharmacy after hours.
- Changes are implemented as appropriate to reduce the amount of times non-pharmacist health care professionals are obtaining medications after the pharmacy is closed.

Survey Procedures §482.25(b)(4)

- Determine through pharmacy records that when the pharmacist is not available, drugs are removed from the pharmacy (drug storage area) only by a designated individual (in accordance with State law if applicable) and only in amounts sufficient for immediate therapeutic needs.

- Review policies and procedures to determine who is designated to remove drugs and biologicals from the pharmacy or storage area and the amount a non-pharmacist may remove in the absence of a pharmacist. The individual(s) designated should be identified by name and qualifications.

- Determine that a system is in place that accurately documents the removal of medications (type and quantity) from either the pharmacy or the after hours supply.

- Determine that the pharmacist reviews all medication removal activity and correlates the removal with current medication orders in the patient medication profile.

- Determine if the pharmacist routinely reviews the contents of the after-hours supply to determine if it is adequate to meet the after-hours needs of the hospital.

A-0507
(Rev. 37, Issued: 10-17-08; Effective/Implementation Date: 10-17-08)

§482.25(b)(5) - Drugs and biologicals not specifically prescribed as to time or number of doses must automatically be stopped after a reasonable time that is predetermined by the medical staff.

Interpretive Guidelines §482.25(b)(5)

In accordance with accepted standards of practice, the medical staff, in coordination and consultation with the pharmacy service, determines and establishes the reasonable time to automatically stop orders for drugs and biologicals not specifically prescribed as to time or number of doses. The hospital must implement, monitor, and enforce this automatic stop system.

Survey Procedures §482.25(b)(5)

Review policies and procedures to determine that there is a protocol established by the medical staff to discontinue and review patients' medical records to determine compliance with stop-order policy.

A-0508
(Rev. 84, Issued: 06-07-13, Effective: 06-07-13, Implementation: 06-07-13)

§482.25(b)(6) - Drug administration errors, adverse drug reactions, and incompatibilities must be immediately reported to the attending physician and, if appropriate, to the hospital's quality assessment and performance improvement program .

Interpretive Guidelines §482.25(b)(6)

Hospitals are required to ensure that the attending physician is made immediately aware of drug administration errors, adverse drug reactions, and incompatibilities. When the attending physician is unavailable, the covering physician must be notified. When the covering physician must be notified, the patient's attending physician must be notified as soon as he/she is available. In addition, when appropriate, such events must also be reported to the hospital-wide Quality Assessment and Performance Improvement (QAPI) program.

The hospital must adopt policies and procedures that identify the types of events that must be reported immediately to the attending physician, as well as those to be reported to the QAPI program.

- Drug administration error:

  The National Coordinating Council Medication Error Reporting and Prevention definition of a medication error is "Any preventable event that may cause or lead to inappropriate medication use or patient harm while the medication is in the control of the health care professional, patient, or consumer. Such events may be related to professional practice, health care products, procedures, and systems, including prescribing; order communication; product labeling, packaging, and nomenclature; compounding; dispensing; distribution; administration; education; monitoring; and use." In the context of this regulation, however, "drug administration error" is limited to those errors in administration that actually reach the patient, i.e., a medication actually is administered to a patient when it should not be, or the wrong dose is administered, or the wrong root of administration is used, etc., or a medication that should have been administered to the patient has not been administered in a timely manner, as discussed in the medication administration standard at 42 CFR 482.23(c).

- Adverse drug reaction:

  The American Society of Health-System Pharmacists (ASHP) defines an adverse drug reaction (ADR) as "Any unexpected, unintended, undesired, or excessive response to a drug that:

  1. Requires discontinuing the drug (therapeutic or diagnostic)
  2. Requires changing the drug therapy
  3. Requires modifying the dose (except for minor dosage adjustments)
  4. Necessitates admission to a hospital
  5. Prolongs stay in a health care facility
  6. Necessitates supportive treatment
  7. Significantly complicates diagnosis
  8. Negatively affects prognosis, or
  9. Results in temporary or permanent harm, disability, or death.

  Consistent with the definition, an allergic reaction (an immunologic hypersensitivity occurring as the result of unusual sensitivity to a drug) and an idiosyncratic reaction (an abnormal susceptibility to a drug that is peculiar to the individual) are also considered ADRs."

- Drug incompatibilities

A drug incompatibility occurs when drugs interfere with one another chemically or physiologically. Drugs known to be incompatible must not be mixed, administered together, or administered within a timeframe where they will interfere with each other.

When IV medications are administered with known incompatibilities, an error has occurred and it needs to be reported to the attending physician immediately. Any unexpected reaction that occurs between IV medications not previously identified as incompatible also needs to be reported.

Hospitals can minimize the risk of administering incompatible medications by making available pertinent resources, such as drug incompatibility charts and online incompatibility references. The incompatibility information needs to be readily available to staff administering medications. The information needs to be kept up-to-date as the information is frequently updated by drug manufacturers.

The immediate reporting requirement applies to drug administration errors, adverse drug reactions or incompatibilities that have harmed or have the potential to harm the patient. If the outcome of the drug administration error is unknown, the physician must also be notified without delay.

Drug administration errors that result in no or insignificant harm to the patient must also be documented in the medical record but do not require immediate reporting to the attending physician. For example, if an analgesic dose is missed during the night shift, it can be reported first thing in the morning. Hospital staff is expected to use their clinical judgment, based on patient presentation and assessment in accordance with hospital policy and procedures, to determine whether immediate reporting is required.

On the other hand, for purposes of reporting to the hospital's QAPI program, hospitals must, in accordance with the requirements of the QAPI CoP at 42 CFR 482.21(c)(2), track and report not only the errors that cause or risk harm to the patient, but also those which do not. Such "near misses" and suspected ADRs may reveal important information about systems vulnerabilities that the hospital should address in order to avoid events that result in harm.

Hospitals must establish policies and procedures for reporting of medication errors, ADRs, and incompatibilities, and ensure that staff is aware of the reporting process. For those events that require immediate reporting, the hospital's policies must establish timeframes for reporting that are based on the clinical effect of the error on the patient.

To improve staff willingness to report medication error incidents, hospitals are encouraged to adopt a non-punitive approach that focuses on system issues rather than individual health care professionals. A non-punitive approach is likely to encourage reporting by those who otherwise may fear retribution or hospital disciplinary action.

In addition to employing broad definitions of medication errors and ADRs for QAPI tracking purposes and encouraging the reporting of medication errors, ADRs and drug incompatibilities, the hospital must take additional steps to identify these events as part of its QAPI program where medical errors and adverse patient events are measured, analyzed and tracked. Reliance solely on incident reporting fails to identify the majority of errors and adverse reactions. Proactive identification includes observation of medication passes, concurrent and retrospective review of a patient's clinical records, ADR surveillance team, implementation of medication usage evaluations for high-alert drugs, and identification of indicator drugs that, when ordered, automatically generate a drug regimen review for a potential adverse drug event.

The hospital must have a method by which to measure the effectiveness of its systems for identifying and reporting to the QAPI program medication errors and ADRs. Such methods could include use of established benchmarks for the size and scope of services provided by the hospital, or studies on reporting rates published in peer-reviewed journals. Hospitals are encouraged, and may be required by State law, to participate in statewide and national reporting of drug administration errors, adverse drug reactions, and incompatibilities. National organizations include, but are not limited to, the Food and Drug Administration's (FDA) MedWatch Reporting Program and the Institute for Safe Medication Practices (ISMP) Medication Errors Reporting Program.

Survey Procedures §482.25(b)(6)

- Does the hospital have policies and procedures that define medications errors, ADRs, and drug incompatibilities? Do they address the circumstances under which they must be reported immediately to the attending physician, as well as to the hospital's QAPI program? Do they address how reporting is to occur?

- Are all medication errors and suspected ADRs promptly recorded in the patient's medical record, including those not subject to immediate reporting?

- If upon review of a sample of records, a suspected ADR or medication error is identified, determine if it was reported immediately to the attending or covering physician, in accordance with the hospital's written policies and procedures. If it is reported to a covering physician, determine if it was also reported to the attending physician when he/she became available.

- Ask hospital staff what they do when they become aware of a medication error, ADR or drug incompatibility. Are staff aware of and do they follow the hospital's policy and procedures?

- Ask hospital staff how they manage drug incompatibilities. What tools do they use in the clinical setting to minimize the risk of incompatibilities? How is the information related to drug incompatibilities made available to the clinical staff administering IV medications (posters, online tools, etc.)? How often is the information updated to ensure accuracy?

- Interview hospital staff to ascertain awareness of the hospital's policy on reporting and documentation of medication errors and adverse drug reactions.

- How does information regarding medication errors, adverse drug reactions, and incompatibilities get reported to the hospital QAPI program? Ask staff to speak to the process.

- For QAPI reporting purposes, is the hospital's definition of an ADR and medication error based on national standards?

A-0509
(Rev. 37, Issued: 10-17-08; Effective/Implementation Date: 10-17-08)

§482.25(b)(7) - Abuses and losses of controlled substances must be reported, in accordance with applicable Federal and State laws, to the individual responsible for the pharmaceutical service, and to the chief executive officer, as appropriate.

Survey Procedures §482.25(b)(7)

- Interview the pharmacists, or pharmacy employees to determine their understanding of the controlled drug policies.

- Conduct a spot check of drug use and other inventory records to ensure that drugs are properly accounted for.

- Review reports of pharmaceutical services to determine if there are reported problems with controlled drugs and what actions have been taken to correct the situation.

- Interview the Pharmacy Director, pharmacist and pharmacy employees to determine their understanding of the controlled drug policies. Is there a policy and procedure for handling controlled drug discrepancies?

- Review reports of pharmaceutical services to determine if there are reported problems with controlled drugs and what actions have been taken to correct the situation.

- Determine if controlled drug losses were reported to appropriate authorities in accordance with State and Federal laws.

A-0510

(Rev. 37, Issued: 10-17-08; Effective/Implementation Date: 10-17-08)

§482.25(b)(8) - Information relating to drug interactions and information of drug therapy, side effects, toxicology, dosage, indications for use, and routes of administration must be available to the professional staff.
Interpretive Guidelines §482.25(b)(8)

The facility has immediately available sufficient texts and other resources on drug therapy. The pharmacist also should be readily available by telephone or other means to discuss drug therapy, interactions, side effects, dosage etc., with practitioners to assist in drug selection and with nursing personnel to assist in the identification of drug-induced problems.

Survey Procedures §482.25(b)(8)

- Examine the sources of drug information available at the nursing station and/or drug storage area and determine if they are current.

- Determine whether staff development programs on drug therapy are available to facility staff to cover such topics as new drugs added to the formulary, how to resolve drug therapy problems, and other general information as the need arises.

A-0511

(Rev. 37, Issued: 10-17-08; Effective/Implementation Date: 10-17-08)

§482.25(b)(9) - A formulary system must be established by the medical staff to assure quality pharmaceuticals at reasonable costs.

Interpretive Guidelines §482.25(b)(9)

The medical staff must establish a formulary system. The formulary lists medications for dispensing or administration that the hospital maintains or that are readily available. In accordance with accepted standards of practice, the medical staff, in consultation with the pharmacy service, should develop written criteria for determining what medications are available for dispensing or administration. At a minimum, the criteria include the indication for use, effectiveness, risks (including propensity for medication errors, abuse potential, and sentinel events), and costs.

Processes and mechanisms should be established to monitor patient responses to a newly added medication before the medication is made available for dispensing or administration within the hospital.

Medications designated as available for dispensing or administration are reviewed periodically based on emerging safety and efficacy information.

The hospital should have processes to approve and procure medications that are not on the hospital's medication list.

The hospital should have processes to address medication shortages and outages, including the following:

- Communicating with appropriate prescribers and staff;

- Developing approved substitution protocols;

- Educating appropriate LIPs, appropriate health care professionals, and staff about these protocols; and

- Obtaining medications in the event of a disaster.

Survey Procedures §482.25(b)(9)

- Interview the pharmacist to determine that the medical staff has established a formulary that lists drugs that actually are available in the hospital.

- Interview the Pharmacy Director to determine that there is a process for creation and periodic review of a formulary system.

- Determine that the formulary lists drugs that are available.

A-0528

(Rev. 37, Issued: 10-17-08; Effective/Implementation Date: 10-17-08)

§482.26 Condition of Participation: Radiologic Services

The hospital must maintain, or have available, diagnostic radiologic services. If therapeutic services are also provided, they, as well as the diagnostic services, must meet professionally approved standards for safety and personnel qualifications.

Interpretive Guidelines §482.26

The hospital must maintain, or have available, diagnostic radiological services according to the needs of their patients. These services must be maintained or available at all times. All radiological services provided by the hospital, including diagnostic and, if offered, therapeutic, must be provided in accordance with acceptable standards of practice and must meet professionally approved standards for safety and personnel qualifications. The scope and complexity of radiological services offered should be specified in writing and approved by the medical staff and governing body.

Acceptable standards of practice include maintaining compliance with applicable Federal and State laws, regulations and guidelines governing radiological services, including facility licensure and/or certification requirements, as well as any standards and recommendations promoted by nationally recognized professional organizations (e.g., the American Medical Association, American College of Radiology, etc).

Radiological services may be provided by the hospital directly or through a contractual arrangement. The same standards apply whether the service is provided by the hospital directly or under contract. Diagnostic radiology services provided under contract may be provided either on the hospital premises or in an adjacent or other nearby, readily accessible facility.

The hospital's radiological services, including any contracted services, must be integrated into its hospital-wide QAPI program.

Survey Procedures §482.26

Verify that radiological services are integrated into the hospital-wide QAPI program.

A-0529

(Rev. 37, Issued: 10-17-08; Effective/Implementation Date: 10-17-08)

§482.26(a) Standard: Radiologic Services

The hospital must maintain, or have available, radiologic services according to the needs of the patients.

Interpretive Guidelines §482.26(a)

The scope and complexity of radiology services provided must meet the needs of the patients.

Radiological services may be provided by the hospital directly or through a contractual arrangement. The same standards apply whether the service is provided by the hospital directly or under contract. Diagnostic radiology services provided under contract may be provided either on the hospital premises or in an adjacent or other nearby, readily accessible facility.

Survey Procedures §482.26(a)

Verify that the hospital maintains, or has available, organized radiology services that meet the needs of the patients, are provided in accordance with accepted standards of practice, and are maintained or available at all times to meet the patient needs.

A-0535

(Rev. 37, Issued: 10-17-08; Effective/Implementation Date: 10-17-08)
§482.26(b) Standard: Safety for Patients and Personnel

The radiologic services, particularly ionizing radiology procedures, must be free from hazards for patients and personnel.

Interpretive Guidelines §482.26(b)

The hospital must adopt and implement policies and procedures that provide safety for patients and personnel.

Survey Procedures §482.26(b)

Observe locations where radiological services are provided. Are they safe for patients and personnel? Are any hazards to patients or personnel observed?

A-0536

§482.26(b)(1) - Proper safety precautions must be maintained against radiation hazards. This includes adequate shielding for patients, personnel, and facilities, as well as appropriate storage, use and disposal of radioactive materials.

Interpretive Guidelines §482.26(b)(1)

The hospital policies must contain safety standards for at least:

- Adequate shielding for patients, personnel and facilities;

- Labeling of radioactive materials, waste, and hazardous areas;

- Transportation of radioactive materials between locations within the hospital;

- Security of radioactive materials, including determining who may have access to radioactive materials and controlling access to radioactive materials;

- Testing of equipment for radiation hazards;

- Maintenance of personal radiation monitoring devices;

- Proper storage of radiation monitoring badges when not in use;

- Storage of radio nuclides and radio pharmaceuticals as well as radioactive waste; and

- Disposal of radio nuclides, unused radio pharmaceuticals, and radioactive waste.

- Methods of identifying pregnant patients.

The hospital must implement and ensure compliance with its established safety standards.

Survey Procedures §482.26(b)(1)

- Verify that patient shielding (aprons, etc) are properly maintained and routinely inspected by the hospital.

- Verify that hazardous materials are stored properly in a safe manner.

- Observe areas where testing is done for violations in safety precautions.

A-0537

(Rev. 37, Issued: 10-17-08; Effective/Implementation Date: 10-17-08)

§482.26(b)(2) - Periodic inspection of equipment must be made and hazards identified must be properly corrected.

Interpretive Guidelines §482.26(b)(2)

The hospital must have policies and procedures in place to ensure that periodic inspections of radiology equipment are conducted, current and that problems identified are corrected in a timely manner. The hospital must ensure that equipment is inspected in accordance with manufacturer's instructions, Federal and State laws, regulations, and guidelines, and hospital policy. The hospital must have a system in place, qualified employees or contracts, to correct hazards. The hospital must be able to demonstrate current inspection and proper correction of all hazards.

Survey Procedures §482.26(b)(2)

- Review the inspection records (logs) to verify that periodic inspections are conducted in accordance with manufacturer's instructions, Federal and State laws, regulations, and guidelines and hospital policy.

- Determine that any problems identified are properly corrected in a timely manner.

A-0538

(Rev. 37, Issued: 10-17-08; Effective/Implementation Date: 10-17-08)

§482.26(b)(3) - Radiation workers must be checked periodically, by the use of exposure meters or badge tests, for amount of radiation exposure.

Interpretive Guidelines §482.26(b)(3)

The requirement that "radiation workers must be checked periodically, by use of exposure meters or badge tests, for amount of radiation exposure" would include radiological services personnel, as well as, other hospital employees who may be regularly exposed to radiation due to working near radiation sources. This could include personnel such as certain nursing and maintenance staff.

Survey Procedures §482.26(b)(3)

- Verify that the hospital requires periodic checks on all radiology personnel and any other hospital staff exposed to radiation and that the personnel are knowledgeable about radiation exposure for month, year, and cumulative/entire working life.

- Observe that appropriate staff have a radiation-detecting device and that they appropriately wear their radiation detecting device.

- Review records to verify that periodic tests of radiology personnel by exposure meters or test badges are performed.

A-0539

(Rev. 37, Issued: 10-17-08; Effective/Implementation Date: 10-17-08)

§482.26(b)(4) - Radiologic services must be provided only on the order of practitioners with clinical privileges or, consistent with State law, of other practitioners authorized by the medical staff and the governing body to order the services.

Survey Procedures §482.26(b)(4)

Review medical records to determine that radiological services are provided only on the orders of practitioners with clinical privileges and to practitioners outside the hospital who have been authorized by the medical staff and the governing body to order radiological services, consistent with State law.

A-0545

(Rev. 37, Issued: 10-17-08; Effective/Implementation Date: 10-17-08)

§482.26(c) Standard: Personnel

Interpretive Guidelines §482.26(c):

The hospital must ensure that specific radiology personnel requirements are met.

A-0546

(Rev. 37, Issued: 10-17-08; Effective/Implementation Date: 10-17-08)

§482.26(c)(1) - A qualified full-time, part-time or consulting radiologist must supervise the ionizing radiology services and must interpret only those radiologic tests that are determined by the medical staff to require a radiologist's specialized knowledge. For purposes of this section, a radiologist is a doctor of medicine or osteopathy who is qualified by education and experience in radiology.

Interpretive Guidelines §482.26(c)(1)

The medical staff must establish, in accordance with this regulation and other Federal and State laws, regulations and guidelines, the qualifications necessary for radiologist appointment to the medical staff.

There must be written policies developed and approved by the medical staff to designate which radiological tests require interpretation by a radiologist.

When telemedicine is used, and the radiologist who interprets radiological tests and the patient are located in different states, the radiologist interpreting the radiological test must be licensed and/or meet the other applicable standards that are required by State or local laws in both the state where the practitioner is located and the state where the patient is located.

Supervision of the radiology services may only be performed by a radiologist who is a member of the medical staff. Supervision should include at least the following:

- Ensuring that radiology reports are signed by the practitioner who interpreted them;
- Assigning duties to radiology personnel appropriate to their level of training, experience, and licensure if applicable;

- Enforcing infection control standards;

- Ensuring that emergency care is provided to patients who experience an adverse reaction to diagnostic agents in the radiology service;

- Ensuring that files, scans, and other image records are kept in a secure area and are readily retrievable; and

- Training radiology staff on how to operate the equipment safely, perform tests offered by the facility and on the management of emergency radiation hazards and accidents.

Survey Procedures §482.26(c)(1)

- Review the radiologist's credentialing file to verify that he/she meets the qualifications established by the medical staff for appointment.

- Review records to determine that a radiologist interprets those tests that have been designated by the medical staff to require interpretation by a qualified radiologist.

- Verify that supervision of the radiology services is restricted to a radiologist who is a member of the medical staff.

A-0547

(Rev. 37, Issued: 10-17-08; Effective/Implementation Date: 10-17-08)

§482.26(c)(2) - Only personnel designated as qualified by the medical staff may use the radiologic equipment and administer procedures.

Interpretive Guidelines §482.26(c)(2)

There should be written policies, developed and approved by the medical staff, consistent with State law, to designate which personnel are qualified to use the radiological equipment and administer procedures.

Survey Procedures §482.26(c)(2)

Determine which staff are using differing pieces of radiological equipment and/or administering patient procedures. Review their personnel folders to determine they meet the qualifications established by the medical staff for the tasks they perform.

A-0553

(Rev. 37, Issued: 10-17-08; Effective/Implementation Date: 10-17-08)

§482.26(d) Standard: Records

Records of radiologic services must be maintained.

Interpretive Guidelines §482.26(d)

The hospital must maintain records for all radiology procedures performed. At a minimum, the records should include copies of reports and printouts, and any films, scans or other image records, as appropriate. The hospital should have written policies and procedures that ensure the integrity of authentication and protect the privacy of radiology records. Patient radiology records are considered patient medical records and the hospital must comply with the medical records CoP (§482.24). The medical records CoP requires that medical records, which would include radiology films, image records, scans, reports, and printouts must be secure, properly stored, be accessible and promptly retrievable for any care, procedure, treatment, or test provided or conducted within the past 5 years.

Survey Procedures §482.26(d)

Determine the hospital's procedures for maintaining radiology records.

A-0554

(Rev. 37, Issued: 10-17-08; Effective/Implementation Date: 10-17-08)

§482.26(d)(1) - The radiologist or other practitioner who performs radiology services must sign reports of his or her interpretations.

Survey Procedures §482.26(d)(1)

Review radiological records to determine that reports are signed by the practitioner who reads and evaluates the roentgenogram.

A-0555

(Rev. 37, Issued: 10-17-08; Effective/Implementation Date: 10-17-08)

§482.26(d)(2) - The hospital must maintain the following for at least 5 years:

(i) Copies of reports and printouts

(ii) Films, scans, and other image records, as appropriate.

Interpretive Guidelines §482.26(d)(2)

Patient radiology records are a type of patient medical record. The hospital must maintain radiology records in compliance with the medical records CoP and this CoP. Medical records, including radiology records, must be maintained for 5 years.

Survey Procedures §482.26(d)(2)

- Verify that the hospital maintains records for at least 5 years.

- Verify that radiology records are maintained in the manner required by the Medical Records CoP.

A-0576

(Rev. 37, Issued: 10-17-08; Effective/Implementation Date: 10-17-08)
§482.27 Condition of Participation: Laboratory Services

The hospital must maintain, or have available, adequate laboratory services to meet the needs of its patients. The hospital must ensure that all laboratory services provided to its patients are performed in a facility certified in accordance with Part 493 of this chapter.

Interpretive Guidelines §482.27

The hospital must maintain or have available laboratory services whenever its patients need those services. The hospital may make laboratory services available directly, through contractual agreements, or through a combination of direct and contractual services. The scope and complexity of the hospital laboratory service must be adequate to meet the needs of its patients. The hospital must maintain, or have available, adequate laboratory services to meet the needs of its patients at each campus or off-campus location of the hospital. All laboratory services, whether direct or contractual, whether conducted in a lab or in another location, must be provided in accordance with Clinical Laboratory Improvement Act (CLIA) requirements. Every hospital laboratory service must be operating under a current CLIA certificate appropriate to the level of services performed.

The hospital's laboratory services, including any contracted services, must be integrated into its hospital-wide QAPI program.

Patient laboratory results and all other laboratory clinical patient records are considered patient medical records and the hospital must comply with the requirements of the Medical Records CoP.

Survey Procedures §482.27

- Determine the total number of laboratories, the location of each laboratory, and every location where laboratory procedures are performed.

- Verify that the laboratory service and all laboratory locations are integrated into the hospital-wide QAPI program.

- If laboratory services are contracted, verify that the review of the quality of those services is integrated into the hospital-wide QAPI program.

A-0582

(Rev. 37, Issued: 10-17-08; Effective/Implementation Date: 10-17-08)

§482.27(a) Standard: - Adequacy of Laboratory Services

The hospital must have laboratory services available, either directly or through a contractual agreement with a certified laboratory that meets requirements of Part 493 of this chapter.

Interpretive Guidelines §482.27(a)

The CLIA certification may be accomplished by having one certificate for the entire hospital's laboratory services, by having one certificate for each laboratory, or by the hospital having a mixture. Whatever the arrangement, all laboratory services must be provided in accordance with CLIA requirements and under a current CLIA certificate, even when those laboratory services take place outside of a lab.

Survey Procedures §482.27(a)

- Determine which services are provided directly by the facility and which are provided through contractual agreements.

- Determine if the referral laboratory is CLIA certified for the appropriate test specialty.

- If the hospital provides laboratory services in multiple locations, verify that all laboratory services are operating under a current CLIA certificate.

- Examine records and determine if the services, including emergency services, are provided in accordance with the hospital's policies.

A-0583

(Rev. 37, Issued: 10-17-08; Effective/Implementation Date: 10-17-08)

§482.27(a)(1) - Emergency laboratory services must be available 24 hours a day.

Interpretive Guidelines §482.27(a)(1)

The hospital must provide emergency laboratory services 24 hours a day, 7 days a week. These onsite emergency services may be provided directly by the hospital or through onsite contracted laboratory services. Emergency lab services include collection, processing, and provision of results to meet a patient's emergency laboratory needs.

In a hospital with multiple hospital campuses, these emergency laboratory services must be available onsite 24/7 at each campus.

The medical staff must determine which laboratory services are to be immediately available to meet the emergency laboratory needs of patients who may be currently at the hospital or those patients who may arrive at the hospital in an emergency condition. The emergency laboratory services (procedures, tests, personnel) available should reflect the scope and complexity of the hospital's operation and be provided in accordance with Federal and State law, regulations and guidelines and acceptable standards of practice.

At a hospital with off-campus locations the medical staff must determine which, if any, laboratory services must be immediately available to meet the emergency laboratory needs of the patients who are likely to seek care at each off-campus location. The emergency laboratory services available must reflect the scope and complexity of the hospital's operations at the location and be provided in accordance with Federal and State law, regulations and guidelines and acceptable standards of practice. The services must be available during the hours of operation of that location.

Survey Procedures §482.27(a)(1)

Review the written description of the emergency laboratory services. Review records (including accession records, worksheets, and test reports) to verify the 24-hour availability of emergency services and that those services are provided when required.

A-0584

(Rev. 37, Issued: 10-17-08; Effective/Implementation Date: 10-17-08)

§482.27(a)(2) - A written description of services provided must be available to the medical staff.

Survey Procedures §482.27(a)(2)

- Verify the existence of a written description of the laboratory services provided, including those furnished on routine and stat basis (either directly or under an arrangement with an outside facility).

- Verify that the description of services is accurate and current.

A-0585

(Rev. 37, Issued: 10-17-08; Effective/Implementation Date: 10-17-08)

§482.27(a)(3) - The laboratory must make provision for proper receipt and reporting of tissue specimens.

Interpretive Guidelines §482.27(a)(3)

The laboratory must have written instructions for the collection, preservation, transportation, receipt, and reporting of tissue specimen results.

Survey Procedures §482.27(a)(3)

Review tissue records (accession records, worksheets, and test reports) to determine whether the laboratory follows the written protocol.

A-0586

(Rev. 37, Issued: 10-17-08; Effective/Implementation Date: 10-17-08)

§482.27(a)(4) - The medical staff and a pathologist must determine which tissue specimens require a macroscopic (gross) examination and which require both macroscopic and microscopic examinations.

Interpretive Guidelines §482.27(a)(4)

Laboratory written policies, approved by the medical staff and a pathologist, must state which tissue specimens require a macroscopic examination and which tissue specimens require both macroscopic and microscopic examination.

Survey Procedures §482.27(a)(4)

- Verify that the hospital has a written policy for examination requirements.

- Review the written policies and tissue reports to assure that tissue specimens are examined in accordance with the written policies.

- Verify that the policies are in accordance with these requirements and other Federal and State laws, regulations, and guidelines.

A-0592

(Rev. 37, Issued: 10-17-08; Effective/Implementation Date: 10-17-08)

§482.27(b) Standard: - Potentially Infectious Blood and Blood Components

(1)   Potentially human immunodeficiency virus (HIV) infectious blood and blood components. Potentially HIV infectious blood and blood components are prior collections from a donor –

(i)   Who tested negative at the time of donation but tests reactive for evidence of HIV infection on a later donation;

(ii)   Who tests positive on the supplemental (additional, more specific) test or other follow-up testing required by FDA; and

(iii)   For whom the timing of seroconversion cannot be precisely estimated.

(2)   Potentially hepatitis C virus (HCV) infectious blood and blood components. Potentially HCV infectious blood and blood components are the blood and blood components identified in 21 CFR 610.47.

(3)   Services furnished by an outside blood collecting establishment. If a hospital regularly uses the services of an outside blood collecting establishment, it must have an agreement with the blood collecting establishment that governs the procurement, transfer, and availability of blood and blood components. The agreement must require that the blood collecting establishment notify the hospital --

(i)   Within 3 calendar days if the blood collecting establishment supplied blood and blood components collected from a donor who tested negative at the time of donation but tests reactive for evidence of HIV or HCV infection on a later donation or who is determined to be at increased risk for transmitting HIV or HCV infection;

(ii)   Within 45 days of the test, of the results of the supplemental (additional, more specific) test for HIV or HCV, as relevant, or other follow-up testing required by FDA;

(iii)   Within 3 calendar days after the blood collecting establishment supplied blood and blood components collected from an infectious donor, whenever records are available, as set forth at 21 CFR 610.48(b)(3).

(4)   Quarantine of blood and blood components pending completion of testing. If the blood collecting establishment (either internal or under an agreement)

notifies the hospital of the reactive HIV or HCV screening test results, the hospital must determine the disposition of the blood or blood component and quarantine all blood and blood components from previous donations in inventory.

    (i)   If the blood collecting establishment notifies the hospital that the result of the supplemental (additional, more specific) test or other follow-up testing required by FDA is negative, absent other informative test results, the hospital may release the blood and blood components from quarantine.

    (ii)   If the blood collecting establishment notifies the hospital that the result of the supplemental (additional, more specific) test or other follow-up testing required by FDA is positive, the hospital must –

        (A)   Dispose of the blood and blood components; and

        (B)   Notify the transfusion recipients as set forth in paragraph (b)(6) of this section.

    (iii)   If the blood collecting establishment notifies the hospital that the result of the supplemental (additional, more specific) test or other follow-up testing required by FDA is indeterminate, the hospital must destroy or label prior collections of blood or blood components held in quarantine as set forth at 21 CFR 610.46(b)(2), 610.47(b)(2), and 610.48(c)(2).

(5)   Recordkeeping by the hospital. The hospital must maintain --

    (i)   Records of the source and disposition of all units of blood and blood components for at least 10 years from the date of disposition in a manner that permits prompt retrieval; and

    (ii)   A fully funded plan to transfer these records to another hospital or other entity if such hospital ceases operation for any reason.

(6)   Patient notification. If the hospital has administered potentially HIV or HCV infectious blood or blood components (either directly through its own blood collecting establishment or under an agreement) or released such blood or blood components to another entity or appropriate individual, the hospital must take the following actions:

    (i)   Make reasonable attempts to notify the patient, or to notify the attending physician who ordered the blood or blood component and ask the physician to notify the patient, or other individual as permitted under paragraph (b)(10) of this section, that potentially HIV or HCV infectious blood or blood components were transfused to the patient and that there may be a need for HIV or HCV testing and counseling.

    (ii)   If the physician is unavailable or declines to make the notification, make reasonable attempts to give this notification to the patient, legal guardian or relative.

    (iii)   Document in the patient's medical record the notification or attempts to give the required notification.

(7)   Time frame for notification.

    (i)   For donors tested on or after February 20, 2008. For notifications resulting from donors tested on or after February 20, 2008 as set forth at 21 CFR 610.46 and 21 CFR 610.47 the notification effort begins when the blood collecting establishment notifies the hospital that it received potentially HIV or HCV infectious blood and blood components. The hospital must make reasonable attempts to give notification over a period of 12 weeks unless--

        (A)   The patient is located and notified; or
        (B)   The hospital is unable to locate the patient and documents in the patient's medical record the extenuating circumstances beyond the hospital's control that caused the notification timeframe to exceed 12 weeks.

    (ii)   For donors tested before February 20, 2008. For notifications from donors tested before February 20, 2008 as set forth at 21 CFR 610.48(b) and (c), the notification effort begins when the blood collecting establishment notifies the hospital that it received potentially HCV infectious blood and blood components. The hospital must make reasonable attempts to give notification and must complete the actions within 1 year of the date on which the hospital received notification from the outside blood collecting establishment.

(8)   Content of notification. The notification must include the following information:

    (i)   A basic explanation of the need for HIV or HCV testing and counseling.

    (ii)   Enough oral or written information so that an informed decision can be made about whether to obtain HIV or HCV testing and counseling.

> (iii)   A list of programs or places where the person can obtain HIV or HCV testing and counseling, including any requirements or restrictions the program may impose.

(9)   Policies and procedures. The hospital must establish policies and procedures for notification and documentation that conform to Federal, State, and local laws, including requirements for the confidentiality of medical records and other patient information.

(10)   Notification to legal representative or relative. If the patient has been adjudged incompetent by a State court, the physician or hospital must notify a legal representative designated in accordance with State law. If the patient is competent, but State law permits a legal representative or relative to receive the information on the patient's behalf, the physician or hospital must notify the patient or his or her legal representative or relative. For possible HIV infectious transfusion recipients that are deceased, the physician or hospital must inform the deceased patient's legal representative or relative. If the patient is a minor, the parents or legal guardian must be notified.

(11)   Applicability. HCV notification requirements resulting from donors tested before February 20, 2008, as set forth at 21 CFR 610.48 will expire on August 24, 2015.

Interpretive Guidelines §482.27(b)

This regulation requires the hospital to have a system in place to take appropriate action when notified that blood or blood components it received are at increased risk of transmitting HIV or HCV.

A-0593

(Rev. 37, Issued: 10-17-08; Effective/Implementation Date: 10-17-08)

§482.27(c) Standard: General blood safety issues. For lookback activities only related to new blood safety issues that are identified after August 24, 2007, hospitals must comply with FDA regulations as they pertain to blood safety issues in the following areas:

(1)   Appropriate testing and quarantining of infectious blood and blood components.

(2)   Notification and counseling of recipients that may have received infectious blood and blood components.

A-0618

(Rev. 37, Issued: 10-17-08; Effective/Implementation Date: 10-17-08)

§482.28 Condition of Participation: Food and Dietetic Services

The hospital must have organized dietary services that are directed and staffed by adequate qualified personnel. However, a hospital that has a contract with an outside food management company may be found to meet this Condition of Participation if the company has a dietician who serves the hospital on a full-time, part-time, or consultant basis, and if the company maintains at least the minimum standards specified in this section and provides for constant liaison with the hospital medical staff for recommendations on dietetic policies affecting patient treatment.

Interpretative Guidelines §482.28

The hospital's food and dietetic services must be organized, directed and staffed in such a manner to ensure that the nutritional needs of the patients are met in accordance with practitioners' orders and acceptable standards of practice.

The hospital should have written policies and procedures that address at least the following:

- Availability of a diet manual and therapeutic diet menus to meet patients' nutritional needs;

- Frequency of meals served;

- System for diet ordering and patient trays delivery;

- Accommodation of non-routine occurrences (e.g., parenteral nutrition (tube feeding), total parenteral nutrition, peripheral parenteral nutrition, change in diet orders, early/late trays, nutritional supplements, etc);

- Integration of the food and dietetic service into the hospital-wide QAPI and Infection Control programs;

- Guidelines for acceptable hygiene practices of food service personnel; and

- Guidelines for kitchen sanitation.

The same standards apply whether the food and dietetic services are provided by the hospital directly, through a contractual agreement, or by off-site vendor.

The hospital must be in compliance with Federal and State licensure requirements for food and dietary personnel as well as food service standards, laws and regulations.

A-0619

(Rev. 37, Issued: 10-17-08; Effective/Implementation Date: 10-17-08)

§482.28(a) Standard: Organization

Interpretive Guidelines §482.28(a):

The hospital must ensure that the specific food and dietetic services organization requirements are met.

A-0620

(Rev. 37, Issued: 10-17-08; Effective/Implementation Date: 10-17-08)

§482.28(a)(1) - The hospital must have a full-time employee who–

> **(i)** Serves as director of the food and dietetic services;
>
> **(ii)** Is responsible for daily management of the dietary services; and
>
> **(iii)** Is qualified by experience or training.

Interpretive Guidelines §482.28(a)(1)

The service director must be a full-time employee who has been granted the authority and delegated responsibility by the hospital's governing body and medical staff for the operation of the dietary services. This authority and delegated responsibility includes, the daily management of the service, implementing training programs for dietary staff, and assuring that established policies and procedures are maintained that address at least the following:

- Safety practices for food handling;

- Emergency food supplies;

- Orientation, work assignments, supervision of work and personnel performance;

- Menu planning, purchasing of foods and supplies, and retention of essential records (e.g., cost, menus, personnel, training records, QAPI reports, etc);

- Service QAPI program.

Additionally, the service director must demonstrate, through education, experience and/or specialized training, the qualifications necessary to manage the service, appropriate to the scope and complexity of the food service operations.

Survey Procedures §482.28(a)(1)

- Verify that the director of the food and dietetic services is a full-time employee.

- Review the service director's job description to verify that it is position-specific and that responsibility and authority for the direction of the food and dietary service has been clearly delineated.
- Review the service director's personnel file to verify that he/she has the necessary education, experience, and training to manage the service, appropriate to the scope and complexity of food service operations.

A-0621

(Rev. 37, Issued: 10-17-08; Effective/Implementation Date: 10-17-08)

§482.28(a)(2) - There must be a qualified dietitian, full-time, part-time or on a consultant basis.

Interpretive Guidelines §482.28(a)(2)

A qualified dietitian must supervise the nutritional aspects of patient care. Responsibilities of a hospital dietitian may include, but are not limited to:

- Approving patient menus and nutritional supplements;

- Patient, family, and caretaker dietary counseling;

- Performing and documenting nutritional assessments and evaluating patient tolerance to therapeutic diets when appropriate;

- Collaborating with other hospital services (e.g., medical staff, nursing services, pharmacy service, social work service, etc) to plan and implement patient care as necessary in meeting the nutritional needs of the patients;

- Maintaining pertinent patient data necessary to recommend, prescribe, or modify therapeutic diets as needed to meet the nutritional needs of the patients.

Qualification is determined on the basis of education, experience, specialized training, State licensure or registration when applicable, and maintaining professional standards of practice.

If the qualified dietitian does not work full-time, and when the dietitian is not available, the hospital must make adequate provisions for dietary consultation that meets the needs of the patients. The frequency of consultation depends on the total number of patients, their nutritional needs and the number of patients requiring therapeutic diets or other nutritional supplementation.

Survey Procedures §482.28(a)(2)

- Review the dietitian's personnel file to determine that he/she is qualified based on education, experience, specialized training, and, if required by State law, is licensed, certified, or registered by the State.

- If the dietitian is not full-time, determine that the number of hours spent working is appropriate to serve the nutritional needs of the patients, and that the hospital makes adequate provisions for a qualified consultant coverage when the dietitian is not available.

A-0622

(Rev. 37, Issued: 10-17-08; Effective/Implementation Date: 10-17-08)

§482.28(a)(3) - There must be administrative and technical personnel competent in their respective duties.

Interpretive Guidelines §482.28(a)(3)

Administrative and technical personnel must be competent in their assigned duties. This competency is demonstrated through education, experience and specialized training appropriate to the task(s) assigned. Personnel files should include documentation that the staff member(s) is competent in their respective duties.

Survey Procedures §482.28(a)(3)

Review personnel files for administrative and technical staff to determine they have appropriate credentials as required and have received adequate training and are competent in their respective duties.

A-0628

(Rev. 37, Issued: 10-17-08; Effective/Implementation Date: 10-17-08)

§482.28(b) Standard: Diets

Menus must meet the needs of the patients.

Interpretive Guidelines §482.28(b)

Menus provided by the hospital must be nutritionally balanced and meet the special needs of the patients. Current menus should be posted in the hospital kitchen. In order to ensure that the hospital is meeting the nutritional needs of its patients, screening criteria should be developed to identify patients at nutritional risk. Once a patient is identified as at altered nutritional status, a nutritional assessment should be performed on the patient. In addition to the initial nutritional assessment, the patient should be re-evaluated as necessary to ensure their ongoing nutritional needs are met. Examples of patients who may require a nutritional assessment include:

- All patients requiring artificial nutrition by any means (i.e., enteral nutrition (tube feeding), total parenteral nutrition, or peripheral parenteral nutrition);

- Patients whose medical condition, surgical intervention, or physical status interferes with their ability to ingest, digest or absorb nutrients;

- Patients whose diagnosis or presenting signs/symptoms indicates a compromised nutritional status (e.g., anorexia nervosa, bulimia, electrolyte imbalances, dysphagia, malabsorption, end stage organ diseases, etc);

- Patients whose medical condition can be adversely affected by their nutritional intake (e.g., diabetes, congestive heart failure, patients taking certain medications, renal diseases, etc).

Patients who refuse the food served should be offered substitutes that are of equal nutritional value in order to meet their basic nutritional needs.

A-0629

(Rev. 37, Issued: 10-17-08; Effective/Implementation Date: 10-17-08)

§482.28(b)(1) - Therapeutic diets must be prescribed by the practitioner or practitioners responsible for the care of the patients.

Interpretive Guidelines §482.28(b)(1)

Therapeutic diets must be:

- Prescribed in writing by the practitioner responsible for the patient's care;

- Documented in the patient's medical record (including documentation about the patient's tolerance to the therapeutic diet as ordered); and

- Evaluated for nutritional adequacy.

In accordance with State law and hospital policy, a dietitian may assess a patient's nutritional needs and provide recommendations or consultations for patients, but the patient's diet must be prescribed by the practitioner responsible for the patient's care.

Survey Procedures §482.28(b)(1)

Verify that therapeutic diet orders are prescribed and authenticated by the practitioner(s) responsible for the care of the patient.

A-0630

(Rev. 37, Issued: 10-17-08; Effective/Implementation Date: 10-17-08)

§482.28(b)(2) - Nutritional needs must be met in accordance with recognized dietary practices and in accordance with orders of the practitioner or practitioners responsible for the care of the patients.

Interpretive Guidelines §482.28(b)(2)

Recognized dietary practices include following current national standards for recommended dietary allowances, i.e., the current Recommended Dietary Allowances (RDA) or the Dietary Reference Intake (DRI) of the Food and Nutrition Board of the National Research Council.

Survey Procedures §482.28(b)(2)

- Ask the hospital to show you what national standard they are following in their menus to meet the nutritional needs of their patients.

- Review patient records to verify that diet orders are provided as prescribed by the practitioner(s) responsible for the care of the patient.

- From the sample patient records, identify patients with special nutritional needs to determine:

  o If their nutritional needs have been met;
  o If appropriate therapeutic diets have been ordered; and

  o As appropriate, if their dietary intake and nutritional status is being monitored.

A-0631

(Rev. 37, Issued: 10-17-08; Effective/Implementation Date: 10-17-08)

§482.28(b)(3) - A current therapeutic diet manual approved by the dietitian and medical staff must be readily available to all medical, nursing, and food service personnel.

Interpretive Guidelines §482.28(b)(3)

The therapeutic diet manual must be approved by the dietitian and the medical staff. The publication or revision date of the approved therapeutic diet manual must not be more than 5 years old. The therapeutic diet manual (or copies of it) must be available to all medical, nursing and food service personnel.

Survey Procedures §482.28(b)(3)

- Determine that the therapeutic diet manual is current, and:

  o Has been approved by both the medical staff and a qualified dietitian;

  o Is readily available to MD/DOs, nursing and food service personnel;

  o Is in accordance with the current national standards, such as RDA or DRI;

  o Includes the different types of therapeutic diets routinely ordered at the hospital; and

  o Is consistently used as guidance for ordering and preparing patient diets.

A-0652

(Rev. 37, Issued: 10-17-08; Effective/Implementation Date: 10-17-08)

§482.30 Condition of Participation: Utilization Review

The hospital must have in effect a utilization review (UR) plan that provides for review of services furnished by the institution and by members of the medical staff to patients entitled to benefits under the Medicare and Medicaid programs.

Interpretive Guidelines §482.30

The Utilization Review CoP is not part of the deemed program for hospitals, per 42 CFR 488.5. As such, State Survey Agencies have jurisdiction over the UR CoP for accredited and non-accredited hospitals.

If the hospital does not satisfy one of the exception criteria at §482.30(a), it must have a UR plan in effect.

The hospital UR plan should include a delineation of the responsibilities and authority for those involved in the performance of UR activities. It should also establish procedures for the review of the medical necessity of admissions, the appropriateness of the setting, the medical necessity of extended stays, and the medical necessity of professional services.

Survey Procedures §482.30

- Determine that the hospital has a utilization review plan for those services furnished by the hospital and its medical staff to Medicare and Medicaid patients.

- Verify through review of records and reports, and interviews with the UR chairman and/or members that UR activities are being performed as described in the hospital UR plan.

- Review the minutes of the UR committee to verify that they include dates, members in attendance, extended stay reviews with approval or disapproval noted in a status report of any actions taken.

A-0653

(Rev. 37, Issued: 10-17-08; Effective/Implementation Date: 10-17-08)

§482.30(a) Standard: Applicability

The provisions of this section apply except in either of the following circumstances:

(1) **A Utilization and Quality Control Quality Improvement Organization (QIO) has assumed binding review for the hospital.**

(2) **CMS has determined that the UR procedures established by the State under title XIX of the Act are superior to the procedures required in this section, and has required hospitals in that State to meet the UR plan requirements under §§456.50 through 456.245 of this chapter.**

Interpretive Guidelines §482.30(a)

The regulation permits two exceptions to the requirement for a hospital UR plan: (1) where the hospital has an agreement with a QIO under contract with the Secretary to assume binding review for the hospital or; (2) where CMS has determined that UR procedures established by the State under Medicaid are superior to the UR requirements for the Medicare program <u>and</u> has required hospitals in that State to meet the UR requirements for the Medicaid program at 42 CFR 456.50 through 456.245.

According to the regulation at 42 CFR 476.86(e), QIO review and monitoring activities fulfill the requirements for compliance activities of State Survey Agencies under §1861(k) of the Social Security Act (Act). The statutory requirements for utilization review at §1861(k) of the Act are reiterated in the UR CoP at 42 CFR 482.30. Therefore, a hospital meets the exception requirements of 42 CFR 482.30 if a QIO has assumed binding review for the hospital. (The hospital may not make requests for work to be performed by the QIO that goes beyond the scope of the QIO's contract with the Secretary.)

The regulation at 42 CFR 489.20(e) requires a hospital to maintain an agreement with a QIO to review the admissions, quality, appropriateness, and diagnostic information related to inpatient services for Medicare patients, if there is a QIO with a contract with CMS in the area where the hospital is located.

CMS anticipates that most hospitals comply with the UR CoP by means of the QIO exception.

With regard to the second exception, CMS would have to determine that UR procedures established by a State under Medicaid are superior to the UR requirements for Medicare. Currently no UR plans established by a State under Medicaid have been approved as exceeding the requirements under Medicare and required for hospital compliance with the Medicare UR CoP within that State. In the event that CMS approves a State's Medicaid UR process for compliance with the Medicare UR CoP, CMS will advise the affected State Survey Agency.

Survey Procedures §482.30(a)

State survey agencies should survey deemed hospitals for compliance with the UR CoP as part of full surveys following a complaint survey with conditions out, or validation surveys. Compliance determinations for all other hospitals should be made during recertification surveys.

Surveyors are to verify either that the hospital:

- Has its own UR plan in place and that it meets the regulatory requirements; or

- If it does not have its own UR plan, that it has an agreement with the QIO that provides for binding UR review. Surveyors should ask to see the signed, dated agreement.

It is not necessary for SAs to conduct routine surveys for compliance with the provider agreement requirement to have a QIO agreement. However, a hospital that does not satisfy the UR CoP through either its own program or a QIO agreement may be cited for violating not only the UR CoP at the condition level, but also the provider agreement requirement at 42 CFR 476.86(e).

A-0654

(Rev. 37, Issued: 10-17-08; Effective/Implementation Date: 10-17-08)
§82.30(b) Standard: Composition of Utilization Review Committee

A UR committee consisting of two or more practitioners must carry out the UR function. At least two of the members of the committee must be doctors of medicine or osteopathy. The other members may be any of the other types of practitioners specified in §482.12(c)(1).

(1)   Except as specified in paragraphs (b)(2) and (3) of this section, the UR committee must be one of the following:

(i) A staff committee of the institution;

(ii)   A group outside the institution--

(A) Established by the local medical society and some or all of the hospitals in the locality; or

(B) Established in a manner approved by CMS.

(2) If, because of the small size of the institution, it is impracticable to have a properly functioning staff committee, the UR committee must be established as specified in paragraph (b)(1)(ii) of this section.

(3) The committee or group's reviews may not be conducted by any individual who--

    (i) Has a direct financial interest (for example, an ownership interest) in that hospital; or

    (ii) Was professionally involved in the care of the patient whose case is being reviewed.

Survey Procedures §482.30(b)

- Determine the composition of the UR committee;

- Determine that the governing body has delegated to the UR committee the authority and responsibility to carry out the UR function;

- Verify that small hospitals delegate the UR function to an outside group if it is impractical to have a staff committee;
- Ascertain that committee members are not financially involved in the hospital (ownership of 5 percent or greater) nor participants in the development or execution of the patient's treatment plan.

A-0655

(Rev. 37, Issued: 10-17-08; Effective/Implementation Date: 10-17-08)

§482.30(c) Standard: Scope and Frequency of Review

(1) The UR plan must provide for review for Medicare and Medicaid patients with respect to the medical necessity of--

    (i) Admissions to the institution;

    (ii) The duration of stays; and

    (iii) Professional services furnished including drugs and biologicals.

(2) Review of admissions may be performed before, at, or after hospital admission.

(3) Except as specified in paragraph (e) of this section, reviews may be conducted on a sample basis.

(4) Hospitals that are paid for inpatient hospital services under the prospective payment system set forth in Part 412 of this chapter must conduct review of duration of stays and review of professional services as follows:

(i) For duration of stays, these hospitals need review only cases that they reasonably assume to be outlier cases based on extended length of stay, as described in §412.80(a)(1)(i) of this chapter; and

(ii) For professional services, these hospitals need review only cases that they reasonably assume to be outlier cases based on extraordinarily high costs, as described in §412.80(a)(1)(ii) of this chapter.

Interpretive Guidelines §482.30(c)

Admissions may be reviewed before, during, or after hospital admission as stated in the hospital's UR plan.

Reviews may be conducted on a sample basis, except for reviews of extended stay cases.

In an Inpatient Prospective Payment System (IPPS) hospital, to determine outlier review compliance, "reasonably assumes" is a good faith test. The question to ask is whether the hospital is reviewing outlier cases. In instances where there was no other review of outlier cases, the question is whether it was reasonable for the hospital not to have known that the cases were in fact outliers. Some medical judgment might be required to determine whether it is reasonable for the hospital to have assumed that a patient fell into a DRG other than the one eventually assigned by the intermediary. This would be an issue in long stay outlier cases where the hospital did not review because the hospital erroneously assumed that the patient was in a DRG under which the case would not have been an outlier.

Survey Procedures §482.30(c)

- Examine the UR plan and other documentation to determine that the medical necessity for Medicare and Medicaid patients is reviewed with respect to admission, duration of the stay, and the professional services furnished.

- Determine if the hospital is reimbursed under IPPS. This requirement does not apply to IPPS excluded hospitals or units.

- Verify that in an IPPS hospital the following are being reviewed:

  o Duration of stay in cases reasonably assumed to be outlier cases; and o Professional services in cases reasonably assumed to be outlier cases.

A-0656

(Rev. 37, Issued: 10-17-08; Effective/Implementation Date: 10-17-08)
§482.30(d) Standard: Determination Regarding Admissions or Continued Stays

(1) The determination that an admission or continued stay is not medically necessary-

(i) May be made by one member of the UR committee if the practitioner or practitioners responsible for the care of the patient, as specified of §482.12(c), concur with the determination or fail to present their views when afforded the opportunity; and

(ii) Must be made by at least two members of the UR committee in all other cases.

(2) Before making a determination that an admission or continued stay is not medically necessary, the UR committee must consult the practitioner or practitioners responsible for the care of the patient, as specified in §482.12(c), and afford the practitioner or practitioners the opportunity to present their views.

(3) If the committee decides that admission to or continued stay in the hospital is not medically necessary, written notification must be given, no later than 2 days after the determination, to the hospital, the patient, and the practitioner or practitioners responsible for the care of the patient, as specified in §482.12(c);

Interpretive Guidelines §482.30(d)

When other than a doctor of medicine or osteopathy makes an initial finding that the written criteria for extended stay are not met, the case must be referred to the committee, or subgroup thereof which contains at least one physician. If the committee or subgroup agrees after reviewing the case that admissions, or extended stay is not medically necessary or appropriate, the attending physician is notified and allowed an opportunity to present his views and any additional information relating to the patient's needs for admissions or extended stay. When a physician member of the committee performs the initial review instead of a non-physician reviewer, and he finds that admissions or extended stay is not necessary no referral to the committee or subgroup is necessary and he may notify the attending practitioner directly.

If the attending practitioner does not respond or does not contest the findings of the committee or subgroup or those of the physician who performed the initial review, then the findings are final.

If the attending physician contests the committee or subgroup findings, or if he presents additional information relating to the patient's need for extended stay, at least one additional physician member of the committee must review the case. If the two physician members determine that the patient's stay is not medically necessary or appropriate after considering all the evidence, their determination becomes final. Written notification of this decision must be sent to the attending physician, patient (or next of kin), facility administrator, and the single State agency (in the case of Medicaid) no later than 2 days after such final decision and in no event later than 3 working days after the end of the assigned extended stay period.

There are only 5 working days in a given week. Normally these days are Monday through Friday, however, the institution has the option to establish 5 other days as working days. When a holiday falls on a working day, that day is not counted as a working day.

In no case may a non-physician make a final determination that a patient's stay is not medically necessary or appropriate.

If, after referral of a questioned case to the committee or subgroup thereof, the physician reviewer determines that an admission or extended stay is justified, the attending physician shall be so notified and an appropriate date for subsequent extended stay review will be selected and noted on the patient's record.

Written notification of this final determination must be sent to the attending physician, the patient (or next of kin), the facility administrator and the single State agency (in the case of Medicaid) no later than 2 days after such final determination and in no event later than 3 working days after the end of the assigned extended stay period.

Where possible, the written notification should be received by all involved parties within the stated time period. Where appropriate and desired, verbal notification may precede written notification.

Survey Procedures §482.30(d)

- Review a sample of "medically unnecessary" decisions involving admissions or continued stay that are not medically necessary and determine that these decisions are made by:

  o One member of the UR committee, if the practitioner(s) responsible for the patient's care concurs with the determination or fails to present his/her views. The practitioner must be one of those specified in §482.12(c), or

  o At least two members of the UR committee in all cases not qualified under the above.

- Review a sample of "medically unnecessary" decisions and verify that the physician or practitioners, as specified in §482.12(c), were informed of the committees expected decision and were given an opportunity to comment.

- Review a sample of "medically unnecessary" cases and verify that all involved parties are notified of the decision that care is medically not necessary no later than two days following the decision.

A-0657

(Rev. 37, Issued: 10-17-08; Effective/Implementation Date: 10-17-08)

§482.30(e) Standard: Extended Stay Review

(1) In hospitals that are not paid under the prospective payment system, the UR committee must make a periodic review, as specified in the UR plan, or each current inpatient receiving hospital services during a continuous period of extended duration.

The scheduling of the periodic reviews may--

(i) Be the same for all cases; or

(ii) Differ for different classes of cases.

(2) In hospitals paid under the prospective payment system, the UR committee must review all cases reasonably assumed by the hospital to be outlier cases because the extended length of stay exceeds the threshold criteria for the diagnosis, as described in §412.80(a)(1)(i). The hospital is not required to review an extended stay that does not exceed the outlier threshold for the diagnosis.

(3) The UR committee must make the periodic review no later than 7 days after the day required in the UR plan.

Survey Procedures §482.30(e)

- Review the facility's definition of extended stay in the UR plan.

- Verify that the hospital's UR plan requires a periodic review of each current Medicare/Medicaid inpatient receiving hospital services of extended duration and that the review is carried out at the specified time stated in the facility's UR plan.

- The review may be the same for all cases or be different for different classes of care.

- If the committee uses a different number of days for different diagnosis or functional categories for the period of extended stay, the surveyor must verify that there is a written list with lengths of stay designated for each diagnosis of functional category.

- Determine if the hospital is under IPPS. Hospitals under IPPS need only review cases reasonably assumed to be outlier cases, and extended stay that exceeds the outlier threshold for the diagnosis.

- Review minutes of the UR committee. Determine that the periodic reviews of extended stay are carried out on or before the expiration of the stated period or no later than 7 days after the day required in the hospital's plan.

A-0658

(Rev. 37, Issued: 10-17-08; Effective/Implementation Date: 10-17-08)
§482.30(f) Standard: Review of Professional Services

The committee must review professional services provided, to determine medical necessity and to promote the most efficient use of available health facilities and services.

Interpretive Guidelines §482.30(f)

"**Professional**" services includes the aspects of care rendered by laboratory personnel, physical therapists, nurses, and others, as well as services provided by MD/DOs.

The review includes medical necessity and efficient use of available health facilities and services. Examples of topics a committee may review are:

- Availability and use of necessary services - underused, overuse, appropriate use

- Timeliness of scheduling of services - operating room, diagnostic

- Therapeutic procedures

Survey Procedures §482.30(f)

Determine that the committee performs a review of professional services.

A-0700

(Rev. 37, Issued: 10-17-08; Effective/Implementation Date: 10-17-08)

§482.41 Condition of Participation: Physical Environment

The hospital must be constructed, arranged, and maintained to ensure the safety of the patient, and to provide facilities for diagnosis and treatment and for special hospital services appropriate to the needs of the community.

Interpretive Guidelines §482.41

This CoP applies to all locations of the hospital, all campuses, all satellites, all provider-based activities, and all inpatient and outpatient locations.

The hospital's Facility Maintenance and hospital departments or services responsible for the hospital's buildings and equipment (both facility equipment and patient care equipment) must be incorporated into the hospital's QAPI program and be in compliance with the QAPI requirements.

Survey Procedures §482.41

Survey of the Physical Environment CoP should be conducted by one surveyor. However, each surveyor as he/she conducts his/her survey assignments should assess the hospital's compliance with the Physical Environment CoP. The Life Safety Code survey may be conducted separately by a specialty surveyor.

A-0701

(Rev. 37, Issued: 10-17-08; Effective/Implementation Date: 10-17-08)

§482.41(a) Standard: Buildings

The condition of the physical plant and the overall hospital environment must be developed and maintained in such a manner that the safety and well-being of patients are assured.

Interpretive Guidelines §482.41(a)

The hospital must ensure that the condition of the physical plant and overall hospital environment is developed and maintained in a manner to ensure the safety and well being of patients. This includes ensuring that routine and preventive maintenance and testing activities are performed as necessary, in accordance with Federal and State laws, regulations, and guidelines and manufacturer's recommendations, by establishing maintenance schedules and conducting ongoing maintenance inspections to identify areas or equipment in need of repair. The routine and preventive maintenance and testing activities should be incorporated into the hospital's **QAPI** plan.

Assuring the safety and well being of patients would include developing and implementing appropriate **emergency preparedness** plans and capabilities. The hospital must develop and implement a comprehensive plan to ensure that the safety and well being of patients are assured during emergency situations. The hospital must coordinate with Federal, State, and local emergency preparedness and health authorities to identify likely risks for their area (e.g., natural disasters, bioterrorism threats, disruption of utilities such as water, sewer, electrical communications, fuel; nuclear accidents, industrial accidents, and other likely mass casualties, etc.) and to develop appropriate responses that will assure the safety and well being of patients. The following issues should be considered when developing the comprehensive emergency plans(s):

- The differing needs of each location where the certified hospital operates;

- The special needs of patient populations treated at the hospital (e.g., patients with psychiatric diagnosis, patients on special diets, newborns, etc.);

- Security of patients and walk-in patients;

- Security of supplies from misappropriation;

- Pharmaceuticals, food, other supplies and equipment that may be needed during emergency/disaster situations;

- Communication to external entities if telephones and computers are not operating or become overloaded (e.g., ham radio operators, community officials, other healthcare facilities if transfer of patients is necessary, etc.);

- Communication among staff within the hospital itself;

- Qualifications and training needed by personnel, including healthcare staff, security staff, and maintenance staff, to implement and carry out emergency procedures;

- Identification, availability and notification of personnel that are needed to implement and carry out the hospital's emergency plans;

- Identification of community resources, including lines of communication and names and contact information for community emergency preparedness coordinators and responders;

- Provisions if gas, water, electricity supply is shut off to the community;

- Transfer or discharge of patients to home, other healthcare settings, or other hospitals;

- Transfer of patients with hospital equipment to another hospital or healthcare setting; and

- Methods to evaluate repairs needed and to secure various likely materials and supplies to effectuate repairs.

Survey Procedures §482.41(a)

- Verify that the condition of the hospital is maintained in a manner to assure the safety and well being of patients (e.g., condition or ceilings, walls, and floors, presence of patient hazards, etc.).

- Review the hospital's routine and preventive maintenance schedules to determine that ongoing maintenance inspections are performed and that necessary repairs are completed.

- Verify that the hospital has developed and implemented a comprehensive plan to ensure that the safety and well being of patients are assured during emergency situations.

A-0702

(Rev. 37, Issued: 10-17-08; Effective/Implementation Date: 10-17-08)

§482.41(a)(1) - There must be emergency power and lighting in at least the operating, recovery, intensive care, and emergency rooms, and stairwells. In all other areas not serviced by the emergency supply source, battery lamps and flashlights must be available.

Interpretive Guidelines §482.41(a)(1)

The hospital must comply with the applicable provisions of the Life Safety Code, National Fire Protection Amendments (NFPA) 101, 2000 Edition and applicable references, such as, NFPA-99: Health Care Facilities, for emergency lighting and emergency power.

Survey Procedures §482.41(a)(1)

Use the Life Safety Code Survey Report Form (CMS-2786) to evaluate compliance with this item.

A-0703

(Rev. 37, Issued: 10-17-08; Effective/Implementation Date: 10-17-08)

§482.41(a)(2) - There must be facilities for emergency gas and water supply.

Interpretive Guidelines §482.41(a)(2)

The hospital must have a system to provide emergency gas and water as needed to provide care to inpatients and other persons who may come to the hospital in need of care. This includes making arrangements with local utility companies and others for the provision of emergency sources of water and gas. The hospital should consider nationally accepted references or calculations made by qualified staff when determining the need for at least water and gas. For example, one source for information on water is the Federal Emergency Management Agency (FEMA).

Emergency gas includes fuels such as propane, natural gas, fuel oil, liquefied natural gas, as well as any gases the hospital uses in the care of patients such as oxygen, nitrogen, nitrous oxide, etc.

The hospital should have a plan to protect these limited emergency supplies, and have a plan for prioritizing their use until adequate supplies are available. The plan should also address the event of a disruption in supply (e.g., disruption to the entire surrounding community).

Survey Procedures §482.41(a)(2)

- Review the system used by hospital staff to determine the hospital's emergency needs for gas and water. Verify that the system accounts for not only inpatients, but also staff and other persons who come to the hospital in need of care during emergencies.

- Determine the source of emergency gas and water, both the quantity of these supplies readily available at the hospital, and that are needed within a short time through additional deliveries.

- Verify that arrangements have been made with utility companies and others for the provision of emergency sources of critical utilities, such as water and gas.

A-0709

(Rev. 37, Issued: 10-17-08; Effective/Implementation Date: 10-17-08)

§482.41(b) Standard: Life Safety from Fire

The hospital must ensure that the life safety from fire requirements are met.

A-0710

§482.41(b)

(1)   **Except as otherwise provided in this section—**

(i) The hospital must meet the applicable provisions of the 2000 edition of the Life Safety Code of the National Fire Protection Association. The Director of the Office of the Federal Register has approved the NFPA 101®2000 edition of the Life Safety Code, issued January 14, 2000, for incorporation by reference in accordance with 5 U.S.C. 552(a) and 1 CFR part 51. A copy of the Code is available for inspection at the CMS Information Resource Center, 7500 Security Boulevard, Baltimore, MD or at the National Archives and Records Administration (NARA). For information on the availability of this material at NARA, call 202–741–6030, or go to:

http://www.archives.gov/federal_register/code_of_federal_regulations/ibr_lo cations.html.

Copies may be obtained from the National Fire Protection Association, 1 Batterymarch Park, Quincy, MA 02269. If any changes in this edition of the Code are incorporated by reference, CMS will publish notice in the Federal Register to announce the changes.

(ii) Chapter 19.3.6.3.2, exception number 2 of the adopted edition of the LSC does not apply to hospitals.

(2)   After consideration of State survey agency findings, CMS may waive specific provisions of the Life Safety Code which, if rigidly applied, would result in unreasonable hardship upon the facility, but only if the waiver does not adversely affect the health and safety of the patients.

(3)   The provisions of the Life Safety Code do not apply in a State where CMS finds that a fire and safety code imposed by State law adequately protects patients in hospitals.

Interpretive Guidelines §482.41(b)(1) –(3)

Medicare-participating hospitals, regardless of size or number of beds, must comply with the hospital/healthcare Life Safety Code requirements for all inpatient care locations. Hospital departments and locations such as emergency departments, outpatient care locations, etc. must comply with hospital/healthcare Life Safety Code Requirements. Additionally, the hospital must be in compliance with all applicable codes referenced in the Life Safety Code, such as, NFPA-99: Health Care Facilities.

Life Safety Code waivers may be recommended by the State survey agency but only CMS (at the Regional Office level) may grant those waivers for Medicare or Medicaid-participating hospitals.

Survey Procedures §482.41(b)(1) - (3)

There is a separate survey form, (Form CMS-2786) used by the Fire Authority surveyor to evaluate compliance with the Life Safety Code.

Consideration, assessment, and recommendation for waivers of specific Life Safety Code provisions are handled by the Fire Authority surveyor as part of the Life Safety Code survey process.

A-0711

(Rev. 37, Issued: 10-17-08; Effective/Implementation Date: 10-17-08)

§482.41(b)(4) - Beginning March 13, 2006, a hospital must be in compliance with Chapter 19.2.9, Emergency Lighting.

Interpretive Guidelines §482.41(b)(4)

Beginning March 13, 2006, Medicare-participating hospitals must be in compliance with Chapter 19.2.9 of the 2000 Edition of NFPA 101. Hospitals have until that date to replace 1-hour batteries with 1-1/2 hour batteries in emergency lighting systems that use batteries as power sources. After March 13, 2006, a hospital with emergency lighting systems with less than 1-1/2 hour batteries will not be in compliance and will be cited.

Survey Procedures §482.41(b)(4)

Determine if the hospital is utilizing 1-1/2 hour batteries for battery-powered emergency lighting systems. After March 13, 2006, cite any noncompliance with this requirement.

A-0712

(Rev. 37, Issued: 10-17-08; Effective/Implementation Date: 10-17-08)

§482.41(b)(5) - Beginning March 13, 2006, Chapter 19.3.6.3.2, exception number 2 does not apply to hospitals.

Interpretive Guidelines §482.41(b)(5)

Beginning March 13, 2006, Medicare-participating hospitals may not keep in service roller latches even when those roller latches are demonstrating the ability to keep the door closed against 5lbf. A hospital with doors in service that have roller latches, where positive latching is required, will not be in compliance and will be cited.

Survey Procedures §482.41(b)(4)

Determine if the hospital is utilizing roller latches on doors that require positive latches.

A-0713

(Rev. 37, Issued: 10-17-08; Effective/Implementation Date: 10-17-08)

§482.41(b)(6) - The hospital must have procedures for the proper routine storage and prompt disposal of trash.

Interpretive Guidelines §482.41(b)(6)

The term trash refers to common garbage as well as biohazardous waste. The storage and disposal of trash must be in accordance with Federal, State and local laws and regulations (i.e., EPA, OSHA, CDC, State environmental, health and safety regulations). The Conditions of Participation for Radiology and Nuclear Medicine Services address handling and storage of radioactive materials.

Survey Procedures §482.41(b)(2)

Verify that the hospital has developed and implemented policies for the proper storage and disposal of trash. Verify through observation that staff adhere to these policies and that the hospital has signage, as appropriate.

A-0714

(Rev. 37, Issued: 10-17-08; Effective/Implementation Date: 10-17-08)

§482.41(b)(7) - The hospital must have written fire control plans that contain provisions for prompt reporting of fires; extinguishing fires; protection of patients, personnel and guests; evacuation; and cooperation with fire fighting authorities.

Survey Procedures §482.41(b)(7)

- Review the hospital's written fire control plans to verify they contain the required provisions of the Life Safety Code or State law.

- Verify that hospital staff reported all fires as required to State officials.

- Interview staff throughout the facility to verify their knowledge of their responsibilities during a fire (this is usually done during the LSC survey, but health surveyors may also verify staff knowledge).

A-0715

(Rev. 37, Issued: 10-17-08; Effective/Implementation Date: 10-17-08)

§482.41(b)(8) - The hospital must maintain written evidence of regular inspection and approval by State or local fire control agencies.

Survey Procedures §482.41(b)(8)

Examine copies of inspection and approval reports from State and local fire control agencies.

A-0716

(Rev. 37, Issued: 10-17-08; Effective/Implementation Date: 10-17-08)

§482.41(b)(9) Notwithstanding any provisions of the 2000 edition of the Life Safety Code to the contrary, a hospital may install alcohol-based hand rub dispensers in its facility if—

(i)   Use of alcohol-based hand rub dispensers does not conflict with any State or local codes that prohibit or otherwise restrict the placement of alcohol-based hand rub dispensers in health care facilities;

(ii)   The dispensers are installed in a manner that minimizes leaks and spills that could lead to falls;

(iii)   The dispensers are installed in a manner that adequately protects against inappropriate access; and

(iv)   The dispensers are installed in accordance with Chapter 18.3.2.7 or Chapter 19.3.2.7 of the 2000 edition of the Life Safety Code, as amended by NFPA Temporary Interim Amendment 00–1(101), issued by the Standards Council of the National Fire Protection Association on April 15, 2004. The Director of the Office of the Federal Register has approved NFPA Temporary Interim Amendment 00–1(101) for incorporation by reference in accordance with 5 U.S.C. 552(a) and 1 CFR part 51. A copy of the amendment is available for inspection at the CMS Information Resource Center, 7500 Security Boulevard, Baltimore, MD and at the Office of the Federal Register, 800 North Capitol Street NW., Suite 700, Washington, DC. Copies may be obtained from the National Fire Protection Association, 1 Batterymarch Park, Quincy, MA 02269.

(v)   The dispensers are maintained in accordance with dispenser manufacturer guidelines.

Interpretive Guidelines, 482.41(b)(9):

CMS amended its regulations, following an NFPA LSC amendment to permit the installation of alcohol-based hand run (ABHR) dispensers in exit access corridors of health care facilities. Previously, ABHR dispensers had been permitted in patient rooms, but not in egress corridors, since they contain flammable materials and could block egress in a fire.

ABHR dispensers have become increasingly common as an infection control method. Healthcare-acquired infections are of increasing concern, and many such infections are transmitted because health care workers do not wash their hands or do so improperly or inadequately.

An important aspect of getting health care workers to use ABHR dispensers is their accessibility. The American Hospital Association commissioned a study to determine the safest method to place ABHR dispensers in egress corridors. As a result of this study, the LSC was amended to permit their use under certain conditions, and CMS has adopted this change in its regulations.

Regular maintenance is seen as a crucial step in making sure that dispensers neither leak nor the contents spill. Hospitals are expected to maintain ABHR dispensers in accordance with manufacturers' guidelines. If the manufacturer does not have specific maintenance requirements, the facility is expected to develop its own policies and procedures to ensure that the dispensers neither leak nor the contents spill.

Survey Procedures §482.41(b)(9):

- Determine whether ABHR dispensers in egress corridors are installed in accordance with the LSC

- Determine whether the hospital maintains the ABHR dispensers in accordance with the manufacturer's guidelines, or, if there are no manufacturer's guidelines, that the hospital has adopted policies and procedures to ensure that the dispensers neither leak nor the contents spill.

A-0722

(Rev. 37, Issued: 10-17-08; Effective/Implementation Date: 10-17-08)

§482.41(c) Standard: Facilities

The hospital must maintain adequate facilities for its services.

Interpretive Guidelines §482.41(c)

Adequate facilities means the hospital has facilities that are:

- Designed and maintained in accordance with Federal, State and local laws, regulations and guidelines; and

- Designed and maintained to reflect the scope and complexity of the services it offers in accordance with accepted standards of practice.

Survey Procedures §482.41(c)

- Observe the facility layout and determine if the patient's needs are met. Toilets, sinks, specialized equipment, etc. should be accessible.

- Review the facility's water supply and distribution system to ensure that the water quality is acceptable for its intended use (drinking water, irrigation water, lab water, etc.). Review the facility water quality monitoring and, as appropriate, treatment system.

A-0723

(Rev. 37, Issued: 10-17-08; Effective/Implementation Date: 10-17-08)

§482.41(c)(1) - Diagnostic and therapeutic facilities must be located for the safety of patients.

Interpretive Guidelines §482.41(c)(1)

Diagnostic and therapeutic facilities must be in rooms or areas specifically designed for the purpose intended.

Survey Procedures §482.41(c)(1)

Determine that x-ray, physical therapy, and other specialized services are provided in areas appropriate for the service provided.

A-0724

(Rev. 37, Issued: 10-17-08; Effective/Implementation Date: 10-17-08)

§482.41(c)(2) - Facilities, supplies, and equipment must be maintained to ensure an acceptable level of safety and quality.

Interpretive Guidelines §482.41(c)(2)

Facilities must be maintained to ensure an acceptable level of safety and quality.

Supplies must be maintained to ensure an acceptable level of safety and quality. This would include that supplies are stored in such a manner to ensure the safety of the stored supplies (protection against theft or damage, contamination, or deterioration), as well as, that the storage practices do not violate fire codes or otherwise endanger patients (storage of flammables, blocking passageways, storage of contaminated or dangerous materials, safe storage practices for poisons, etc.).

Additionally, "supplies must be maintained to ensure an acceptable level of safety" would include that the hospital identifies the supplies it needs to meet its patients' needs for both day-to-day operations and those supplies that are likely to be needed in likely emergency situations such as mass casualty events resulting from natural disasters, mass trauma, disease outbreaks, etc.; and that the hospital makes adequate provisions to ensure the availability of those supplies when needed.

Equipment must be maintained to ensure an acceptable level of safety and quality.

Equipment includes both facility equipment (e.g., elevators, generators, air handlers, medical gas systems, air compressors and vacuum systems, etc.) and medical equipment (e.g., biomedical equipment, radiological equipment, patient beds, stretchers, IV infusion equipment, ventilators, laboratory equipment, etc.).
There must be a regular periodical maintenance and testing program for medical devices and equipment. A qualified individual such as a clinical or biomedical engineer, or other qualified maintenance person must monitor, test, calibrate and maintain the equipment periodically in accordance with the manufacturer's recommendations and Federal and State laws and regulations. Equipment maintenance may be conducted using hospital staff, contracts, or through a combination of hospital staff and contracted services.

"Equipment must be maintained to ensure an acceptable level of safety" would include that the hospital identifies the equipment it needs to meet its patients' needs for both day-to-day operations and equipment that is likely to be needed in likely emergency/disaster situations such as mass casualty events resulting from natural disasters, mass trauma, disease outbreaks, internal disasters, etc.; and that the hospital makes adequate provisions to ensure the availability of that equipment when needed.

Survey Procedures §482.41(c)(2)

- Interview the person in charge of medical equipment and determine if there is an adequate repair/periodical maintenance program.

- Verify that all medical devices and equipments are routinely checked by a clinical or biomedical engineer.

- Review maintenance logs for significant medical equipment (e.g., cardiac monitors, IV infusion pumps, ventilators, etc.).

- Are supplies maintained in such a manner as to ensure that safety?

- Are supplies stored as recommended by the manufacturer?

- Are supplies stored in such a manner as to endanger patient safety?

- Has the hospital identified supplies and equipment that are likely to be needed in emergency situations?

- Has the hospital made adequate provisions to ensure the availability of those supplies and equipment when needed?

A-0725

(Rev. 37, Issued: 10-17-08; Effective/Implementation Date: 10-17-08)

§482.41(c)(3) - The extent and complexity of facilities must be determined by the services offered.

Interpretive Guidelines §482.41(c)(3)

Physical facilities must be large enough, numerous enough, appropriately designed and equipped, and of appropriate complexity to provide the services offered in accordance with Federal and State laws, regulations and guidelines and accepted standards of practice for that location or service.

Survey Procedures §482.41(c)(3)

Verify through observation that the physical facilities are large enough and properly equipped for the scope of services provided and the number of patients served.

0726
(Rev. 89, Issued: 08-30-13, Effective: -8-30-13, Implementation: 08-30-13)

§482.41(c)(4) - There must be proper ventilation, light, and temperature controls in pharmaceutical, food preparation, and other appropriate areas.

Interpretive Guidelines §482.41(c)(4)

There must be proper ventilation in at least the following areas:

- Areas using ethylene oxide, nitrous oxide, guteraldehydes, xylene, pentamidine, or other potentially hazardous substances;

- Locations where oxygen is transferred from one container to another;

- Isolation rooms and reverse isolation rooms (both must be in compliance with Federal and State laws, regulations, and guidelines such as OSHA, CDC, NIH, etc.);

- Pharmaceutical preparation areas (hoods, cabinets, etc.);

- Laboratory locations*; and*

- *Anesthetizing locations. According to NFPA 99, anesthetizing locations are "Any area of a facility that has been designated to be used for the administration of nonflammable inhalation anesthetic agents in the course of examination or treatment, including the use of such agents for relative analgesia." NFPA 99 defines relative analgesia as "A state of sedation and partial block of pain perception produced in a patient by the inhalation of concentrations of nitrous oxide insufficient to produce loss of consciousness (conscious sedation)." (Note that this definition is applicable only for LSC purposes and does not supercede other guidance we have issued for other purposes concerning anesthesia and analgesia.)*

There must be adequate lighting in all the patient care areas, and food and medication preparation areas. Temperature, humidity and airflow in *anesthetizing locations* must be maintained within acceptable standards to inhibit *microbial* growth, *reduce risk of* infection, *control odor,* and promote patient comfort. *Hospitals must maintain relative humidity (RH) levels at 35 percent or greater in each anesthetizing location, unless the hospital elects to use the CMS categorical waiver, which permits it to maintain a RH of at least 20 percent (see Appendix I, Section II for additional information). Hospitals must maintain records that demonstrate they have achieved the required levels. Although not required, CMS recommends that hospitals maintain the upper range of RH at 60 percent or less, as e*xcessive humidity is conducive to *microbial* growth and compromises the integrity of wrapped sterile instruments and supplies. Each operating room should have separate temperature control. Acceptable standards such as from the Association of Operating Room Nurses (AORN) or the *Facilities Guidelines* Institute *(FGI)* should be incorporated into hospital policy.

The hospital must ensure that an appropriate number of refrigerators and/or heating devices are provided and ensure that food and pharmaceuticals are stored properly and in accordance with nationally accepted guidelines (food) and manufacturer's recommendations (pharmaceuticals).

Survey Procedures §482.41(c)(4)

- Verify that all food and medication preparation areas are well lighted.

- Verify that the hospital is in compliance with ventilation requirements for patients with contagious airborne diseases, such as tuberculosis, patients receiving treatments with hazardous chemical, surgical areas, and other areas where hazardous materials are stored.

- Verify that food products are stored under appropriate conditions (e.g., time, temperature, packaging, location) based on a nationally-accepted source such as the United States Department of Agriculture, the Food and Drug Administration, or other nationally-recognized standard.

- Verify that pharmaceuticals are stored at temperatures recommended by the product manufacturer.

- Review *monitoring records for* temperature to ensure that appropriate levels are maintained.

- *Review humidity maintenance records for anesthetizing locations to ensure, if monitoring determined humidity levels were not within acceptable parameters, that corrective actions were performed in a timely manner to achieve acceptable levels.*

A-0747
(Rev. 37, Issued: 10-17-08; Effective/Implementation Date: 10-17-08)

§482.42 Condition of Participation: Infection Control

The hospital must provide a sanitary environment to avoid sources and transmission of infections and communicable diseases. There must be an active program for the prevention, control, and investigation of infections and communicable diseases.

Interpretive Guidelines §482.42

This regulation requires the hospital to develop, implement, and maintain an active, hospital-wide program for the prevention, control, and investigation of infections and communicable diseases. The National Institute of Allergy and Infectious Diseases defines an infectious disease as a change from a state of health to a state in which part or all of a host's body cannot function normally because of the presence of an infectious agent or its product. An infectious agent is defined by the NIAID as a living or quasi-living organism or particle that causes an infectious disease, and includes bacteria, viruses, fungi, protozoa, helminthes, and prions. NIAID defines a communicable disease as a disease associated with an agent that can be transmitted from one host to another. (NIAID website glossary)

According to the Centers for Disease Control and Prevention (CDC), healthcare-associated infections, i.e., infections that patients acquire during the course of receiving treatment for other conditions within a healthcare setting, are one of the top ten leading causes of death in the United States. The CDC estimates that there are 1.7 million healthcare-associated infections in American hospitals each year, with 99,000 associated deaths. (CDC website, Estimates of Healthcare-Associated Infections, date last modified May 30, 2007)

The hospital must provide and maintain a sanitary environment to avoid sources and transmission of infections and communicable diseases. All areas of the hospital must be clean and sanitary. This includes all hospital units, campuses and off-site locations. The infection prevention and control program must include appropriate monitoring of housekeeping, maintenance (including repair, renovation and construction activities), and other activities to ensure that the hospital maintains a sanitary environment. Examples of areas to monitor would include: food storage, preparation, serving and dish rooms, refrigerators, ice machines, air handlers, autoclave rooms, venting systems, inpatient rooms, treatment areas, labs, waste handling, surgical areas, supply storage, equipment cleaning, etc.

The hospital's program for prevention, control and investigation of infections and communicable diseases should be conducted in accordance with nationally recognized infection control practices or guidelines, as well as applicable regulations of other federal or state agencies. Examples of organizations that promulgate nationally recognized infection and communicable disease control guidelines, and/or recommendations include: the Centers for Disease Control and Prevention (CDC), the Association for Professionals in Infection Control and Epidemiology (APIC), the Society for Healthcare Epidemiology of America (SHEA), and the Association of periOperative Registered Nurses (AORN). The U.S. Occupational Health and Safety Administration (OSHA) also issues federal regulations applicable to infection control practices.

In order to prevent, control and investigate infections and communicable diseases, the hospital's program must include an active surveillance component that covers both hospital patients and personnel working in the hospital. Surveillance includes infection detection, data collection and analysis, monitoring, and evaluation of preventive interventions.

The hospital must conduct surveillance on a hospital-wide basis in order to identify infectious risks or communicable disease problems at any particular location. This does not imply "total hospital surveillance," but it does mean that hospitals must have reliable sampling or other mechanisms in place to permit identifying and monitoring infections and communicable diseases occurring throughout the hospital's various locations or departments. The hospital must document its surveillance activities, including the measures selected for monitoring, and collection and analysis methods. Surveillance activities should be conducted in accordance with recognized infection control surveillance practices, such as, for example, those utilized by the CDC's National Healthcare Safety Net (NHSN).

The hospital must develop and implement appropriate infection control interventions to address issues identified through its detection activities, and then monitor the effectiveness of interventions through further data collection and analysis.

The hospital's infection prevention and control program must be integrated into its hospital-wide Quality Assurance and Performance Improvement (QAPI) program. (See 42 CFR 482.42(b)(1).)

SPECIAL CHALLENGES IN INFECTION CONTROL

MULTI-DRUG RESISTANT ORGANISMS (MDROs)

According to the Centers for Disease Control's (CDC) publication, Management of Multi-drug Resistant Organisms in Healthcare Settings 2006, http://www.cdc.gov/ncidod/dhqp/pdf/ar/mrdoGuideline2006.pdf, MDROs are microorganisms that are resistant to one or more antimicrobial agents. Options for treating patients with MDRO infections are very limited, resulting in increased mortality, as well as increased hospital length of stay and costs. During the last several decades the prevalence of MDROs in hospitals has increased steadily. Hospitals are encouraged to have mechanisms in place for the early identification of patients with targeted MDROs prevalent in their hospital and community, and for the prevention of transmission of such MDROs. When ongoing transmission of targeted MDROs in the hospital is identified, the infection prevention and control program should use this event to identify potential breaches in infection control practice.

AMBULATORY CARE

The ambulatory care setting, including emergency departments, presents unique challenges for infection control, because: patients remain in common areas, often for prolonged periods of time, until they can be seen by a healthcare practitioner; examination or treatment rooms are turned around quickly with minimal cleaning; and infectious patients may not be recognized immediately. Furthermore, immuno-compromised patients may receive treatments in rooms among other patients who pose risks of infection.

The hospital's infection prevention and control program should be designed with these ambulatory care setting challenges in mind. After assessing the likely level of risk in its various ambulatory care settings, including off-site settings, a hospital might identify particular settings, such as the emergency department, where it would be appropriate to employ measures for screening individuals with potentially contagious diseases during their initial patient encounter, and taking appropriate control measures for those individuals who may present risk for the transmission of infectious agents by the airborne or droplet route. Guidelines promulgated by the CDC's Healthcare Infection Control Practices Advisory Committee (HICPAC) are a resource for hospitals in developing their infection control program for ambulatory care. For example, when potentially infectious individuals are identified, prevention measures should include prompt physical separation wherever possible, implementation of respiratory hygiene/cough etiquette protocols, and/or appropriate isolation precautions based on the routes of transmission of the suspected infection.

COMMUNICABLE DISEASE OUTBREAKS

Community-wide outbreaks of communicable diseases (such as measles, SARS, or influenza) present many of the same issues and require many of the same considerations and strategies as other hospital infectious disease threats. If a communicable disease outbreak occurs, an understanding of the epidemiology, likely modes of transmission, and clinical course of the disease is essential for responding to and managing the event. Among the infection control issues that may need to be addressed are:

- Preventing transmission among patients, healthcare personnel, and visitors;

- Identifying persons who may be infected and exposed;

- Providing treatment or prophylaxis to large numbers of people; and

- Logistics issues (staff, medical supplies, resupply, continued operations, and capacity).

Pandemics, or very widespread and clinically serious outbreaks of an infection, present additional challenges due to the widespread effect on the availability of back-up resources that would typically be available to address an outbreak confined to a smaller geographic area. Additionally, the duration of a pandemic may present special challenges for staffing, supplies, resupply, etc. Hospitals should work with local, State, and Federal public health agencies to identify likely communicable disease threats and develop appropriate preparedness and response strategies.

BIOTERRORISM

Healthcare facilities would confront a set of issues similar to naturally occurring communicable disease threats when dealing with a suspected bioterrorism event. The required response is likely to differ based on whether exposure is a result of a biological release or person-to-person transmission. A variety of sources offer guidance for the management of persons exposed to likely agents of bioterrorism, including Federal agency websites (e.g., http://www.ahrq.gov/prep; http://www.usamrid.army.mil/publications/index.html; http://www.bt.cdc.gov) Because of the many similarities between man-made and naturally occurring threats, an all-hazards approach to developing emergency response plans is preferred, and hospitals are encouraged to work with their State and local emergency response agencies to develop their plans.

The hospital must be in compliance with the Occupational Health and Safety Administration's Bloodborne Pathogens regulation at 29 CFR 1910.1030.

Survey Procedures §482.42

- Survey of the Infection Control Condition of Participation (CoP) should be coordinated by one surveyor. However, each surveyor should assess the hospital's compliance with the Infection Control CoP as he/she conducts his/her survey assignments.

- Determine whether there are hospital-wide policies and procedures for preventing, identifying, reporting, investigating, and controlling infections and communicable diseases of patients and hospital personnel, including contract workers and volunteers. Determine whether the infection control program can identify all hospital locations and that the policies and procedures take the various hospital locations into account.

- Determine whether the policies and procedures are implemented correctly in an active infection control program.
- Determine whether the program is hospital-wide and program specific in gathering and assessing infection and communicable disease data. Review the parameters of the active surveillance program to determine whether it is consistent

with infection control standards of practice and suitable to the scope and complexity of the hospital's services.

- Throughout the hospital, observe the sanitary condition of the environment of care, noting the cleanliness of patient rooms, floors, horizontal surfaces, patient equipment, air inlets, mechanical rooms, food service activities, treatment and procedure areas, surgical areas, central supply, storage areas, etc.

- Determine whether the hospital's infection prevention and control program is integrated into its hospital-wide QAPI program.

A-0748
(Rev. 84, Issued: 06-07-13, Effective: 06-07-13, Implementation: 06-07-13)

§482.42(a) Standard: Organization and Policies

A person or persons must be designated as infection control officer or officers to develop and implement policies governing control of infections and communicable diseases....

Interpretive Guidelines §482.42(a)

Hospital infection control officers are often referred to as "hospital epidemiologists (HEs)," "infection control professionals (ICPs)" or "infection preventionists." CDC has defined "infection control professional" as "a person whose primary training is in either nursing, medical technology, microbiology, or epidemiology and who has acquired specialized training in infection control."

The hospital must designate in writing an individual or group of individuals as its infection control officer or officers. In designating infection control officers, hospitals should assure that the individuals so designated are qualified through education, training, experience, or certification (such as that offered by the Certification Board of Infection Control and Epidemiology Inc. (CBIC), or by the specialty boards in adult or pediatric infectious diseases offered for physicians by the American Board of Internal Medicine (for internists) and the American Board of Pediatrics (for pediatricians)). Infection control officers should maintain their qualifications through ongoing education and training, which can be demonstrated by participation in infection control courses, or in local and national meetings organized by recognized professional societies, such as APIC and SHEA.

CMS does not specify either the number of infection control officers to be designated or the number of infection control officer hours that must be devoted to the infection prevention and control programs. However, resources must be adequate to accomplish the tasks required for the infection control program. A prudent hospital would consider patient census, characteristics of the patient population, and complexity of the healthcare services it offers in determining the size and scope of the resources it commits to infection control. The CDC's HICPAC as well as professional infection control organizations such as the APIC and the SHEA publish studies and recommendations on resource allocation that hospitals may find useful.

The infection control officer(s) must develop and implement policies governing the control of infections and communicable diseases. Infection control policies should address the roles and responsibilities for infection control within the hospital; how the various hospital committees and departments interface with the infection control program; and how to prevent infectious/communicable diseases; and how to report infectious/communicable diseases to the infection control program.

Survey Procedures §482.42(a)

- Determine whether an infection control officer(s) is designated and has the responsibility for the infection prevention and control program.

- Review the personnel file of the infection control officer(s) to determine whether he/she is qualified through ongoing education, training, experience, or certification to oversee the infection control program.

- Determine whether the infection control officer(s) have developed and implemented hospital infection control policies.

A-0749
(Rev. 84, Issued: 06-07-13, Effective: 06-07-13, Implementation: 06-07-13)

§482.42(a)–….The infection control officer or officers must develop a system for identifying, reporting, investigating, and controlling infections and communicable diseases of patients and personnel.

Interpretive Guidelines §482.42(a)

The infection control officer or officers must develop, implement and evaluate measures governing the identification, investigation, reporting, prevention and control of infections and communicable diseases within the hospital, including both healthcare–associated infections and community-acquired infections. Infection control policies should be specific to each department, service, and location, including off-site locations, and be evaluated and revised when indicated. The successful development, implementation and evaluation of a hospital-wide infection prevention and control program requires frequent collaboration with persons administratively and clinically responsible for inpatient and outpatient departments and services, as well as, non-patient-care support staff, such as maintenance and housekeeping staff.

Implicit in the infection control officer(s)' responsibility for measures to identify, investigate, report, prevent and control infections and communicable diseases are the following activities:

- Maintenance of a sanitary hospital environment;

- Development and implementation of infection control measures related to hospital personnel; hospital staff, for infection control purposes, includes all hospital staff, contract workers (e.g., agency nurses, housekeeping staff, etc), and volunteers;

- Mitigation of risks associated with patient infections present upon admission:

- Mitigation of risks contributing to healthcare-associated infections:

- Active surveillance;

- Monitoring compliance with all policies, procedures, protocols and other infection control program requirements;

- Program evaluation and revision of the program, when indicated;

- Coordination as required by law with federal, state, and local emergency preparedness and health authorities to address communicable disease threats, bioterrorism, and outbreaks;

- Complying with the reportable disease requirements of the local health authority; For example, a hospital with a comprehensive hospital-wide infection control program should have and implement policies and procedures, based as much as possible on national guidelines that address the following:

- Maintenance of a sanitary physical environment:

  ° Ventilation and water quality control issues, including measures taken to maintain a safe environment during internal or external construction/renovation;

  ° Maintaining safe air handling systems in areas of special ventilation, such as operating rooms, intensive care units, and airborne infection isolation rooms;

  ° Techniques for food sanitation;

- ○ Techniques for cleaning and disinfecting environmental surfaces, carpeting and furniture;

- ○ Techniques for textiles reprocessing, storage and distribution;

- ○ Techniques for disposal of regulated and non-regulated waste; and

- ○ Techniques for pest control.

- Hospital staff-related measures:

  - ○ Measures – and authority - for evaluating hospital staff immunization status for designated infectious diseases, as recommended by the CDC and its Advisory Committee on Immunization Practices (ACIP);

  - ○ Policies articulating the authority and circumstances under which the hospital screens hospital staff for infections likely to cause significant infectious disease or other risk to the exposed individual, and for reportable diseases, as required under local, state, or federal public health authority;

  - ○ Policies articulating when infected hospital staff are restricted from providing direct patient care and/or are required to remain away from the healthcare facility entirely;

  - ○ New employee and regular update training in preventing and controlling healthcare-associated infections and methods to prevent exposure to and transmission of infections and communicable diseases;

  - ○ Measures to evaluate staff and volunteers exposed to patients with infections and communicable disease;

- Mitigation of risks associated with patient infections present upon admission:

  - ○ Measures for the early identification of patients who require isolation in accordance with CDC guidelines;

  - ○ Appropriate use of personal protective equipment including gowns, gloves, masks and eye protection devices;

  - ○ Use and techniques for "isolation" precautions as recommended by the CDC.

- Mitigation of risks contributing to healthcare-associated infections:

° Surgery-related infection risk mitigation measures:

- Implementing appropriate prophylaxis to prevent surgical site infection (SSI), such as a protocol to assure that antibiotic prophylaxis to prevent surgical site infection for appropriate procedures is administered at the appropriate time, done with an appropriate antibiotic, and discontinued appropriately after surgery;

- Addressing aseptic technique practices used in surgery and invasive procedures performed outside the operating room, including sterilization of instruments;

° Other hospital healthcare-associated infection risk mitigation measures:

- Promotion of hand washing hygiene among staff and employees, including utilization of alcohol-based hand sanitizers;

- Measures specific to prevention of infections caused by organisms that are antibiotic-resistant;

- Measures specific to prevention of device-associated bloodstream infection (BSI), such as a protocol for reducing infections of central venous catheters specifying aseptic precautions for line insertions, care of inserted lines, and prompt removal when a line is no longer needed;

- Measures specific to prevention of other device-associated infections, e.g., those associated with ventilators, tube feeding, indwelling urinary catheters, etc;

- Isolation procedures and requirements for highly immuno-suppressed patients who require a protective environment.

- Care techniques for tracheostomy care, respiratory therapy, burns and other situations that reduce a patient's resistance to infection;
- Requiring disinfectants, antiseptics, and germicides to be used in accordance with the manufacturers' instructions;

- Appropriate use of facility and medical equipment, including negative and positive pressure isolation room equipment, portable air filtration equipment, treatment booths and enclosed beds, UV lights, and other equipment used to control the spread of infectious agents;

- Adherence to nationally recognized infection prevention and control precautions, such as current CDC guidelines and recommendations, for infections/communicable diseases identified as present in the hospital; and

- Educating patients, visitors, caregivers, and staff, as appropriate, about infections and communicable diseases and methods to reduce transmission in the hospital and in the community;

- Active surveillance:

  ○ The hospital is expected to identify and track infections and communicable diseases in any of the following categories occurring throughout the hospital, whether in patients or staff (patient care staff and non-patient care staff, including employees, contract staff and volunteers). Hospitals are not required to organize their surveillance according to these categories. The categories are:

    - Healthcare-associated infections selected by the hospital's Infection Prevention and Control Program as part of a targeted surveillance strategy based on nationally recognized guidelines and periodic risk assessment;
    - Patients or staff with identified communicable diseases that local, State, or Federal health agencies require be reported;
    - Patients identified by laboratory culture as colonized or infected with multi-drug-resistant organisms (MDROs), as defined by the hospital's Infection Prevention and Control Program;

    - Patients who meet CDC criteria for requiring isolation precautions (other than "Standard Precautions" or a protective environment) during their hospitalization;

    - Patients or staff with signs and symptoms that have been requested be reported or recorded by local, State, or Federal health agencies; and

    - Staff or patients who are known or suspected to be infected with epidemiologically-significant pathogens that are identified by the hospital or local, State, or Federal health agencies.

For Information – Not Required/Not to be Cited

Many hospitals are using automated surveillance technology (AST) or "data mining" for identification and control of hospital-acquired infections (HAI) and implementation of evidence-based infection control practices. Use of AST or similar technology is encouraged in hospitals, but is not required.

- Provisions to monitor compliance with all policies, procedures, protocols and other infection control program requirements;

- Provision for program evaluation and revision of the program, when indicated;

- Policies and procedures developed in coordination with federal, state, and local emergency preparedness and health authorities to address communicable disease threats, bioterrorism, and outbreaks; and

- Procedures for meeting the reporting requirements of the local health authority.

Survey Procedures §482.42(a)

- Determine whether the hospital has an active, hospital-wide infection control program reflecting the infection control officer responsibilities specified in the interpretive guidelines. Specifically, surveyors should determine whether the hospital:

  - Maintains a sanitary environment;
  - Develops and implements infection control measures related to hospital personnel;
  - Mitigates risks associated with patient infections present upon admission;
  - Mitigates risks contributing to healthcare-associated infections (for example, observe whether staff exhibit good hand washing hygiene);

  - Conducts active surveillance;

  - Monitors compliance with all infection control program requirements;

  - Evaluates the infection control program regularly and revises it, when indicated;

  - Coordinates as required by law with federal, state, and local emergency preparedness and health authorities to address communicable disease threats, bioterrorism, and outbreaks; and

  - Complies with the reportable disease requirements of the local health authority.

A-0756
(Rev. 84, Issued: 06-07-13, Effective: 06-07-13, Implementation: 06-07-13)

§482.42(b) Standard: Responsibilities of Chief Executive Officer, Medical Staff, and Director of Nursing Services

The chief executive officer, the medical staff, and the director of nursing must--

(1)   Ensure that the hospital-wide quality assessment and performance improvement (QAPI) program and training programs address problems identified by the infection control officer or officers; and

(2)   Be responsible for the implementation of successful corrective action plans in affected problem areas.

Interpretive Guidelines §482.42(b)

The chief executive officer (CEO), the medical staff and the director of nursing (DON) must ensure that the hospital-wide Quality Assessment and Performance Improvement (QAPI) program and staff in-service training programs address problems identified through the infection prevention and control program.

To reflect the importance of infection control the regulations specifically require that the hospital's QAPI and training programs must be involved in addressing problems identified by the infection control program, and hold the CEO, medical staff and DON jointly responsible for linking the infection control program with the QAPI and training programs. Requirements for the hospital's QAPI program are found at 42 CFR 482.21.

These hospital leaders are also held explicitly responsible for implementing successful corrective action plans. In order to accomplish this, hospital leaders must monitor adherence to corrective action plans, as well as assess the effectiveness of actions taken, with implementation of revised corrective actions as needed.

Education on the principles and practices for preventing transmission of infectious agents within the hospital should be provided to anyone who has an opportunity for contact with patients or medical equipment, e.g., nursing and medical staff; therapists and technicians, such as those involved in respiratory, physical, and occupational therapy and radiology and cardiology services; phlebotomists; housekeeping and maintenance staff; volunteers; and all students and trainees in healthcare professions.

Survey Procedures §482.42(b)

- Determine whether the hospital's QAPI program and staff in-service training programs address problems identified by the infection control officer(s).

- Determine whether infection control problems identified are reported to the Medical Staff, CEO and DON. Verify that hospital leadership takes steps to assure that corrective actions are implemented and successful.

A-0799
(Rev. 87, Issued: 07-19-13, Effective: 07-19-13, Implementation: 07-19-13)

§482.43 Condition of Participation: Discharge Planning

The hospital must have in effect a discharge planning process that applies to all patients. The hospital's policies and procedures must be specified in writing.

Interpretive Guidelines §482.43

Hospital discharge planning is a process that involves determining the appropriate post-hospital discharge destination for a patient; identifying what the patient requires for a smooth and safe transition from the hospital to his/her discharge destination; and beginning the process of meeting the patient's identified post-discharge needs. Newer terminology, such as "transition planning" or "community care transitions" is preferred by some, since it moves away from a focus primarily on a patient's hospital stay to consideration of transitions among the multiple types of patient care settings that may be involved at various points in the treatment of a given patient. This approach recognizes the shared responsibility of health care professionals and facilities as well as patients and their support persons throughout the continuum of care, and the need to foster better communication among the various groups. Much of the interpretive guidance for this CoP has been informed by newer research on care transitions, understood broadly. At the same time, the term "discharge planning" is used both in Section 1861(ee) of the Social Security Act as well as in §482.43. In this guidance, therefore, we continue to use the term "discharge planning."

When the discharge planning process is well executed, and absent unavoidable complications or unrelated illness or injury, the patient continues to progress towards the goals of his/her plan of care after discharge. However, it is not uncommon in the current health care environment for patients to be discharged from inpatient hospital settings only to be readmitted within a short timeframe for a related condition. Some readmissions may not be avoidable. Some may be avoidable, but are due to factors beyond the control of the hospital that discharged the patient. On the other hand, a poor discharge planning process may slow or complicate the patient's recovery, may lead to readmission to a hospital, or may even result in the patient's death.

Jencks[5] et al. analyzed Medicare claims data for a two-year period in an attempt to more accurately identify readmission (called "rehospitalization") rates and associated costs. They found approximately 19.6% of Medicare fee-for-service beneficiaries were rehospitalized within 30 days of discharge and 34.0% within 60 days of discharge. 70.5% of those surgical patients subsequently readmitted within 30 days had a medical cause for the readmission. Only approximately 10% of rehospitalizations were estimated to have been planned.

[5] *Jencks, F. J., Williams, M. V., Coleman, E. A. Rehospitalizations among Patients in the Medicare Fee-for-Service program. The New England Journal of Medicine 2009; 360;14: 1418-1428.*

Reducing the number of preventable hospital readmissions is a major priority for patient safety, and holding hospitals accountable for complying with the discharge planning CoP is one key element of an overall strategy for reducing readmissions.

With respect to the causes of the high rate of preventable readmissions, "Multiple factors contribute to the high level of hospital readmissions in the U.S.... They may result from poor quality care or from poor transitions between different providers and care settings. Such readmissions may occur if patients are discharged from hospitals or other health care settings prematurely; if they are discharged to inappropriate settings; or if they do not receive adequate information or resources to ensure a continued progression of services. System factors, such as poorly coordinated care and incomplete communication and information exchange between inpatient and community-based providers, may also lead to unplanned readmissions."[6] The discharge planning CoP requirements address all of these factors. While hospitals are not solely responsible for the success of their patients' post-hospital care transitions, under the discharge planning CoP hospitals are expected to employ a discharge planning process that improves the quality of care for patients and reduces the chances of readmission.

For Information – Not to be Cited under the CoP

These interpretive guidelines address hospital discharge requirements under the Medicare statute and regulations. However, hospitals should be aware that, as entities receiving Federal financial assistance (including Medicaid and Medicare payments) and public accommodations, they are subject to the requirements of Section 504 of the Rehabilitation Act and the Americans with Disabilities Act. These statutes and their implementing regulations require that covered entities administer their services, programs and activities in the most integrated setting appropriate to individuals with disabilities and prohibit covered entities from utilizing criteria or methods of administration that lead to discrimination. CMS does not interpret or enforce these requirements. However, hospitals should ensure that their discharge practices comply with applicable Federal civil rights laws and do not lead to needless segregation.

The plain language of the regulation requires hospitals to have a discharge planning process in effect for "all" patients. However, the preamble to the adoption of this regulation on December 13, 1994 makes it clear that this "all patients" language was meant to distinguish the final rule from the proposed rule, which would have applied only to hospital inpatients who were Medicare beneficiaries. It was not intended to apply the discharge planning process to outpatients as well as inpatients. Specifically, the preamble stated, "Discharge planning presupposes hospital admission and section 9305(c) of OBRA '86 specifically indicates that discharge planning follows hospitalization." (59 FR

---

[6] *Modifications to the Maryland Hospital Preventable Readmissions (MHPR) Draft Recommendations, Staff Report, Maryland Health Services Cost Review Commission, December 1, 2010, accessed via the agenda for the December 8, 2010 Commission meeting.*

at 64141, December 13, 1994). Accordingly, under the regulation, hospitals are required to have a discharge planning process that applies to all inpatients; discharge planning is not required for outpatients.

For Information – Not Required/Not to be Cited

Hospitals might consider utilizing, on a voluntary basis, an abbreviated post-hospital planning process for certain categories of outpatients, such as patients discharged from observation services, from same day surgery (including invasive procedures – see the definition of surgery in the guidance for the surgical services CoP), and for certain categories of emergency department discharges. Given the increasing complexity of services offered in the outpatient setting, many of the same concerns for effective post-hospital care coordination arise as for inpatients.

The discharge planning CoP (and Section 1861(ee) of the Act on which the CoP is based) provides for a four-stage discharge planning process:

- Screening all inpatients to determine which ones are at risk of adverse health consequences post-discharge if they lack discharge planning;

- Evaluation of the post-discharge needs of inpatients identified in the first stage, or of inpatients who request an evaluation, or whose physician requests one;

- Development of a discharge plan if indicated by the evaluation or at the request of the patient's physician; and

- Initiation of the implementation of the discharge plan prior to the discharge of an inpatient.

The hospital is required to specify in writing its discharge planning policies and procedures. The policies and procedures must address all of the requirements of 42 CFR 482.43(a) – 482.43(e). The hospital must take steps to assure that its discharge planning policies and procedures are implemented consistently.

For Information – Not Required/Not to be Cited

It would be advisable for the hospital to develop its discharge planning policies and procedures with input from the hospital's medical staff prior to review and approval by the governing body.

Hospitals are also encouraged to obtain input from:

> - Other healthcare facilities and professionals who provide care to discharged patients, including but not limited to: nursing homes/skilled nursing facilities, home health agencies, primary care physicians and clinics, etc.; and
>
> - Patients and patient advocacy groups.

The discharge planning CoP specifically addresses the role of the patient, or the patient's representative, by requiring the hospital to develop a discharge planning evaluation at the patient's request, and to discuss the evaluation and plan with the patient. This is consistent with the regulations at 42 CFR 482.13(b)(1) & (2), that provide the patient has the right to participate in the development and implementation of his/her plan of care, and to make informed decisions regarding his/her care. Accordingly, hospitals must actively involve patients or their representatives throughout the discharge planning process. Further, the specific discharge planning evaluation requirement to assess a patient's capability for post-discharge self-care requires the hospital, as needed, to actively solicit information not only from the patient or the patient's representative, but also from family/friends/support persons.

For Information – Not Required/Not to be Cited

If a patient exercises the right to refuse to participate in discharge planning or to implement a discharge plan, documentation of the refusal is recommended.

Survey Procedures §482.43

- Determine whether the hospital has written policies and procedures for discharge planning.

Evaluate compliance with each standard within the discharge planning CoP in accordance with the guidance below. Following standard practice, depending on the manner and degree of deficiencies identified related to specific discharge planning standards, determine whether deficiencies in one or more of these areas rises to the level of substantial, i.e., condition-level, noncompliance with this CoP.

A-0800
(Rev. 87, Issued: 07-19-13, Effective: 07-19-13, Implementation: 07-19-13)

§482.43(a) Standard: Identification of Patients in Need of Discharge Planning

The hospital must identify at an early stage of hospitalization all patients who are likely to suffer adverse health consequences upon discharge if there is no adequate discharge planning.

Interpretive Guidelines §482.43(a)

For Information – Not Required/Not to be Cited

Given the high level of readmissions that hospitals experience, a hospital would be well advised to assume that every inpatient requires a discharge plan to reduce the risk of adverse health consequences post-discharge. Providing a discharge plan for every inpatient means the hospital avoids the problems that result if it utilizes a screening process that fails to predict adequately which patients need a discharge plan to avoid adverse consequences.

This does not mean that every discharge plan will be equally detailed or complex; some may be comparatively simple, for example, focusing on clear instructions for self-care for patients whose post-care needs may be readily met in their home environment. On the other hand, other patients may have complex needs for care after discharge. It is common for many patients to be discharged with a need for numerous on-going services/therapies, such as intravenous (IV) medications, intensive physical and occupational therapy, remote monitoring, wound care, etc. The key is that the discharge plan must reflect a thorough evaluation of the patient's post hospital care needs and must address the needs identified.

If a hospital does not voluntarily adopt a policy of developing a discharge plan for every inpatient, then the hospital must evaluate all inpatients to identify those patients for whom the lack of an adequate discharge plan is likely to result in an adverse impact on the patient's health. While there is no one nationally accepted tool or criteria for identifying those patients who require discharge planning, the following factors have been identified as important: the patient's functional status and cognitive ability; the type of post-hospital care the patient requires, and whether such care requires the services of health care professionals or facilities; the availability of the required post-hospital health care services to the patient; and the availability and capability of family and/or friends to provide follow-up care in the home.

For hospitals that do not develop a discharge plan for every inpatient, the hospital's discharge planning policies and procedures must document the criteria and screening process it uses to identify patients likely to need discharge planning, including the evidence or basis for the criteria and process. They must also identify which staff are responsible for carrying out the evaluation to identify patients likely to need discharge planning.

The regulation requires that the identification of patients must be made at an early stage of the patient's hospitalization. This is necessary in order to allow sufficient time to complete discharge planning evaluations and develop appropriate discharge plans, for those patients who need them. (See §482.43((b)(5)) Ideally the identification process will be completed when the patient is admitted as an inpatient, or shortly thereafter. However, no citations will be made if the identification of patients likely to need discharge planning is completed at least 48 hours in advance of the patient's discharge and there is no evidence that the patient's discharge was delayed due to the hospital's failure to complete an appropriate discharge planning evaluation on a timely basis or that the patient was placed unnecessarily in a setting other than where he/she was admitted from primarily due to a delay in discharge planning. For example, a delay in identification of a patient in need of discharge planning might result in discharging the patient to a nursing facility, because such placements can be arranged comparatively quickly, when the patient preferred to return home, and could have been supported in the home environment with arrangement of appropriate community services.

If the patient's stay is for less than 48 hours, hospitals must nevertheless ensure that they are screened so that, if needed, the discharge planning process is completed before the patient's discharge.

Changes in the patient's condition may warrant development of a discharge plan for a patient not identified during the initial screening process. The hospital's discharge planning policies and procedures must address how the staff responsible for discharge planning will be made aware of changes in a patient's condition that require a discharge planning evaluation.

In the event that a patient is transferred to another hospital, any pertinent information concerning the identification of the patient's post-hospital needs should be in the patient's medical record that is transferred with the patient. The receiving hospital then becomes responsible for the discharge planning process for the patient.

Survey Procedures §482.43(a)

- In every inpatient unit surveyed is there evidence of timely screening to determine if a discharge planning evaluation is needed? (Not applicable in hospitals that require a discharge planning evaluation for all inpatients.)

- Conduct discharge tracers for several open and closed inpatient records to determine:

  o When was the screening done to identify inpatients needing a discharge planning evaluation?

    - If the hospital conducts an evaluation for all inpatients, or if it documents in the medical record screening of an inpatient before or at time of admission, or at least 48 hours prior to discharge, it is in compliance.

- For patients whose stay was less than 48 hours is there any evidence of a screening to determine if discharge planning was needed?

  o Can hospital staff demonstrate that the hospital's criteria and screening process for a discharge planning evaluation are correctly applied?

o For patients not initially identified as in need of a discharge plan, is there a process for updating this determination based on changes in the patient's condition or circumstances?

- Does the discharge planning policy address changes in patient condition that would call for a discharge planning evaluation of patients not previously identified as in need of one?

- Are inpatient unit staff aware of how, when, and whom to notify of changes in the patient's clinical condition that might warrant a change in the discharge planning process?

A-0806
(Rev. 87, Issued: 07-19-13, Effective: 07-19-13, Implementation: 07-19-13)

§482.43(b) Standard: Discharge Planning Evaluation

(1) The hospital must provide a discharge planning evaluation to the patients identified in paragraph (a) of this section, and to other patients upon the patient's request, the request of a person acting on the patient's behalf, or the request of the physician.

* * *

(3) - The discharge planning evaluation must include an evaluation of the likelihood of a patient needing post-hospital services and of the availability of the services.

(4) - The discharge planning evaluation must include an evaluation of the likelihood of a patient's capacity for self-care or of the possibility of the patient being cared for in the environment from which he or she entered the hospital.

Interpretive Guidelines §482.43(b)(1), §482.43(b)(3) & §482.43(b)(4)

For every inpatient identified under the process required at §482.43(a) as at potential risk of adverse health consequences without a discharge plan, a discharge planning evaluation must be completed by the hospital. In addition, an evaluation must also be completed if the patient, or the patient's representative, or the patient's attending physician requests one. Unless the hospital has adopted a voluntary policy of developing an evaluation for every inpatient, the hospital must also have a process for making patients, including the patient's representative, and attending physicians aware that they may request a discharge planning evaluation, and that the hospital will perform an evaluation upon request. Hospitals must perform the evaluation upon request, regardless of whether the patient meets the hospital's screening criteria for an evaluation.

In contrast to the screening process, the evaluation entails a more detailed review of the individual patient's post-discharge needs, in order to identify the specific areas that must be addressed in the discharge plan.

§482.43(b)(4) requires that the evaluation include assessment of the patient's capacity for self-care or, alternatively, to be cared for by others in the environment, i.e., the setting, from which the patient was admitted to the hospital. In general, the goal upon discharge is for a patient to be able to return to the setting in which they were living prior to admission. This may be the patient's home in the community or residence in a nursing home. In the case of transfer from another hospital, generally the preferred goal is to return the patient to the setting from which he/she presented to the transferring hospital.

The evaluation must consider what the patient's care needs will be immediately upon discharge, and whether those needs are expected to remain constant or lessen over time. If the patient was admitted from his/her private residence, the evaluation must include an assessment of whether the patient is capable of addressing his/her care needs through self-care. The evaluation must include assessment of whether the patient will require specialized medical equipment or permanent physical modifications to the home, and the feasibility of acquiring the equipment or the modifications being made. If the patient is not able to provide some or all of the required self-care, the evaluation must also address whether the patient has family or friends available who are willing and able to provide the required care at the times it will be needed, or who could, if willing, be trained by the hospital sufficiently to provide the required care.

§482.43(b)(3) requires the evaluation to consider the patient's likelihood of needing post-hospital services and the availability of such services.

If neither the patient nor the patient's family or informal caregiver(s) are able to address all of the required care needs, then the evaluation must determine whether there are community-based services that are available to meet the patient's needs while allowing the patient to continue living at home.

Such health care services include, but are not limited to:

- Home health, attendant care, and other community-based services;
- Hospice or palliative care;
- Respiratory therapy;
- Rehabilitation services (PT, OT, Speech, etc.);
- End Stage Renal Dialysis services;
- Pharmaceuticals and related supplies;
- Nutritional consultation/supplemental diets; and/or

- Medical equipment and related supplies.

However, services may also include those that are not traditional health care services, but which may be essential to a patient's ongoing ability to live in the community, including, but not limited to:

- Home and physical environment modifications;
- Transportation services;
- Meal services; and/or
- Household services, such as housekeeping, shopping, etc.

Some of the information related to needed services will emerge from the required evaluation of the patient's ability to receive care in the home, either as self-care or provided by someone else. All patients, even those with a high capability for self-care, are likely to require some follow-up ambulatory health care services, e.g., a post-discharge appointment with their surgeon, specialist or primary care physician, or a series of appointments for physical or occupational therapy. Some patients might have more complex care needs which nevertheless may still be met in the home setting, depending on the specific clinical needs and the services available in the patient's community.

For example, some patients require wound care that exceeds the capabilities of their family or others who act as informal caregivers. But they may be able to receive sufficient care in the home setting through a home health service, if such services are available. Some patients with chronic conditions may prefer to remain in their home and would be able to do so using available community-based services, but also require financial supports, such as Medicaid-financed home and community-based waiver services. If such supports are not immediately available at the time of discharge while an application for waiver services is pending, the evaluation should consider the availability of other short term supports that would allow the patient to be discharged home. If the result of the evaluation is that the patient cannot receive required care if he/she returns to home, then an assessment must be made of options for transfer to another inpatient or residential health care facility that can address the patient's needs, including other types of hospitals, such as rehabilitation hospitals; skilled nursing facilities; assisted living facilities; nursing homes; or inpatient hospice facilities.

If prior to the hospital admission the patient was a resident in a facility that he or she wishes to return to, such as an assisted living or nursing facility or skilled nursing facility, the evaluation must address whether that facility has the capability to provide the post-hospital care required by the patient. The post-discharge care requirements may be different than the care that was previously provided. This requires dialogue and cooperation between hospitals and post-hospital care facilities in the area served by the hospital, as well as with the physicians who provide care to patients in either or both of these settings.

Long term care facilities often express concern that hospitals discharge patients to their facilities with care needs that exceed their care capabilities, necessitating sending the patient to the emergency department for care and possible readmission. On the other hand, hospitals often express concern that long term care facilities send patients to the emergency department with ambulatory care-sensitive conditions, i.e., conditions that either do not require an acute level of care, or which could have been prevented from escalating to an acute level had appropriate primary care been provided in a timely manner.

While hospitals cannot address these concerns in isolation, they are expected to be knowledgeable about the care capabilities of area long term care facilities and to factor this knowledge into the discharge planning evaluation.

Hospitals are expected to have knowledge of the capabilities and capacities of not only of long term care facilities, but also of the various types of service providers in the area where most of the patients it serves receive post-hospital care, in order to develop a discharge plan that not only meets the patient's needs in theory, but also can be implemented. This includes knowledge of community services, as well as familiarity with available Medicaid home and community-based services (HCBS), since the State's Medicaid program plays a major role in supporting post-hospital care for many patients. If the hospital is one with specialized services that attract a significant number of patients who will receive their post-hospital care in distant communities, the hospital is expected to take reasonable steps to identify the services that will be available to the patient.

Once the determination has been made that services will be necessary post-discharge, the team must then determine availability of those services or identify comparable substitutions. Included in the evaluation is coordination with insurers and other payors, including the State Medicaid agency, as necessary to ensure resources prescribed are approved and available.

For Information– Not Required/Not to be Cited

Although not required under the regulations, hospitals would be well advised to develop collaborative partnerships with post-hospital care providers to improve care transitions of care that might support better patient outcomes. This includes not only skilled nursing facilities and nursing facilities, but also providers of community-based services. For example, Centers for Independent Living (CIL) and Aging and Disability Resource Centers (ADRC) are resources for community-based services and housing available to persons with disabilities and older adults. Hospitals can find local CIL's at http://www.ilru.org/html/publications/directory/index.html and ADRC's and other resources at http://www.adrc-tae.org/tiki-index.php?page=HomePage.

The ability to pay out of pocket for services must also be discussed with the family or other support persons. Although hospitals are not expected to have definitive knowledge of the terms of any given patient's insurance coverage or eligibility for community-based services, or for Medicaid coverage, they are expected to have a general awareness of these matters and their impact on the patient's post-discharge needs and prospects for recovery. For example, if the patient is a Medicare beneficiary, the hospital is expected to be aware of Medicare coverage requirements for home health care or admission to a rehabilitation hospital, a skilled nursing facility, or a long term care hospital, etc. and to make the beneficiary aware that they may have to pay out of pocket for services not meeting the coverage requirements.

Similarly, for Medicaid, they should know coverage options for home health, attendant care, and long term care services or have contacts at the State Medicaid agency that can assist with these issues. As noted above, hospitals are also expected to have knowledge of community resources to assist in arranging services. Some examples include Aging and Disability Resource Centers and Centers for Independent Living (see box above).

For Information– Not Required/Not to be Cited

Providing a discharge planning tool to patients and their family or other support persons may help to reinforce the discharge plan. Use of the tools may encourage patients' participation in developing the plan as well as provide them an easy-to-follow guide to prepare them for a successful transition from the hospital. The tool should be given to patients on admission, reviewed throughout their stay, and updated prior to discharge.

Examples of available tools include:

- Medicare's "Your Discharge Planning Checklist," (available at http://www.medicare.gov/publications/pubs/pdf/11376.pdf)

- Agency for Healthcare, Research and Quality's (AHRQ) "Taking Care of Myself: A Guide For When I Leave the Hospital," (available at http://www.ahrq.gov/qual/goinghomeguide.pdf)

- Consumers Advancing Patient Safety (CAPS) "Taking Charge of Your Healthcare: Your Path to Being an Empowered Patient Toolkit" (available at http://www.patientsafety.org/page/transtoolkit/).

The hospital CoP governing patients' rights at §482.13(b) provides that "The patient has the right to participate in the development and implementation of his or her plan of care." (CMS views discharge planning as part of the patient's plan of care). "The patient or his/her representative (as allowed under State law) has the right to make informed decisions regarding his/her care" and "The patient's rights include...being involved in care planning and treatment." Accordingly, hospitals are expected to engage the patient, or the patient's representative, actively in the development of the discharge evaluation, not only as a source of information required for the assessment of self-care capabilities, but also to incorporate the patient's goals and preferences as much as possible into the evaluation. A patient's goals and preferences may be, in the hospital's view, unrealistic. Identifying divergent hospital and patient assessments of what is realistic enables a discussion of these differences and may result in an assessment and subsequent development of a discharge plan that has a better chance of successful implementation.

For Information – Not Required/Not to be Cited

If a patient exercises the right to refuse to participate in the discharge planning evaluation, documentation of the refusal is recommended in the medical record.

Survey Procedures §482.43(b)(1), §482.43(b)(3) & §482.43(b)(4)

- In every unit with inpatient beds surveyed, is there evidence of discharge planning evaluation activities?

- Are staff members who are responsible for discharge planning evaluation correctly following the hospital's policies and procedures?

- If the hospital does not require a discharge planning evaluation for all inpatients:

  - Does the hospital have a standard process for notifying patients, their representative, and physicians that they may request a discharge planning evaluation and that the hospital will conduct an evaluation upon request?

  - Can discharge planning and unit nursing staff describe the process for a patient or the patient's representative to request a discharge planning evaluation?

  - Interview patients and their representatives. If they say they were not aware they could request a discharge planning evaluation, can the hospital provide evidence they received notice of their right?

  - Interview attending physicians to see if they are aware they can request a discharge planning evaluation. If they are not aware, can the hospital provide evidence of how they inform the medical staff about this?

- Review a sample of cases to determine if the discharge planning evaluation documents the patient's (or the patient's representatives) goals and preferences for post-discharge placement and care.

- Review a sample of cases to determine if the discharge planning evaluation includes an assessment of:

  - The patient's post-discharge care needs being met in the environment from which he/she entered the hospital? What the patient's care needs will be immediately upon discharge, and whether those needs are expected to remain constant or lessen over time?

  - The patient's insurance coverage (if applicable) and how that coverage might or might not provide for necessary services post-hospitalization?

  - For patients admitted from home --

    - Whether the patient can perform activities of daily living (personal hygiene and grooming, dressing and undressing, feeding, voluntary control over bowel and bladder, ambulation, etc.)?

    - The patient's or family/other support person's ability to provide self-care/care?

    - Whether the patient will require specialized medical equipment or home modification?

      - If yes, did the evaluation include an assessment of whether the equipment is available or if the modifications can be made to safely discharge the patient to that setting?

    - If the patient or family/support person is unable to meet care needs or there are additional care needs above their capabilities, did the evaluation include an assessment of available community-based services to meet post-hospital needs?

  - For patients admitted from a nursing facility, skilled nursing facility or assisted living facility did the evaluation assess whether the prior facility has the capability to provide necessary post-hospital services to the patient (i.e. is the same, higher, or lower level of care required and can those needs be met?)If yes, is there any documentation that the patient's care needs fall within the capabilities of the facility?

  - Are the results of the discharge planning evaluation documented in the medical record?

A-0807
(Rev. 87, Issued: 07-19-13, Effective: 07-19-13, Implementation: 07-19-13)

§482.43(b)(2) - A registered nurse, social worker, or other appropriately qualified personnel must develop, or supervise the development of, the evaluation.

Interpretive Guidelines §482.43(b)(2)

The patient's discharge planning evaluation must be developed by a registered nurse, social worker, or other appropriate qualified personnel, or by a person who is supervised by such personnel. State law governs the qualifications required to be considered a registered nurse or a social worker. The hospital's written discharge planning policies and procedures must specify the qualifications for personnel other than registered nurses or social workers who develop or supervise the development of the evaluation.

The qualifications must include such factors as previous experience in discharge planning, knowledge of clinical and social factors that affect the patient's functional status at discharge, knowledge of community resources to meet post-discharge clinical and social needs, and assessment skills. All personnel performing or supervising discharge planning evaluations, including registered nurses and social workers, must have knowledge of clinical, social, insurance/financial and physical factors that must be considered when evaluating how a patient's expected post-discharge care needs can be met. It is acceptable for a hospital to include new staff who may not have had previous discharge planning experience, but who are being trained to perform discharge planning duties and whose work is reviewed by qualified personnel.

For Information – Not Required/Not to be Cited

A well designed discharge planning evaluation process uses a multidisciplinary team approach. Team members may include representatives from nursing, case management, social work, medical staff, pharmacy, physical therapy, occupational therapy, respiratory therapy, dietary, and other health care professionals involved with the patient's care. The team approach helps to ensure that all of the patient's post-discharge care needs are identified, so that they can be taken into consideration when developing the evaluation.

Survey Procedures §482.43(b)(2)

- Review a sample of cases to determine if the discharge planning evaluation was developed by an RN, Social Worker, or other qualified personnel, as defined in the hospital discharge planning policies and procedures, or someone they supervise? In order to assess this:

  o Review the hospital's written policy and procedure governing who is responsible for developing or supervising the development of the discharge planning evaluation. Does the policy permit someone other than a RN or social worker to be responsible for developing or supervising such evaluations? If yes, does the policy specify the qualifications of the personnel other than a RN or social worker to perform this function?

- Determine which individual(s) is(are) responsible for developing or supervising discharge planning evaluations. Review their personnel folders to determine if they are a RN, social worker, or meet the hospital's criteria for developing/supervising the discharge planning evaluation. If they are not, are they supervised by an individual who is an RN, social worker or is qualified according to the hospital's policies? Are their discharge planning evaluations reviewed by their supervisor before being finalized?

- Ask personnel who supervise or develop discharge planning evaluations to give examples illustrating how they apply their knowledge of clinical, social, insurance/financial and physical factors when performing an evaluation.

A-0810
(Rev. 87, Issued: 07-19-13, Effective: 07-19-13, Implementation: 07-19-13)

§482.43(b)(5) - The hospital personnel must complete the evaluation on a timely basis so that appropriate arrangements for post-hospital care are made before discharge, and to avoid unnecessary delays in discharge.

Interpretive Guidelines §482.43(b)(5)

After a patient has been identified as needing an evaluation, or after a request for an evaluation has been made by the physician, patient and/or patient's representative, the evaluation must be completed timely. This means there must be sufficient time after completion to allow arrangements for post-hospital care to be made, without having to delay the patient's discharge in order to do so, or requiring the patient to transfer to a different setting from where he/she was admitted from primarily due to the delay in making appropriate arrangements. The comparatively short average length of stay of a short term acute care hospital inpatient necessitates prompt attention to patients' discharge planning needs in that type of hospital. Failure to complete the evaluation in a timely manner could make it more difficult to implement the patient's final discharge plan, and/or may cause an unnecessary delay in the patient's discharge from the hospital. While other types of hospitals with a longer average length of stay may be able to complete the evaluation at a later point after admission, they too must complete it on a timely basis to avoid delays in discharge.

Where a team approach is utilized by the hospital in developing the discharge planning evaluation, there must be a process to promote efficient collaboration among team members to complete the evaluation in a timely manner. Changes in patient condition throughout the hospitalization warrant adjustments to the discharge plan.

Survey Procedures §482.43(b)(5)

* Review a sample of cases to determine if the discharge planning evaluation was completed on a timely basis to allow for appropriate arrangements to be made for post-hospital care and to avoid delays in discharge. In order to assess this:

  * Determine when the discharge planning evaluation was initiated. If the evaluation was not begun within 24 hours of the request or identification of the need for an evaluation, ask why.

  * Is there a pattern of delayed start or completion of the evaluation? If so, is the delay due to circumstances beyond the hospital's control (e.g., inability to reach the beneficiary's support person(s), continuing changes in the patient's condition) and/or is the delay due to the hospital's failure to develop timely discharge planning evaluations?

A-0811
(Rev. 87, Issued: 07-19-13, Effective: 07-19-13, Implementation: 07-19-13)

§482.43(b)(6) - The hospital … must discuss the results of the evaluation with the patient or individual acting on his or her behalf.

Interpretive Guidelines §482.43(b)(6)

The results of the discharge planning evaluation must be discussed with the patient or the patient's representative. Documentation of this communication must be included in the medical record, including if the patient rejects the results of the evaluation. It is not necessary for the hospital to obtain a signature from the patient (or the patient's representative, as applicable) documenting the discussion.

The patient or the patient's representative must be actively engaged in the development of the plan, so that the discussion of the evaluation results represents a continuation of this active engagement. It would not be appropriate for a hospital to conduct an evaluation without the participation of the patient or the patient's representative, and then present the results of the evaluation to the patient as a finished product, since this would place the patient in a passive position that is not consistent with the requirements of the patients' rights CoP at §482.13(b).

Survey Procedures §482.43(b)(6)

* Review a sample of cases to determine if the discharge planning evaluation results were discussed with the patient or the patient's representative.

A-0812
(Rev. 87, Issued: 07-19-13, Effective: 07-19-13, Implementation: 07-19-13)

§482.43(b)(6) – [The hospital must] include the discharge planning evaluation in the patient's medical record for use in establishing an appropriate discharge plan….

Interpretive Guidelines §482.43(b)(6)

The hospital must include the discharge planning evaluation in the patient's medical record in order for it to guide the development of the patient's discharge plan. Timely placement of the evaluation in the medical record facilitates communication among members of the patient's healthcare team who should participate in a multidisciplinary process to develop and implement the discharge plan. The evaluation and subsequent planning process may be a continuous one and hospitals may choose not to divide the process into distinct documents. The key requirement is that the evaluation results are included in the patient's medical record and are used in the development of the features of the discharge plan.

Survey Procedures §482.43(b)(6)

- Review a sample of cases to determine if the discharge planning evaluation results are included in the medical record.

A-0818
(Rev. 87, Issued: 07-19-13, Effective: 07-19-13, Implementation: 07-19-13)

§482.43(c) Standard: Discharge Plan

(1) - A registered nurse, social worker, or other appropriately qualified personnel must develop, or supervise the development of, a discharge plan if the discharge planning evaluation indicates a need for a discharge plan.

Interpretive Guidelines §482.43(c)(1)

The discharge plan that is based on the findings of the discharge planning evaluation must be developed by a registered nurse, social worker, or other appropriate qualified personnel, or by a person who is supervised by such personnel. State law governs the qualifications required to be considered a registered nurse or a social worker. The hospital's written discharge planning policies and procedures must specify the qualifications for personnel other than registered nurses or social workers who develop or supervise the development of the plan.

The qualifications should include such factors as previous experience in discharge planning, knowledge of clinical and social factors that affect the patient's functional status at discharge, knowledge of community resources to meet post-discharge clinical and social needs, and assessment skills. All personnel performing or supervising development of discharge plans, including registered nurses and social workers, must have knowledge of clinical, social, insurance/financial and physical factors that must be considered when evaluating how a patient's expected post-discharge care needs can be met.

For Information – Not Required/Not to be Cited

A well designed discharge planning process uses a multidisciplinary team approach. Team members may include representatives from nursing, case management, social work, medical staff, pharmacy, physical therapy, occupational therapy, respiratory therapy, dietary, and other healthcare professionals involved with the patient's care. The team approach helps to ensure all of the patient's post-discharge care needs are addressed in the plan, increasing the likelihood of successful recovery and avoidance of complications and readmissions.

The hospital CoP governing patients' rights at §482.13(b) provides that "The patient has the right to participate in the development and implementation of his or her plan of care." (CMS views discharge planning as part of the patient's plan of care). "The patient or his/her representative (as allowed under State law) has the right to make informed decisions regarding his/her care" and "The patient's rights include...being involved in care planning and treatment." Accordingly, hospitals are expected to engage the patient, or the patient's representative, actively in the development of the discharge plan, not only to provide them the necessary education and training to provide self-care/care, but also to incorporate the patient's goals and preferences as much as possible into the plan. A patient will be more likely to cooperate in the implementation of a discharge plan that reflects his/her preferences, increasing the likelihood of a successful care transition and better health outcomes.

A patient's goals and preferences may be, in the hospital's view, unrealistic. A hospital is not obligated to develop a discharge plan that cannot be implemented. However, the fact that a plan incorporating the patient's goals and preferences might be more time-consuming for the hospital to develop and implement than another alternative does not make the patient's preferred plan unrealistic.

For Information – Not Required/Not to be Cited

If a patient exercises the right to refuse to participate in discharge planning or to implement a discharge plan, documentation of the refusal in the medical record is recommended.

Survey Procedures §482.43(c)(1)

- Review a sample of cases to determine if the discharge plan was developed by an RN, Social Worker, or other qualified personnel, as defined in the hospital discharge planning policies and procedures, or someone they supervise? In order to assess this:

  - Review the hospital's written policy and procedure governing who is responsible for developing or supervising the development of the discharge plan. Does the policy permit someone other than a RN or social worker to be responsible for developing or supervising development of such plans? If yes, does the policy specify the qualifications of the personnel other than a RN or social worker to perform this function?

  - Determine which individual(s) are responsible for developing or supervising the development of discharge plans. Review their personnel folders to determine if they are a RN, social worker, or meet the hospital's criteria for developing/supervising the discharge plan. If they are not, are they supervised by an individual who is an RN, social worker or qualified according to the hospital's policies? Are their discharge plans reviewed by their supervisor before being finalized?

  - Ask personnel who supervise or develop discharge plans to give examples illustrating their knowledge of healthcare and other resources available in the community that could be utilized to meet patients' expected post-discharge care needs.

- Ask the discharge planner how the patient or patient's representative is engaged to participate in the development of the discharge plan. Does the discharge plan identify the patient's or patient's representative discharge preferences?

- Does the discharge plan match the identified needs as determined by the discharge planning evaluation?

A-0819
(Rev. 87, Issued: 07-19-13, Effective: 07-19-13, Implementation: 07-19-13)

§482.43(c)(2) In the absence of a finding by the hospital that a patient needs a discharge plan, the patient's physician may request a discharge plan. In such a case, the hospital must develop a discharge plan for the patient.

Interpretive Guidelines §482.43(c)(2)

If a patient is not identified through the hospital's discharge planning evaluation process as requiring a discharge plan, the patient's physician may nevertheless request a discharge plan. The hospital must develop a discharge plan when requested to do so by the patient's physician.

If the hospital's policies and procedures call for a discharge plan for every hospital inpatient, then it is not necessary to include a separate provision in those policies requiring development of a plan upon physician request, since such a provision would be superfluous.

Survey Procedures §482.43(c)(2)

- Review the hospital's discharge planning policies and procedures to determine whether it requires the development of a discharge plan for all inpatients, or only for those identified as needing a plan through a risk-based identification and evaluation process.

- If the hospital does not require a discharge planning evaluation for all inpatients:

    - Does the hospital have a standard process for notifying physicians that they may request a discharge plan evaluation and that the hospital will develop a plan upon request?

        - Interview attending physicians to see if they are aware they can request a discharge plan. If they are not aware they can request a discharge plan, can the hospital provide evidence of how they inform the medical staff about this?

A-0820
(Rev. 87, Issued: 07-19-13, Effective: 07-19-13, Implementation: 07-19-13)

§482.43(c)(3) - The hospital must arrange for the initial implementation of the patient's discharge plan....

§482.43(c)(5) - As needed, the patient and family members or interested persons must be counseled to prepare them for post-hospital care.

Interpretive Guidelines §482.43(c)(3) & §482.43(c)(5)

The hospital is required to arrange for the initial implementation of the discharge plan. This includes providing in-hospital education/training to the patient for self-care or to the patient's family or other support person(s) who will be providing care in the patient's home. It also includes arranging:

- Transfers to rehabilitation hospitals, long term care hospitals, or long term care facilities;

- Referrals to home health or hospice agencies;

- Referral for follow-up with physicians/practitioners, occupational or physical therapists, etc.;

- Referral to medical equipment suppliers; and

- Referrals to pertinent community resources that may be able to assist with financial, transportation, meal preparation, or other post-discharge needs.

(See §482.43(d) for more discussion about the hospital's transfer or referral obligations and the initial implementation of the plan relating to transfer/referral.)

The discharge planning process is a collaborative one that must include the participation of the patient and the patient's informal caregiver or representative, when applicable. In addition, other family or support persons who will be providing care to the patient after discharge need to be engaged in the process. Keeping the patient, and, when applicable, the patient's representative and other support persons informed throughout the development of the plan is essential for its success. Providing them with information on post-discharge options, what to expect after discharge and, as applicable, instruction and training in how to provide care is essential. The patient needs clear instructions regarding what to do when concerns, issues, or problems arise, including who to call and when they should seek emergency assistance. Although it may be an important component of the discharge instructions, it is not acceptable to only advise a patient to "return to the ED" whenever problems arise.

There are a variety of tools and techniques that have focused on improving the support provided to patients who are discharged back to their homes. A comprehensive approach employing combinations of these techniques has been found to improve patient outcomes and reduce hospital readmission rates, including, but not limited to:

- Improved education) to patients and support persons regarding disease processes, medications, treatments, diet and nutrition, expected symptoms, and when and how to seek additional help. Teaching methods must be based on recognized methodologies. CMS does not prescribe any specific methodologies, but examples include the teach-back, repeat-back approach and simulation laboratories;

- Written discharge instructions, in the form of checklists when possible, that are legible, in plain language, culturally sensitive and age appropriate;

- Providing supplies, such as materials for changing dressings on wounds, needed immediately post-discharge; and

- A list of all medications the patient should be taking after discharge, with clear indication of changes from the patient's pre-admission medications;

The education and training provided to the patient or the patient's caregiver(s) by the hospital must be tailored to the patient's identified needs related to medications, treatment modalities, physical and occupational therapies, psychosocial needs, appointments, and other follow-up activities, etc. Repeated review of instructions with return demonstrations and/or repeat-backs by the patient, and their support persons will improve their ability to deliver care properly. This includes providing instructions in writing as well as verbally reinforcing the education and training.

It is also necessary to provide information to patients and their support persons when the patient is being transferred to a rehabilitation or a long term care hospital, or to a long term care setting, such as a skilled nursing facility or nursing facility. The information should address questions such as: the goal of treatment in the next setting and prospects for the patient's eventual discharge home.

The hospital must document in the patient's medical record the arrangements made for initial implementation of the discharge plan, including training and materials provided to the patient or patient's informal caregiver or representative, as applicable.

For Information – Not Required/Not to be Cited

Additional actions hospitals might consider taking to improve the patient's post-discharge care transition:

- Scheduling follow-up appointments with the patient's primary care physician/practitioner and in-home providers of service as applicable;

- Filling prescriptions prior to discharge;

- If applicable, arranging remote monitoring technologies, e.g., pulse oximetry and daily weights for congestive heart failure (CHF) patients; pulse and blood pressure monitoring for cardiac patients; and blood glucose levels for diabetic patients; and

- Follow-up phone calls within 24 -72 hours by the hospital to the patient after discharge.

The communication with the patient to ensure implementation of the discharge plan does not stop at discharge. An initiative showing significant success in reducing preventable readmissions involves the hospital contacting the patient by phone in the first 24 to 72 hours after discharge. The phone contact provides an opportunity for the patient to pose questions and for the hospital to address any confusion related to medications, diet, activity, etc., and to reinforce the education/instruction that took place in the hospital prior to discharge. This also helps to reduce patient and family member anxieties as they

---

manage post-hospital care needs.

Hospital staff placing the calls should be familiar with the patient's discharge plan and qualified to address typical questions that might be expected. They should also be knowledgeable about when to instruct the patient to seek a more immediate evaluation, including where to go for such evaluation. Although this follow-up phone call can serve as a customer service initiative for the hospital, the primary intent would be to provide an opportunity for questions and to reduce or eliminate any confusion or concerns regarding post-hospital care.

Survey Procedures §482.43(c)(3) & §482.43(c)(5)

- Review cases of discharged patients to determine if the hospital arranges initial implementation of the discharge plan by providing:

  - For patients discharged to home:

  - In-hospital training to patient and family/support persons, using recognized methods;

  - Written discharge instructions that are legible and use non-technical language;

  - A legible, complete, reconciled medication list that highlights changes from the post hospital regimen;
  - Referrals as applicable to specialized ambulatory services, e.g. physical therapy, occupational therapy, home health, hospice, mental health, etc.;

  - Referrals as applicable to community-based resources other than health services, e.g. Departments of Aging, elder services, transportation services, Centers for Independent Living, Aging and Disability Resource Centers, etc.;

  - Arranging essential durable medical equipment, e.g. oxygen, wheel chair, hospital bed, commode, etc.;

  - Sending necessary medical information to providers that the patient was referred to prior to the first post-discharge appointment or within 7 days of discharge, whichever comes first; and

  - For patients transferred to another inpatient facility, was necessary medical information ready at time of transfer and sent to the receiving facility with the patient?

- Were there portions of the plan the hospital failed to begin implementing, resulting in delays in discharge?

A-0821
(Rev. 87, Issued: 07-19-13, Effective: 07-19-13, Implementation: 07-19-13)

§482.43(c)(4) - The hospital must reassess the patient's discharge plan if there are factors that may affect continuing care needs or the appropriateness of the discharge plan.

Interpretive Guidelines §482.43(c)(4)

Changes in a patient's condition may warrant adjustments to the discharge plan. Hospitals must have in place either a routine reassessment of all plans or a process for triggering a reassessment of the patient's post-discharge needs, capabilities and discharge plan when significant changes in the patient's condition or available supports occur.

Survey Procedures §482.43(c)(4)

- Review a sample of cases to determine if any significant changes in the patient's condition were noted in the medical record that changed post-discharge needs, and if the discharge plan was updated accordingly.

    - In making this determination, ask staff responsible for discharge planning when and how they reassess a patient's discharge plan. If none of the records being used for the tracers suggest a need to revise the discharge plan, ask staff to present one or more clinical records that document reassessment.

A-0823
(Rev. 87, Issued: 07-19-13, Effective: 07-19-13, Implementation: 07-19-13)

§482.43(c)(6) - The hospital must include in the discharge plan a list of HHAs or SNFs that are available to the patient, that are participating in the Medicare program, and that serve the geographic area (as defined by the HHA) in which the patient resides, or in the case of a SNF, in the geographic area requested by the patient. HHAs must request to be listed by the hospital as available.

(i) - This list must only be presented to patients for whom home health care or post-hospital extended care services are indicated and appropriate as determined by the discharge planning evaluation.

(ii) - For patients enrolled in managed care organizations, the hospital must indicate the availability of home health and post-hospital extended care services through individuals and entities that have a contract with the managed care organizations. (iii) The hospital must document in the patient's medical record that the list was presented to the patient or to the individual acting on the patient's behalf.

§482.43(c)(7) The hospital, as part of the discharge planning process, must inform the patient or the patient's family of their freedom to choose among participating Medicare providers of post-hospital care services and must, when possible, respect patient and family preferences when they are expressed. The hospital must not specify or otherwise limit the qualified providers that are available to the patient.

§482.43(c)(8) The discharge plan must identify any HHA or SNF to which the patient is referred in which the hospital has a disclosable financial interest, as specified by the Secretary, and any HHA or SNF that has a disclosable financial interest in a hospital under Medicare. Financial interests that are disclosable under Medicare are determined in accordance with the provisions of Part 420, Subpart C, of this chapter.

Interpretative Guidelines §482.43(c)(6), §482.43(c)(7) & §482.43(c)(8)

The hospital must include a list of Medicare-participating home health agencies (HHAs) and skilled nursing facilities (SNFs) in the discharge plan for those patients for whom the plan indicates home health or post-hospital extended care services are required.

- "Extended care services" are defined at sections 1861(h) and (i) of the Social Security Act as items or services furnished in a skilled nursing facility (SNF). SNFs included on the list must be located in a geographic area that the patient or patient's representative indicated he/she prefers.

- For Home Health Agencies (HHAs) the list must consist of Medicare-participating HHAs that have requested the hospital to be listed and which serve the geographic area where the patient lives. Hospitals may expect the HHA to define its geographic service area when it submits its request to be listed.

During the discharge planning process the hospital must inform the patient of his/her freedom to choose among Medicare-participating post-hospital providers and must not direct the patient to specific provider(s) or otherwise limit which qualified providers the patient may choose among. Hospitals have the flexibility either to develop their own lists or to print a list of skilled nursing facilities and home health agencies in the applicable geographic areas from the CMS websites, Nursing Home Compare (www.medicare.gov/NHcompare) and Home Health Compare (www.medicare.gov/homehealthcompare). If hospitals develop their own lists, they are expected to update them at least annually. (69 FR 49226, August 11, 2004)

For Information – Not Required/Not to be Cited

Hospitals may also refer patients and their families to the Nursing Home Compare and Home Health Compare websites for additional information regarding Medicare-certified skilled nursing facilities and home health agencies, as well as Medicaid-participating

---

nursing facilities.

The data on the Nursing Home Compare website include an overall performance rating, nursing home characteristics, performance on quality measures, inspection results, and nursing staff information.

Home Health Compare provides details about every Medicare-certified home health agency in the country. Included on the website are quality indicators such as managing daily activities, managing pain and treating symptoms, treating wounds and preventing pressure sores, preventing harm, and preventing unplanned hospital care.

The hospital might also refer the patient and their representatives to individual State agency websites, Long-Term Care Ombudsmen Program, Protection and Advocacy Organizations, Citizen Advocacy Groups, Area Agencies on Aging, Centers for Independent Living, and Aging and Disability Resource Centers for additional information on long term care facilities and other types of providers of post-hospital care. Having access to the information found at these sources may assist in the decision making process regarding post-hospital care options.

If the patient is enrolled in a managed care insurance program that utilizes a network of exclusive or preferred providers, the hospital must make reasonable attempts, based on information from the insurer, to limit the list to HHAs and SNFs that participate in the insurer's network of providers.

If the hospital has a disclosable financial interest in a HHA or SNF on a patient's list, or an HHA or SNF on the list has a disclosable financial interest in the hospital, these facts must also be stated on the list provided to the patient. Surveyors are not expected to know the requirements for a disclosable financial interest under Part 420, Subpart C, but hospitals are expected to know and comply with these requirements, and to identify for the surveyor whether there are such disclosable financial interests between the hospital and any specific HHAs or SNFs to which they refer/transfer patients.

When the patient or the patient's family has expressed a preference, the hospital must attempt to arrange post-hospital care with an HHA or SNF, as applicable, which meets these preferences. If the hospital is unable to make the preferred arrangement, e.g., if there is no bed available in the preferred SNF, it must document the reason the patient's preference could not be fulfilled and must explain that reason to the patient.

Survey Procedures §482.43(c)(6), §482.43(c)(7) & §482.43(c)(8):

- Review a sample of cases of patients discharged to HHAs or SNFs to determine if, when applicable, the hospital provided the patient with lists of Medicare-participating HHAs or SNFs. In making this determination:

- Is there documentation of a list of multiple HHAs or SNFs being provided (including electronically) to the patient? If not, is there documentation for an acceptable rationale for providing only one option, e.g., the patient's home is included in the service area of only one Medicare-participating HHA that requested to be included on hospital lists, or there is only one Medicare-participating SNF in the area preferred by the patient?

- Ask to see examples of lists of HHAs and SNFs provided to patients prior to discharge.

- Ask the hospital if it has any disclosable financial interests in any HHA or SNF on its lists, or if an HHA or SNF has a disclosable financial interest in the hospital. If yes, is this stated clearly on the lists?

- Interview staff members involved with the discharge planning process. Ask them to describe how patient preferences are taken into account in the selection of post-hospital HHA or SNF services.

- Ask the hospital to identify current patients for whom HHA or SNF services are planned. Interview the patient or the patient's family to ask them:

  - Were they presented with a list of HHAs or SNFs, as applicable, to choose from?

  - Did the hospital emphasize their freedom of choice?

  - Did the hospital arrange for their referral/transfer to an HHA or SNF reflecting their preferences? If not, did the hospital explain why their choice was not feasible?

  - If applicable, were they made aware of disclosable financial interest?

A-0837
(Rev. 87, Issued: 07-19-13, Effective: 07-19-13, Implementation: 07-19-13)

§482.43(d) Standard: Transfer or Referral

The hospital must transfer or refer patients, along with necessary medical information, to appropriate facilities, agencies, or outpatient services, as needed, for follow-up or ancillary care.

Interpretive Guidelines §482.43(d)

The hospital must take steps to ensure that patients receive appropriate post-hospital care by arranging, as applicable, transfer to appropriate facilities or referrals to follow-up ambulatory care services.

"Appropriate facilities, agencies, or outpatient services" refers to entities such as skilled nursing facilities, nursing facilities, home health agencies, hospice agencies, mental health agencies, dialysis centers, suppliers of durable medical equipment, suppliers of physical and occupational therapy, physician offices, etc. which offer post-acute care services that address the patient's post-hospital needs identified in the patient's discharge planning evaluation. The term does not refer to non-healthcare entities, but hospitals also are encouraged to make appropriate referrals to community-based resources that offer transportation, meal preparation, and other services that can play an essential role in the patient's successful recovery.

"Appropriate facilities" may also include other hospitals to which a patient is transferred for follow-up care, such as rehabilitation hospitals, long term care hospitals, or even other short-term acute care hospitals.

Necessary medical information must be provided not only for patients being transferred, but also for those being discharged home, to make the patient's physician aware of the outcome of hospital treatment or follow-up care needs. This is particularly important since the increasing use of hospitalists in the inpatient hospital setting means the patient's physician may have had no interaction with the patient throughout the hospital stay. When the hospital provides the patient's physician with necessary medical information promptly, among other things, this provides an opportunity for the patient's physician to discuss with the hospital care team changes to the patient's preadmission medication regimen or other elements of the post-discharge care plan about which the physician may have questions. Facilitating opportunities for such communication and dialogue enhances the likelihood of better patient outcomes after discharge.

The "medical information" that is necessary for the transfer or referral includes, but is not limited to:

- Brief reason for hospitalization (or, if hospital policy requires a discharge summary for certain types of outpatient services, the reason for the encounter) and principal diagnosis;
- Brief description of hospital course of treatment;

- Patient's condition at discharge, including cognitive and functional status and social supports needed;

- Medication list (reconciled to identify changes made during the patient's hospitalization) including prescription and over-the-counter medications and herbal. (Note, an actual list of medications needs to be included in the discharge information, not just a referral to an electronic list available somewhere else in the medical record.);

- List of allergies (including food as well as drug allergies) and drug interactions;

- Pending laboratory work and test results, if applicable, including information on how the results will be furnished;

- For transfer to other facilities, a copy of the patient's advance directive, if the patient has one; and

- For patients discharged home:

  - Brief description of care instructions reflecting training provided to patient and/or family or other informal caregiver(s);

  - If applicable, list of all follow-up appointments with practitioners with which the patient has an established relationship and which were scheduled prior to discharge, including who the appointment is with, date and time.

  - If applicable, referrals to potential primary care providers, such as health clinics, if available, for patients with no established relationship with a practitioner.

The regulation requires transfer or referral "along" with necessary medical information. In the case of a patient being transferred to another inpatient or residential health care facility, the necessary information must accompany the patient to the facility. However, in the case of a patient discharged home who is being referred for follow-up ambulatory care, the transmittal of the information to the patient's physician may take place up to 7 days after discharge or prior to the first appointment for ambulatory care services that may have been scheduled, whichever comes first. If the patient's physician is not yet able to accept the information electronically from the hospital, the hospital may provide the information to the patient with instructions to give this information to the physician at their next appointment.

For Information – Not Required/Not to be Cited

Scheduling of follow-up appointments for ambulatory care services by the hospital prior to discharge has been found to be an effective tool to ensure prompt follow-up and reduce the likelihood of a preventable readmission. This follow-up visit shortly after discharge provides an opportunity for the patient to address any issues or concerns experienced after the inpatient stay. It also provides an opportunity for the primary care physician or practitioner to review and reinforce the post-hospital plan of care with the patient, for

---

> rehabilitation therapy to begin in a timely manner, to clarify any concerns related to medication reconciliation or other adjustments to the patient's pre-hospital regimen, etc.

It is recognized that hospitals have certain constraints on their ability to accomplish patient transfers and referrals:

- They must operate within the constraints of their authority under State law;

- A patient may refuse transfer or referral; or

- There may be financial barriers limiting a facility's, agency's, or ambulatory care service provider's willingness to accept the patient. In such cases the hospital does not have financial responsibility for the post-acute care services. However, hospitals are expected to be knowledgeable about resources available in their community to address such financial barriers, such as Medicaid services, availability of Federally Quality Health Centers, Area Agencies on Aging, etc., and to take steps to make those resources available to the patient. For example, in most states hospitals work closely with the Medicaid program to expedite enrollment of patients eligible for Medicaid.

Survey Procedures §482.43(d)

- Review a sample of records for discharged patients who had a discharge plan to determine if:

  - For patients discharged home:

    - Necessary medical information was sent to a practitioner with which the patient has an established relationship prior to the first post-discharge appointment or within 7 days of discharge, whichever comes first;

    - For patients without an established relationship with a practitioner, information was provided on potential primary care providers, such as health clinics, if available.

  - For patients transferred to another inpatient facility, was necessary medical information ready at time of transfer and sent to the receiving facility with the patient?

  - When applicable, there is documentation in the medical record of providing the results of tests, pending at time of discharge, to the patient and/or post-hospital provider of care?

A-0843
(Rev. 87, Issued: 07-19-13, Effective: 07-19-13, Implementation: 07-19-13)

§483.43(e) Standard: Reassessment

The hospital must reassess its discharge planning process on an on-going basis. The reassessment must include a review of discharge plans to ensure that they are responsive to discharge needs.

Interpretive Guidelines §483.43(e)

The hospital must reassess the effectiveness of its discharge planning process on an ongoing basis. Since the QAPI CoP at §482.21 requires the QAPI program to be hospital-wide, the discharge planning reassessment process is considered an integral component of the overall hospital QAPI program.

The hospital must have a mechanism in place for ongoing reassessment of its discharge planning process. The reassessment process must include a review of discharge plans in closed medical records to determine whether they were responsive to the patient's post-discharge needs. One indicator of the effectiveness of the discharge plan is whether or not the discharge was followed by a preventable readmission. Accordingly, hospitals are expected to track their readmission rates and identify potentially preventable readmissions.

Typically readmissions at 7, 15, 30 days, or even longer, after discharge are tracked by analysts studying readmissions to short-term acute care hospitals. Hospitals must choose at least one interval to track. Since there are National Quality Forum-endorsed readmissions measures that use a 30-day interval, and since such measures are permitted by law to be used by CMS for payment-related purposes, it might be prudent for a hospital to track its 30-day readmissions rate, but other intervals are permissible. It is understood that information on post-discharge admissions to other hospitals may not be not readily available to hospitals, but all hospitals are expected to track readmissions to their own hospital, and to do so on an ongoing basis, i.e., at least quarterly. Hospitals may employ various methodologies to identify potentially preventable readmissions. There are proprietary products that, for example, use claims data to identify such cases. Hospitals are expected to document their methodology for tracking their readmissions rates.

Once the hospital has identified potentially preventable readmissions, it is expected to conduct an in-depth review of the discharge planning process for a sample of such readmissions (at least 10% of potentially preventable readmissions, or 15 cases/quarter, whichever is larger is suggested but not required) in order to determine whether there was an appropriate discharge planning evaluation, discharge plan, and implementation of the discharge plan.

Hospitals are also expected to follow up on trends identified through analysis of their readmissions, such as a concentration of readmissions related to post-surgical infections, discharges from a particular service or unit, discharges to a particular extended care facility or home health agency, discharges with the same primary diagnosis on the first admission, etc. Such clustering or concentration may identify areas requiring more follow-up analysis and potential remedial actions.

Having identified factors that contribute to preventable readmissions, hospitals are expected to revise their discharge planning and related processes to address these factors. Consistent with the requirements under the QAPI CoP, the hospital's governing body, medical leadership and administrative leadership are all expected to ensure that identified problems are addressed, with further ongoing reassessment to achieve improvement.

Survey Procedures §482.43(e)

- Review hospital policies and procedures to determine whether the discharge planning process is reassessed on an ongoing basis, i.e., at least quarterly.

- Does the hospital's discharge planning reassessment policy include tracking and analysis of readmissions?

    - Do staff know how to obtain data on readmissions that enables them to review the discharge plans for the initial admission? Ask them to identify medical records for patients who were readmitted and to show you the documentation of the review of the discharge planning process for the initial admission.

- Does the assessment of readmissions include an evaluation of whether the readmissions were potentially preventable?

    - Is there evidence of in-depth analysis of a sample of discharge plans in cases where preventable readmissions were identified?

    - Is there evidence that the hospital took action to address factors identified as contributing to preventable readmissions?

A-0884
(Rev. 37, Issued: 10-17-08; Effective/Implementation Date: 10-17-08)

§482.45 Condition of Participation: Organ, Tissue and Eye Procurement

Interpretive Guidelines §482.45:

The hospital must ensure the specific organ, tissue, and eye procurement requirements are met.

A-0885

(Rev. 37, Issued: 10-17-08; Effective/Implementation Date: 10-17-08)

The hospital must have and implement written protocols that:

Interpretive Guidelines §482.45(a)

The hospital must have written policies and procedures to address its organ procurement responsibilities.

A-0886

(Rev. 37, Issued: 10-17-08; Effective/Implementation Date: 10-17-08)

§482.45(a)(1) - Incorporate an agreement with an OPO designated under part 486 of this chapter, under which it must notify, in a timely manner, the OPO or a third party designated by the OPO of individuals whose death is imminent or who have died in the hospital. The OPO determines medical suitability for organ donation and, in the absence of alternative arrangements by the hospital, the OPO determines medical suitability for tissue and eye donation, using the definition of potential tissue and eye donor and the notification protocol developed in consultation with the tissue and eye banks identified by the hospital for this purpose;

Interpretive Guidelines §482.45(a)(1)

The hospital must have a written agreement with an Organ Procurement Organization (OPO), designated under 42 CFR Part 486. At a minimum, the written agreement must address the following:

- The criteria for referral, including the referral of all individuals whose death is imminent or who have died in the hospital;

- Includes a definition of "imminent death";

- Includes a definition of "timely notification";

- Addresses the OPO's responsibility to determine medical suitability for organ donation;

- Specifies how the tissue and/or eye bank will be notified about potential donors using notification protocols developed by the OPO in consultation with the hospital-designated tissue and eye bank(s);

- Provides for notification of each individual death in a timely manner to the OPO (or designated third party) in accordance with the terms of the agreement;

- Ensures that the designated requestor training program offered by the OPO has been developed in cooperation with the tissue bank and eye bank designated by the hospital;

- Permits the OPO, tissue bank, and eye bank access to the hospital's death record information according to a designated schedule, e.g., monthly or quarterly;

- Includes that the hospital is not required to perform credentialing reviews for, or grant privileges to, members of organ recovery teams as long as the OPO sends only "qualified, trained individuals" to perform organ recovery; and

- The interventions the hospital will utilize to maintain potential organ donor patients so that the patient organs remain viable.

Hospitals must notify the OPO of every death or imminent death in the hospital. When death is imminent, the hospital must notify the OPO both before a potential donor is removed from a ventilator and while the potential donor's organs are still viable. The hospital should have a written policy, developed in coordination with the OPO and approved by the hospital's medical staff and governing body, to define "imminent death." The definition for "imminent death" should strike a balance between the needs of the OPO and the needs of the hospital's care givers to continue treatment of a patient until brain death is declared or the patient's family has made the decision to withdraw supportive measures. Collaboration between OPOs and hospitals will create a partnership that furthers donation, while respecting the perspective of hospital staff.

The definition for "imminent death" might include a patient with severe, acute brain injury who:

- Requires mechanical ventilation;

- Is in an intensive care unit (ICU) or emergency department; **AND**

- Exhibits clinical findings consistent with a Glasgow Coma Score that is less than or equal to a mutually-agreed-upon threshold; **or**

- MD/DOs are evaluating a diagnosis of brain death; **or**

- An MD/DO has ordered that life sustaining therapies be withdrawn, pursuant to the family's decision.

Hospitals and their OPO should develop a definition of "imminent death" that includes specific triggers for notifying the OPO about an imminent death.

In determining the appropriate threshold for the Glascow Coma Score (GCS), it is important to remember that if the threshold is too low, there may be too many "premature" deaths or situations where there is a loss of organ viability. Standards for appropriate GCS thresholds may be obtained from the hospital's OPO or organizations such as The Association of Organ Procurement Organizations.

Note that a patient with "severe, acute brain injury" is not always a trauma patient. For example, post myocardial infarction resuscitation may result in a patient with a beating heart and no brain activity.

The definition agreed to by the hospital and the OPO may include all of the elements listed above or just some of the elements. The definition should be tailored to fit the particular circumstances in each hospital.

Hospitals may not use "batch reporting" for deaths by providing the OPO with periodic lists of patient deaths, even if instructed to do so by the OPO. If the patient dies during a transfer from one hospital to another, it is the receiving hospital's responsibility to notify the OPO.

"**Timely notification**" means a hospital must contact the OPO by telephone as soon as possible after an individual has died, has been placed on a ventilator due to a severe brain injury, or who has been declared brain dead (ideally within 1 hour). That is, a hospital must notify the OPO while a brain dead or severely brain-injured, ventilator-dependent individual is still attached to the ventilator and as soon as possible after the death of any other individual, including a potential non-heart-beating donor. Even if the hospital does not consider an individual who is not on a ventilator to be a potential donor, the hospital must call the OPO as soon as possible after the death of that individual has occurred.

Referral by a hospital to an OPO is timely if it is made:

- As soon as it is anticipated that a patient will meet the criteria for imminent death agreed to by the OPO and hospital or as soon as possible after a patient meets the criteria for imminent death agreed to by the OPO and the hospital (ideally, within one hour); **AND**

- Prior to the withdrawal of any life sustaining therapies (i.e., medical or pharmacological support).

Whenever possible, referral should be made early enough to allow the OPO to assess the patient's suitability for organ donation before brain death is declared and before the option of organ donation is presented to the family of the potential donor. Timely assessment of the patient's suitability for organ donation increases the likelihood that the patient's organs will be viable for transplantation (assuming there is no disease process identified by the OPO that would cause the organs to be unsuitable), assures that the family is approached only if the patient is medically suitable for organ donation, and assures that an OPO representative is available to collaborate with the hospital staff in discussing donation with the family.

It is the OPO's responsibility to determine medical suitability for organ donation, and, in the absence of alternative arrangements by the hospital, the OPO determines medical suitability for tissue and eye donation, using the definition of potential tissue and eye donor and the notification protocol developed in consultation with the tissue and eye banks identified by the hospital for this purpose.

Survey Procedures §482.45(a)(1)

- Review the hospital's written agreement with the OPO to verify that it addresses all required information.

- Verify that the hospital's governing body has approved the hospital's organ procurement policies.

- Review a sample of death records to verify that the hospital has implemented its organ procurement policies.

- Interview the staff to verify that they are aware of the hospital's policies and procedures for organ, tissue and eye procurement.

- Verify that the organ, tissue and eye donation program is integrated into the hospital's QAPI program.

A-0887

(Rev. 37, Issued: 10-17-08; Effective/Implementation Date: 10-17-08)

§482.45(a)(2) - Incorporate an agreement with at least one tissue bank and at least one eye bank to cooperate in the retrieval, processing, preservation, storage and distribution of tissues and eyes, as may be appropriate to assure that all usable tissues and eyes are obtained from potential donors, insofar as such an agreement does not interfere with organ procurement;

Interpretative Guidelines §482.45(a)(2)

The hospital must have an agreement with at least one tissue bank and at least one eye bank. The OPO may serve as a "gatekeeper" receiving notification about every hospital death and should notify the tissue bank or eye bank chosen by the hospital about potential tissue and eye donors.

It is not necessary for a hospital to have a separate agreement with a tissue bank if it has an agreement with its OPO to provide tissue procurement services; nor is it necessary for a hospital to have a separate agreement with an eye bank if its OPO provides eye procurement services. The hospital is not required to use the OPO for tissue or eye procurement but is free to have an agreement with the tissue bank or eye bank of its choice. The tissue banks and eye banks define "usable tissues" and "usable eyes."

The requirements of this regulation may be satisfied through a single agreement with an OPO that provides services for organ, tissue and eye, or by a separate agreement with another tissue and/or eye bank outside the OPO, chosen by the hospital. The hospital may continue current successful direct arrangements with tissue and eye banks as long as the direct arrangement does not interfere with organ procurement.

Survey Procedures §482.45(a)(2)

Verify that the hospital has an agreement with at least one tissue bank and one eye bank that specifies criteria for referral of all potential tissue and eye donors, or an agreement with an OPO that specifies the tissue bank and eye bank to which referrals will be made. The agreement should also acknowledge that it is the OPO's responsibility to determine medical suitability for tissue and eye donation, unless the hospital has an alternative agreement with a different tissue and/or eye bank.

A-0888

(Rev. 37, Issued: 10-17-08; Effective/Implementation Date: 10-17-08)

§482.45(a)(3) - Ensure, in collaboration with the designated OPO, that the family of each potential donor is informed of its options to donate organs, tissues, or eyes, or to decline to donate.

Interpretive Guidelines §482.45(a)(3)

It is the responsibility of the OPO to screen for medical suitability in order to select potential donors. Once the OPO has selected a potential donor, that person's family must be informed of the family's donation options.

Ideally, the OPO and the hospital will decide together how and by whom the family will be approached.

Survey Procedures §482.45(a)(3)

- Verify that the hospital ensures that the family of each potential donor is informed of its options to donate organs, tissues, or eyes, including the option to decline to donate.

- Does the hospital have QAPI mechanisms in place to ensure that the families of all potential donors are informed of their options to donate organs, tissues, or eyes, or to decline to donate?

A-0889

(Rev. 37, Issued: 10-17-08; Effective/Implementation Date: 10-17-08)

§482.45(a)(3) - (Continued)

The individual designated by the hospital to initiate the request to the family must be an organ procurement representative or a designated requestor. A designated requestor is an individual who has completed a course offered or approved by the OPO and designed in conjunction with the tissue and eye bank community in the methodology for approaching potential donor families and requesting organ or tissue donation;

Interpretive Guidelines §482.45(a)(3)

The individual designated by the hospital to initiate the request to a family must be an organ procurement representative, an **organizational representative of a tissue or eye bank**, or a designated requestor. Any individuals involved in a request for organ, tissue, and eye donation must be formally trained in the donation request process.

The individual designated by the hospital to initiate the request to the family must be an OPO, tissue bank, or eye bank representative or a designated requestor. A "**designated requestor**" is defined as a hospital-designated individual who has completed a course offered or approved by the OPO and designed in conjunction with the tissue and eye bank community.

Ideally, the OPO and the hospital will decide together how and by whom the family will be approached. If possible, the OPO representative and a designated requestor should approach the family together.

The hospital must ensure that any "designated requestor" for organs, tissues or eyes has completed a training course either offered or approved by the OPO, which addresses methodology for approaching potential donor families.

Survey Procedures §482.45(a)(3)

- Review training schedules and personnel files to verify that all designated requestors have completed the required training.

- How does the hospital ensure that only OPO, tissue bank, or eye bank staff or designated requestors are approaching families to ask them to donate?

A-0890

(Rev. 37, Issued: 10-17-08; Effective/Implementation Date: 10-17-08)

§482.45(a)(4) - Encourage discretion and sensitivity with respect to the circumstances, views, and beliefs of the families of potential donors;

Interpretive Guidelines §482.45(a)(4)

Using discretion does not mean a judgment can be made by the hospital that certain families should not be approached about donation. Hospitals should approach the family with the belief that a donation is possible and should take steps to ensure the family is treated with respect and care. The hospital staff's perception that a family's grief, race, ethnicity, religion or socioeconomic background would prevent donation should never be used as a reason not to approach a family.
All potential donor families must be approached and informed of their donation rights.

Survey Procedures §482.45(a)(4)

- Interview a hospital-designated requestor regarding approaches to donation requests.

- Review the designated requestor training program to verify that it addresses the use of discretion.

- Review the hospital's complaint file for any relevant complaints.

A-0891

(Rev. 37, Issued: 10-17-08; Effective/Implementation Date: 10-17-08)

§482.45(a)(5) - Ensure that the hospital works cooperatively with the designated OPO, tissue bank and eye bank in educating staff on donation issues;

Interpretive Guidelines §482.45(a)(5)

Appropriate hospital staff, including all patient care staff, must be trained on donation issues. The training program must be developed in cooperation with the OPO, tissue bank and eye bank, and should include, at a minimum:

- Consent process;

- Importance of using discretion and sensitivity when approaching families;

- Role of the designated requestor;

- Transplantation and donation, including pediatrics, if appropriate;

- Quality improvement activities; and

- Role of the organ procurement organization.

Training should be conducted with new employees annually, whenever there are policy/procedure changes, or when problems are determined through the hospital's QAPI program.

Those hospital staff who may have to contact or work with the OPO, tissue bank and eye bank staff must have appropriate training on donation issues including their duties and roles.

Survey Procedures §482.45(a)(5)

- Review in-service training schedules and attendance sheets.

- How does the hospital ensure that all appropriate staff has attended an educational program regarding donation issues and how to work with the OPO, tissue bank, and eye bank?

A-0892

(Rev. 37, Issued: 10-17-08; Effective/Implementation Date: 10-17-08)

§482.45(a)(5) - (Continued)

[Ensure that the hospital works cooperatively with the designated OPO, tissue bank and eye bank in educating staff on…] reviewing death records to improve identification of potential donors, and

Interpretive Guidelines §482.45(a)(5)

Hospitals must cooperate with the OPOs, tissue banks and eye banks in regularly or periodically reviewing death records. This means that the hospital must develop policies and procedures which permit the OPO, tissue bank, and eye bank access to death record information that will allow the OPO, tissue bank and eye bank to assess the hospital's donor potential, assure that all deaths or imminent deaths are being referred to the OPO in a timely manner, and identify areas where the hospital, OPO, tissue bank and eye bank staff performance might be improved. The policies must address how patient confidentiality will be maintained during the review process.

Survey Procedures §482.45(a)(5)

- Verify by review of policies and records that the hospital works with the OPO, tissue bank, and eye bank in reviewing death records.
- Verify that the effectiveness of any protocols and policies is monitored as part of the hospital's quality improvement program.

- Validate how often the reviews are to occur. Review the protocols that are in place to guide record reviews and analysis.

- Determine how confidentiality is ensured.

A-0893

(Rev. 37, Issued: 10-17-08; Effective/Implementation Date: 10-17-08)

§482.45(a)(5) - (Continued)

[Ensure that the hospital works cooperatively with the designated OPO, tissue bank and eye bank in educating staff on...] maintaining potential donors while necessary testing and placement of potential donated organs, tissues, and eyes take place.

Interpretive Guidelines §482.45(a)(5)

The hospital must have policies and procedures, developed in cooperation with the OPO, that ensure that potential donors are maintained in a manner that maintains the viability of their organs. The hospital must have policies in place to ensure that potential donors are identified and declared dead within an acceptable time frame by an appropriate practitioner.

Survey Procedures §482.45(a)(5)

- Determine by review, what policies and procedures are in place to ensure that potential donors are identified and declared dead by an appropriate practitioner within an acceptable timeframe.

- Verify that there are policies and procedures in place to ensure the coordination between facility staff and OPO staff in maintaining the potential donor.

A-0899

(Rev. 37, Issued: 10-17-08; Effective/Implementation Date: 10-17-08)

§482.45(b) Standard: Organ Transplantation Responsibilities

(1)   A hospital in which organ transplants are performed must be a member of the Organ Procurement and Transplantation Network (OPTN) established and operated in accordance with section 372 of the Public Health Service (PHS) Act (42 U.S.C. 274) and abide by its rules. The term "rules of the OPTN" means those rules provided for in regulations issued by the Secretary in accordance with section 372 of the PHS Act which are enforceable under 42 CFR 121.10. No hospital is considered to be out of compliance with section 1138(a)(1)(B) of the Act, or with the requirements of this paragraph, unless the Secretary has given the OPTN formal notice that he or she approves the decision to exclude the hospital from the OPTN and has notified the hospital in writing.

(2)   For purposes of these standards, the term "organ" means a human kidney, liver, heart, lung, or pancreas.

(3)   If a hospital performs any type of transplants, it must provide organ transplant related data, as requested by the OPTN, the Scientific Registry, and the OPOs. The hospital must also provide such data directly to the Department when requested by the Secretary.

Interpretive Guidelines §482.45(b)(1) –(3)

If you have questions concerning the facility membership in the Organ Procurement and Transplantation Network; you may verify the membership by contacting the CMS regional office or by calling the United Network for Organ sharing (UNOS) at 1-804-330-8500.

Survey Procedures §482.45(b)(1) – (3)

Verify by review, one year of reports submitted by the facility to the OPTN, the Scientific Registry, the OPOs, and any data submitted to the Department per request of the Secretary.

A-0940

(Rev. 37, Issued: 10-17-08; Effective/Implementation Date: 10-17-08)

§482.51 Condition of Participation: Surgical Services

If the hospital provides surgical services, the services must be well organized and provided in accordance with acceptable standards of practice. If outpatient surgical services are offered the services must be consistent in quality with inpatient care in accordance with the complexity of services offered.

Interpretive Guidelines §482.51

The provision of surgical services is an optional hospital service. However, if a hospital provides any degree of surgical services to its patients, the hospital must comply with all the requirements of this Condition of Participation (CoP).

What constitutes "surgery"?

For the purposes of determining compliance with the hospital surgical services CoP, CMS relies, with minor modification, upon the definition of surgery developed by the American College of Surgeons. Accordingly, the following definition is used to determine whether or not a procedure constitutes surgery and is subject to this CoP:

> Surgery is performed for the purpose of structurally altering the human body by the incision or destruction of tissues and is part of the practice of medicine. Surgery also is the diagnostic or therapeutic treatment of conditions or disease processes by any instruments causing localized alteration or transposition of live human tissue which include lasers, ultrasound, ionizing radiation, scalpels, probes, and needles. The tissue can be cut, burned, vaporized, frozen, sutured, probed, or manipulated by closed reductions for major dislocations or fractures, or

otherwise altered by mechanical, thermal, light-based, electromagnetic, or chemical means. Injection of diagnostic or therapeutic substances into body cavities, internal organs, joints, sensory organs, and the central nervous system also is considered to be surgery (this does not include the administration by nursing personnel of some injections, subcutaneous, intramuscular, and intravenous, when ordered by a physician). All of these surgical procedures are invasive, including those that are performed with lasers, and the risks of any surgical procedure are not eliminated by using a light knife or laser in place of a metal knife, or scalpel. Patient safety and quality of care are paramount and, therefore, patients should be assured that individuals who perform these types of surgery are licensed physicians (physicians as defined in 482.12(c)(1)) who are working within their scope of practice, hospital privileges, and who meet appropriate professional standards.

If surgical services are provided, they must be organized and staffed in such a manner to ensure the health and safety of patients.

Acceptable standards of practice include maintaining compliance with applicable Federal and State laws, regulations and guidelines governing surgical services or surgical service locations, as well as, any standards and recommendations promoted by or established by nationally recognized professional organizations (e.g., the American Medical Association, American College of Surgeons, Association of Operating Room Nurses, Association for Professionals in Infection Control and Epidemiology, etc.)

Outpatient surgical services must be in compliance with all hospital CoPs including the surgical services CoP. Outpatient surgical services must be provided in accordance with acceptable standards of practice. Additionally, the hospital's outpatient surgical services must be consistent in quality with the hospital's inpatient surgical services. Post-operative care planning, coordination for the provision of needed post-operative care and appropriate provisions for follow-up care of outpatient surgery patients must be consistent in quality with inpatient care in accordance with the complexity of the services offered and the needs of the patient.

The hospital's inpatient and outpatient surgical services must be integrated into its hospital-wide QAPI program.

Survey Procedures §482.51

Inspect all inpatient and outpatient operative rooms/suites. Request the use of proper attire for the inspection. Observe the practices to determine if the services are provided in accordance with acceptable standards of practice. Observe:

- That access to the operative and recovery area is limited to authorized personnel and that the traffic flow pattern adheres to accepted standards of practice;

- The conformance to aseptic and sterile technique by all individuals in the surgical area;

- That there is appropriate cleaning between surgical cases and appropriate terminal cleaning applied;

- That operating room attire is suitable for the kind of surgical case performed, that persons working in the operating suite must wear only clean surgical costumes, that surgical costumes are designed for maximum skin and hair coverage;

- That equipment is available for rapid and routine sterilization of operating room materials;

- That equipment is monitored, inspected, tested, and maintained by the hospital's biomedical equipment program and in accordance with Federal and State law, regulations and guidelines and manufacturer's recommendations;

- That sterilized materials are packaged, handled, labeled, and stored in a manner that ensures sterility e.g., in a moisture and dust controlled environment and policies and procedures for expiration dates have been developed and are followed in accordance with accepted standards of practice.

- That temperature and humidity are monitored and maintained within accepted standards of practice;

- That medical/surgical devices and equipment are checked and maintained routinely by clinical/biomedical engineers.

- Verify that all surgical service activities and locations are integrated into the hospital-wide QAPI program.

A-0941

(Rev. 37, Issued: 10-17-08; Effective/Implementation Date: 10-17-08)
§482.51(a) Standard: Organization and Staffing

The organization of the surgical services must be appropriate to the scope of the services offered.

Interpretive Guidelines §482.51(a)

When the hospital offers surgical services, the hospital must provide the appropriate equipment and the appropriate types and numbers of qualified personnel necessary to furnish the surgical services offered by the hospital in accordance with acceptable standards of practice.

The scope of surgical services provided by the hospital should be defined in writing and approved by the medical staff.

Survey Procedures §482.51(a)

Review the hospital's organizational chart displaying the relationship of the operating room service to other services. Confirm that the operating room's organization chart indicates lines of authority and delegation of responsibility within the department or service.

A-0942

(Rev. 37, Issued: 10-17-08; Effective/Implementation Date: 10-17-08)

§482.51(a)(1) - The operating rooms must be supervised by an experienced registered nurse or a doctor of medicine or osteopathy.

Interpretive Guidelines §482.51(a)(1)

The operating room (inpatient and outpatient) must be supervised by an experienced RN or MD/DO. The RN or MD/DO supervising the operating room must demonstrate appropriate education, background working in surgical services, and specialized training in the provision of surgical services/management of surgical service operations. The hospital should address its required qualifications for the supervisor of the hospital's operating rooms in its policies and the supervisor's personnel file should contain information demonstrating compliance with the hospital's established qualifications.

Survey Procedures §482.51(a)(1)

- Verify that an RN or a doctor of medicine or osteopathy is assigned responsibility for supervision of the operating rooms.

- Request a copy of the supervisor's position description to determine that it specifies qualifications, duties and responsibilities of the position. Verify that the supervisor is experienced and competent in the management of surgical services.

A-0943

(Rev. 37, Issued: 10-17-08; Effective/Implementation Date: 10-17-08)

§482.51(a)(2) - Licensed practical nurses (LPNs) and surgical technologists (operating room technicians) may serve as "scrub nurses" under the supervision of a registered nurse.

Interpretive Guidelines §482.51(a)(2)

If the hospital utilizes LPN or operating room technicians as "scrub nurses," those personnel must be under the supervision of an RN who is immediately available to physically intervene and provide care.

Survey Procedures §482.51(a)(2)

- Determine that an RN is available for supervision in the department or service. Validate the availability by requesting and reviewing a staffing schedule for the OR.

- Review staffing schedules to determine adequacy of staff and RN supervision.

A-0944

(Rev. 37, Issued: 10-17-08; Effective/Implementation Date: 10-17-08)

§482.51(a)(3) - Qualified registered nurses may perform circulating duties in the operating room. In accordance with applicable State laws and approved medical staff policies and procedures, LPNs and surgical technologists may assist in circulatory duties under the supervision of a qualified registered nurse who is immediately available to respond to emergencies.

Interpretive Guidelines §482.51(a)(3)

The circulating nurse must be an RN. An LPN or surgical technologist may assist an RN in carrying out circulatory duties (in accordance with applicable State laws and medical-staff approved hospital policy) but the LPN or surgical technologist must be under the supervision of the circulating RN who is in the operating suite and who is available to immediately and physically respond/intervene to provide necessary interventions in emergencies. The supervising RN would not be considered immediately available if the RN was located outside the operating suite or engaged in other activities/duties which prevent the RN from immediately intervening and assuming whatever circulating activities/duties that were being provided by the LPN or surgical technologist. The hospital, in accordance with State law and acceptable standards of practice, must establish the qualifications required for RNs who perform circulating duties and LPNs and surgical technologists who assist with circulating duties.

Survey Procedures §482.51(a)(3)

- If LPNs and surgical technologists (STs) are assisting with circulating duties, verify that they do so in accordance with applicable State laws and medical-staff approved policies and procedures.

- Verify in situations where LPNs and STs are permitted to assist with circulating duties that a qualified RN supervisor is immediately available to respond to emergencies.

- Verify that RNs working as circulating nurses are working in accordance with applicable State laws and medical-staff approved policies and procedures.

A-0945

(Rev. 37, Issued: 10-17-08; Effective/Implementation Date: 10-17-08)

§482.51(a)(4) - Surgical privileges must be delineated for all practitioners performing surgery in accordance with the competencies of each practitioner. The surgical service must maintain a roster of practitioners specifying the surgical privileges of each practitioner.

Interpretive Guidelines §482.51(a)(4)

Surgical privileges should be reviewed and updated at least every 2 years. A current roster listing each practitioner's specific surgical privileges must be available in the surgical suite and area/location where the scheduling of surgical procedures is done. A current list of surgeons suspended from surgical privileges or whose surgical privileges have been restricted must also be retained in these areas/locations.
The hospital must delineate the surgical privileges of all practitioners performing surgery and surgical procedures. The medical staff is accountable to the governing body for the quality of care provided to patients. The medical staff bylaws must include criteria for determining the privileges to be granted to an individual practitioner and a procedure for applying the criteria to individuals requesting privileges. Surgical privileges are granted in accordance with the competencies of each practitioner. The medical staff appraisal procedures must evaluate each individual practitioner's training, education, experience, and demonstrated competence as established by the hospital's QAPI program,

credentialing process, the practitioner's adherence to hospital policies and procedures, and in accordance with scope of practice and other State laws and regulations.

The hospital must specify the surgical privileges for each practitioner that performs surgical tasks. This would include practitioners such as MD/DO, dentists, oral surgeons, podiatrists, RN first assistants, nurse practitioners, surgical physician assistants, surgical technicians, etc. When a practitioner may perform certain surgical procedures under supervision, the specific tasks/procedures and the degree of supervision (to include whether or not the supervising practitioner is physically present in the same OR, in line of sight of the practitioner being supervised) be delineated in that practitioner's surgical privileges and included on the surgical roster.

If the hospital utilizes RN First Assistants, surgical PA, or other non-MD/DO surgical assistants, the hospital must establish criteria, qualifications and a credentialing process to grant specific privileges to individual practitioners based on each individual practitioner's compliance with the privileging/credentialing criteria and in accordance with Federal and State laws and regulations. This would include surgical services tasks conducted by these practitioners while under the supervision of an MD/DO.

When practitioners whose scope of practice for conducting surgical procedures requires the direct supervision of an MD/DO surgeon, the term "supervision" would mean the supervising MD/DO surgeon is present in the same room, working with the same patient.

Surgery and all surgical procedures must be conducted by a practitioner who meets the medical staff criteria and procedures for the privileges granted, who has been granted specific surgical privileges by the governing body in accordance with those criteria, and who is working within the scope of those granted and documented privileges.

Survey Procedures §482.51(a)(4)

- Review the hospital's method for reviewing the surgical privileges of practitioners. This method should require a written assessment of the practitioner's training, experience, health status, and performance.

- Determine that a current roster listing each practitioner's specific surgical privileges is available in the surgical suite and the area where the scheduling of surgical procedures is done.

- Determine that a current list of surgeons suspended from surgical privileges or who have restricted surgical privileges is retained in these areas/locations.

A-0951

(Rev. 37, Issued: 10-17-08; Effective/Implementation Date: 10-17-08)

§482.51(b) Standard: Delivery of Service

Surgical services must be consistent with needs and resources. Policies governing surgical care must be designed to assure the achievement and maintenance of high standards of medical practice and patient care.

Interpretive Guidelines §482.51(b)

Policies governing surgical care should contain:

- Aseptic and sterile surveillance and practice, including scrub techniques;

- Identification of infected and non-infected cases;

- Housekeeping requirements/procedures;

- Patient care requirements:

  o Preoperative work-up;

  o Patient consents and releases;

  o Clinical procedures;

  o Safety practices;

  o Patient identification procedures;

- Duties of scrub and circulating nurse;

- Safety practices;

- The requirement to conduct surgical counts in accordance with accepted standards of practice;

- Scheduling of patients for surgery;

- Personnel policies unique to the O.R.;

- Resuscitative techniques;

- DNR status;

- Care of surgical specimens;

- Malignant hyperthermia;

- Appropriate protocols for all surgical procedures performed. These may be procedure-specific or general in nature and will include a list of equipment, materials, and supplies necessary to properly carry out job assignment;

- Sterilization and disinfection procedures;

- Acceptable operating room attire;

- Handling infections and biomedical/medical waste; and

- Outpatient surgery post-operative care planning and coordination, and provisions for follow-up care.

Policies and procedures must be written, implemented and enforced. Surgical services' policies must be in accordance with acceptable standards of medical practice and surgical patient care.

NOTE: Use of Alcohol-based Skin Preparations in Anesthetizing Locations. Alcohol-based skin preparations are considered the most effective and rapid-acting skin antiseptic, but they are also flammable and contribute to the risk of fire.

It is estimated that approximately 100 surgical fires occur each year in the United States, resulting in roughly 20 serious patient injuries, including one to two deaths annually. (ECRI, "Surgical Fire Safety," Health Devices 35 no 2 (February, 2006) 45-66)) Fires occur when an ignition source, a fuel source, and an oxidizer come together. Heat-producing devices are potential ignition sources, while alcohol-based skin preparations provide fuel. Procedures involving electro-surgery or the use of cautery or lasers involve heat-producing devices. There is concern that an alcohol-based skin preparation, combined with the oxygen-rich environment of an anesthetizing location could ignite when exposed to a heat-producing device in an operating room. Specifically, if the alcohol-based skin preparation is improperly applied, the solution may wick into the patient's hair and linens or pool on the patient's skin, resulting in prolonged drying time. Then, if the patient is draped before the solution is completely dry, the alcohol vapors can become trapped under the surgical drapes and channeled to the surgical site. (ECRI for Pennsylvania Patient Safety Advisory 2, No. 2 (June, 2005) 13)

On the other hand, surgical site infections (SSI) also pose significant risks to patients; according to the Centers for Disease Control and Prevention (CDC), such infections are the third most commonly reported hospital-acquired infections. Although the CDC has stated that there are no definitive studies comparing the effectiveness of the different types of skin antiseptics in preventing SSI, it also states that "Alcohol is readily available, inexpensive, and remains the most effective and rapid-acting skin antiseptic." (CDC Hospital Infection Control Practices Advisory Committee, "Guideline for Prevention of Surgical Site Infection, 1999," Infection Control and Hospital Epidemiology April 1999 (Vol 20 No. 4) 251, 257) Hence, in light of alcohol's effectiveness as a skin antiseptic, there is a need to balance the risks of fire related to use of alcohol-based skin preparations with the risk of surgical site infection.

The use of an alcohol-based skin preparation in inpatient or outpatient anesthetizing locations is not considered safe, unless appropriate fire risk-reduction measures are taken, preferably as part of a systematic approach by the hospital to preventing surgery-related fires. A review of recommendations produced by various expert organizations concerning use of alcohol-based skin preparations in anesthetizing locations indicates there is general consensus that the following risk reduction measures are appropriate:

- Using skin prep solutions that are: 1) packaged to ensure controlled delivery to the patient in unit dose applicators, swabs, or other similar applicators; and 2) provide clear and explicit manufacturer/supplier instructions and warnings. These instructions for use should be carefully followed.

- Ensuring that the alcohol-based skin prep solution does not soak into the patient's hair or linens. Sterile towels should be placed to absorb drips and runs during application and should then be removed from the anesthetizing location prior to draping the patient.

- Ensuring that the alcohol-based skin prep solution is completely dry prior to draping. This may take a few minutes or more, depending on the amount and location of the solution. The prepped area should be inspected to confirm it is dry prior to draping.

- Verifying that all of the above has occurred prior to initiating the surgical procedure. This can be done, for example, as part of a standardized pre-operative "time out" used to verify other essential information to minimize the risk of medical errors during the procedure.

Hospitals that employ alcohol-based skin preparations in anesthetizing locations should establish appropriate policies and procedures to reduce the associated risk of fire. They should also document the implementation of these policies and procedures in the patient's medical record.

Failure by a hospital to develop and implement appropriate measures to reduce the risk of fires associated with the use of alcohol-based skin preparations in anesthetizing locations should be cited as condition-level noncompliance.

Survey Procedures §482.51(b)

- Review policies and procedures to determine whether they address the elements specified in the interpretive guidelines. If the hospital uses alcohol-based skin preparations in anesthetizing locations, determine whether it has adopted policies and procedures to minimize the risk of surgical fires.

- Interview surgical services staff to determine whether they are aware of and follow hospital policies and procedures.

A-0952

(Rev. 37, Issued: 10-17-08; Effective/Implementation Date: 10-17-08)

§482.51(b) (1) - Prior to surgery or a procedure requiring anesthesia services and except in the case of emergencies:

(i)   A medical history and physical examination must be completed and documented no more than 30 days before or 24 hours after admission or registration.

(ii)   An updated examination of the patient, including any changes in the patient's condition, must be completed and documented within 24 hours after admission or registration when the medical history and physical examination are completed within 30 days before admission or registration.

Interpretive Guidelines §482.51(b)(1)

There must be a complete history and physical examination (H & P), and an update, if applicable, in the medical record of every patient prior to surgery, or a procedure requiring anesthesia services, except in emergencies.

- The H&P must be conducted in accordance with the requirements of 42 CFR 482.22(c)(5).

- The H&P must be completed and documented no more than 30 days before or 24 hours after admission or registration. In all cases, except for emergencies, the H&P must be completed and documented **before** the surgery or procedure takes place, even if that surgery or procedure occurs less than 24 hours after admission or registration.

- If the H&P was completed within 30 days before admission or registration, then an updated examination must be completed and documented within 24 hours after admission or registration. In all cases, except for emergencies, the update must be completed and documented **before** the surgery or procedure takes place, even if that surgery or procedure occurs less than 24 hours after admission or registration.

Survey Procedures §482.51(b)(1)

Review a sample of open and closed medical records of patients (both inpatient and outpatient) who have had surgery or a procedure requiring anesthesia.

- Determine whether an H&P was conducted and documented in a timely manner.

- Determine whether the H&P was conducted in accordance with the requirements of 42 CFR 482.22(c)(5).

- Determine whether the records of patients who did not have a timely H&P or update indicate that the surgery or procedure was conducted on an emergency basis.

A-0955

(Rev. 37, Issued: 10-17-08; Effective/Implementation Date: 10-17-08)

§482.51(b)(2) - A properly executed informed consent form for the operation must be in the patient's chart before surgery, except in emergencies.

Interpretive Guidelines §482.51(b)(2)

Informed consent is addressed in two other portions of the CMS Hospital CoPs and the SOMl. Surveyors should review the guidelines for §482.13(b)(2) under Patients' Rights and the guidelines for §482.24(c)(2)(v) under Medical Records to understand all requirements related to informed consent.

The primary purpose of the informed consent process for surgical services is to ensure that the patient, or the patient's representative, is provided information necessary to enable him/her to evaluate a proposed surgery before agreeing to the surgery. Typically, this information would include potential short- and longer-term risks and benefits to the patient of the proposed intervention, including the likelihood of each, based on the available clinical evidence, as informed by the responsible practitioner's professional judgment. Informed consent must be obtained, and the informed consent form must be placed in the patient's medical record, prior to surgery, except in the case of emergency surgery.

Hospitals must assure that the practitioner(s) responsible for the surgery obtain informed consent from patients in a manner consistent with the hospital's policies governing the informed consent process.

It should be noted that there is no specific requirement for informed consent within the regulation at §482.52 governing anesthesia services. However, given that surgical procedures generally entail use of anesthesia, hospitals may wish to consider specifically extending their informed consent policies to include obtaining informed consent for the anesthesia component of the surgical procedure.

Surgical Informed Consent Policy

The hospital's surgical informed consent policy should describe the following:

- Who may obtain the patient's informed consent;

- Which procedures require informed consent;

- The circumstances under which surgery is considered an emergency, and may be undertaken without an informed consent;

- The circumstances when a patient's representative, rather than the patient, may give informed consent for a surgery;

- The content of the informed consent form and instructions for completing it;

- The process used to obtain informed consent, including how informed consent is to be documented in the medical record;

- Mechanisms that ensure that the informed consent form is properly executed and is in the patient's medical record prior to the surgery (except in the case of emergency surgery); and

- If the informed consent process and informed consent form are obtained outside the hospital, how the properly executed informed consent form is incorporated into the patient's medical record prior to the surgery.

If there are additional requirements under State law for informed consent, the hospital must comply with those requirements.

Example of a Well-Designed Informed Consent Process

A well-designed informed consent process would include discussion of the following elements:

- A description of the proposed surgery, including the anesthesia to be used;

- The indications for the proposed surgery;

- Material risks and benefits for the patient related to the surgery and anesthesia, including the likelihood of each, based on the available clinical evidence, as informed by the responsible practitioner's clinical judgment. Material risks could include risks with a high degree of likelihood but a low degree of severity, as well as those with a very low degree of likelihood but high degree of severity;

- Treatment alternatives, including the attendant material risks and benefits;

- The probable consequences of declining recommended or alternative therapies;

- Who will conduct the surgical intervention and administer the anesthesia;

- Whether physicians other than the operating practitioner, including but not limited to residents, will be performing important tasks related to the surgery, in accordance with the hospital's policies. Important surgical tasks include: opening and closing, dissecting tissue, removing tissue, harvesting grafts, transplanting tissue, administering anesthesia, implanting devices and placing invasive lines;

  o For surgeries in which residents will perform important parts of the surgery, discussion is encouraged to include the following:

    - That it is anticipated that physicians who are in approved post graduate residency training programs will perform portions of the surgery, based on their availability and level of competence;

- That it will be decided at the time of the surgery which residents will participate and their manner or participation, and that this will depend on the availability of residents with the necessary competence; the knowledge the operating practitioner/teaching surgeon has of the resident's skill set; and the patient's condition;

- That residents performing surgical tasks will be under the supervision of the operating practitioner/teaching surgeon; and

- Whether, based on the resident's level of competence, the operating practitioner/teaching surgeon will not be physically present in the same operating room for some or all of the surgical tasks performed by residents.

  NOTE: A "moonlighting" resident or fellow is a postgraduate medical trainee who is practicing independently, outside the scope of his/her residency training program and would be treated as a physician within the scope of the privileges granted by the hospital.

- Whether, as permitted by State law, qualified medical practitioners who are not physicians will perform important parts of the surgery or administer the anesthesia, and if so, the types of tasks each type of practitioner will carry out; and that such practitioners will be performing only tasks within their scope of practice for which they have been granted privileges by the hospital.

Informed Consent Forms

See the guidelines for §482.24(c)(2)(v) under Medical Records for discussion of the content of a properly executed informed consent form.

Survey Procedures §482.51(b)(2)

- Verify that the hospital has assured that the medical staff has specified which procedures are considered surgery and, thus, are those that require a properly executed informed consent form.

- Verify that the hospital's informed consent policies address the circumstances when a surgery would be considered an emergency and thus not require an informed consent form be placed in the medical record prior to surgery.

- Review a minimum of six medical records of surgical patients and verify that they did not involve emergency surgery and that they contain informed consent forms that were executed prior to the surgery. When possible, review medical records of patients who are about to undergo surgery, or who are located in a surgical recovery area.

- Interview two or three post-surgical patients, as appropriate based on their ability to provide a cogent response, or the patients' representatives to see how satisfied they are with the informed consent discussion prior to their surgery.

A-0956

(Rev. 37, Issued: 10-17-08; Effective/Implementation Date: 10-17-08)

§482.51(b)(3) - The following equipment must be available to the operating room suites: call-in system, cardiac monitor, resuscitator, defibrillator, aspirator, and tracheotomy set.

Survey Procedures §482.51(b)(3)

- Check to determine that the operating room suite has available the items listed:

  o On-call system;

  o Cardiac monitor;

  o Resuscitator;

  o Defibrillator;

  o Aspirator (suction equipment); and

  o Tracheotomy set (a cricothyroidotomy set is not a substitute).

Verify that all equipment is working and, as applicable, in compliance with the hospital's biomedical equipment inspection, testing, and maintenance program.

A-0957

(Rev. 37, Issued: 10-17-08; Effective/Implementation Date: 10-17-08)

§482.51(b)(4) - There must be adequate provisions for immediate post-operative care.

Interpretive Guidelines §482.51(b)(4)

Adequate provisions for immediate post-operative care means:

- Post operative care must be in accordance with acceptable standards of practice.

- The post-operative care area or recovery room is a separate area of the hospital. Access is limited to authorized personnel.

- Policies and procedures specify transfer requirements to and from the recovery room. Depending on the type of anesthesia and length of surgery, the post-operative check before transferring the patient from the recovery room should include some of the following:

    o Level of activity;

    o Respirations;

    o Blood pressure;

    o Level of consciousness;

    o Patient color; and

- If the patients are not transferred to the recovery room, determine that provisions are made for close observation until they have regained consciousness, e.g., direct observation by a qualified RN in the patient's room.

Survey Procedures §482.51(b)(4)

- Verify that the hospital has provisions for post-operative care.

- Determine that there are policies and procedures that govern the recovery room area.

A-0958
(Rev. 37, Issued: 10-17-08; Effective/Implementation Date: 10-17-08)

§482.51(b)(5) - The operating room register must be complete and up-to-date.

Interpretive Guidelines §482.51(b)(5)

The register includes at least the following information:

- Patient's name;

- Patient's hospital identification number;

- Date of the operation;

- Inclusive or total time of the operation;

- Name of the surgeon and any assistant(s);

- Name of nursing personnel (scrub and circulating);

- Type of anesthesia used and name of person administering it;

- Operation performed;

- Pre and post-op diagnosis; and

- Age of patient.

Survey Procedures §482.51(b)(5)

Examine the OR register or equivalent record which lists all surgery performed by the surgery service. Determine that the register includes items specified in the interpretive guidelines.

A-0959
(Rev. 37, Issued: 10-17-08; Effective/Implementation Date: 10-17-08)

§482.51(b)(6) - An operative report describing techniques, findings, and tissues removed or altered must be written or dictated immediately following surgery and signed by the surgeon.

Interpretive Guidelines §482.51(b)(6)

The operative report includes at least:

- Name and hospital identification number of the patient;

- Date and times of the surgery;

- Name(s) of the surgeon(s) and assistants or other practitioners who performed surgical tasks (even when performing those tasks under supervision);

- Pre-operative and post-operative diagnosis;

- Name of the specific surgical procedure(s) performed;

- Type of anesthesia administered;

- Complications, if any;

- A description of techniques, findings, and tissues removed or altered;

- Surgeons or practitioners name(s) and a description of the specific significant surgical tasks that were conducted by practitioners other than the primary surgeon/practitioner (significant surgical procedures include: opening and closing, harvesting grafts, dissecting tissue, removing tissue, implanting devices, altering tissues); and

- Prosthetic devices, grafts, tissues, transplants, or devices implanted, if any.

Survey Procedures §482.51(b)(6)

Review a minimum of six random medical records of patients who had a surgical encounter. Verify that they contain a surgical report that is dated and signed by the responsible surgeon and includes the information specified in the interpretive guidelines.

A-1000

(Rev. 74, Issued: 12-02-11, Effective: 12-02-11, Implementation: 12-02-11)

§482.52 Condition of Participation: Anesthesia Services

If the hospital furnishes anesthesia services, they must be provided in a well-organized manner under the direction of a qualified doctor of medicine or osteopathy. The service is responsible for all anesthesia administered in the hospital.

Interpretive Guidelines §482.52

The provision of anesthesia services is an optional hospital service. However, if a hospital provides any degree of anesthesia service to its patients, the hospital must comply with all the requirements of this Condition of Participation (CoP).

"Anesthesia" involves the administration of a medication to produce a blunting or loss of:

- pain perception (analgesia);
- voluntary and involuntary movements;
- autonomic function; and
- memory and/or consciousness,

depending on where along the central neuraxial (brain and spinal cord) the medication is delivered.

In contrast, "analgesia" involves the use of a medication to provide relief of pain through the blocking of pain receptors in the peripheral and/or central nervous system. The patient does not lose consciousness, but does not perceive pain to the extent that may otherwise prevail.

Anesthesia exists along a continuum. For some medications there is no bright line that distinguishes when their pharmacological properties bring about the physiologic transition from the analgesic to the anesthetic effects. Furthermore, each individual patient may respond differently to different types of medications. The additional definitions below illustrate distinctions among the various types of "anesthesia services" that may be offered by a hospital. These definitions are generally based on American Society of Anesthesiologists definitions found in its most recent set of practice guidelines (Anesthesiology 2002; 96:1004-17).

- **General anesthesia**: a drug-induced loss of consciousness during which patients are not arousable, even by painful stimulation. The ability to independently maintain ventilatory support is often impaired. Patients often require assistance in maintaining a patent airway, and positive pressure ventilation may be required because of depressed spontaneous ventilation or drug-induced depression of neuromuscular function. Cardiovascular function may be impaired. For example, a patient undergoing major abdominal surgery involving the removal of a portion or all of an organ would require general anesthesia in order to tolerate such an extensive surgical procedure. General anesthesia is used for those procedures when loss of consciousness is required for the safe and effective delivery of surgical services;

- **Regional anesthesia**: the delivery of anesthetic medication at a specific level of the spinal cord and/or to peripheral nerves, including epidurals and spinals and other central neuraxial nerve blocks, is used when loss of consciousness is not desired but sufficient analgesia and loss of voluntary and involuntary movement is required. Given the potential for the conversion and extension of regional to general anesthesia in certain procedures, it is necessary that the administration of regional and general anesthesia be delivered or supervised by a practitioner as specified in 42 CFR 482.52(a).

- **Monitored anesthesia care (MAC)**: anesthesia care that includes the monitoring of the patient by a practitioner who is qualified to administer anesthesia as defined by the regulations at §482.52(a). Indications for MAC depend on the nature of the procedure, the patient's clinical condition, and/or the potential need to convert to a general or regional anesthetic. Deep sedation/analgesia is included in MAC.

  - Deep sedation/analgesia: a drug-induced depression of consciousness during which patients cannot be easily aroused but respond purposefully following repeated or painful stimulation. The ability to independently maintain ventilatory function may be impaired. Patients may require assistance in maintaining a patent airway, and spontaneous ventilation may be inadequate. Cardiovascular function is usually maintained. Because of the potential for the inadvertent progression to general anesthesia in certain procedures, it is necessary that the administration of deep sedation/analgesia be delivered or supervised by a practitioner as specified in 42 CFR 482.52(a).

- **Moderate sedation/analgesia: ("Conscious Sedation")**: a drug-induced depression of consciousness during which patients respond purposefully to verbal commands, either alone or accompanied by light tactile stimulation. No interventions are required to maintain a patent airway, and spontaneous ventilation is adequate. Cardiovascular function is usually maintained. CMS, consistent with ASA guidelines, does not define moderate or conscious sedation as anesthesia (71 FR 68690-1).

- **Minimal sedation**: a drug-induced state during which patients respond normally to verbal commands. Although cognitive function and coordination may be impaired, ventilator and cardiovascular functions are unaffected. This is also not anesthesia.

- **Topical or local anesthesia**: the application or injection of a drug or combination of drugs to stop or prevent a painful sensation to a circumscribed area of the body where a painful procedure is to be performed. There are generally no systemic effects of these medications, which also are not anesthesia, despite the name.

Rescue Capacity: As stated above, because the level of sedation of a patient receiving anesthesia services is a continuum, it is not always possible to predict how an individual patient will respond. Further, no clear boundary exists between some of these services. Hence, hospitals must ensure that procedures are in place to rescue patients whose level of sedation becomes deeper than initially intended, for example, patients who inadvertently enter a state of Deep Sedation/Analgesia when Moderate Sedation was intended. "Rescue" from a deeper level of sedation than intended requires an intervention by a practitioner with expertise in airway management and advanced life support. The qualified practitioner corrects adverse physiologic consequences of the deeper-than-intended level of sedation and returns the patient to the originally intended level of sedation. (Rescue capacity is not only required as an essential component of anesthesia services, but is also consistent with the requirements under the Patients' Rights standard at §482.13(c)(2), guaranteeing patients care in a safe setting.)

Anesthesia services throughout the hospital (including all departments in all campuses and off-site locations where anesthesia services are provided) must be organized into one anesthesia service.

Areas where anesthesia services are furnished may include (but are not limited to):

• Operating room suite(s), both inpatient and outpatient;

• Obstetrical suite(s);

• Radiology department;

• Clinics;

• Emergency department;

• Psychiatry department;

• Outpatient surgery areas;

• Special procedures areas (e.g., endoscopy suite, pain management clinic, etc.)

The anesthesia services must be under the direction of one individual who is a qualified doctor of medicine (MD) or doctor of osteopathy (DO). Consistent with the requirement at §482.12(a)(4) for it to approve medical staff bylaws, rules and regulations, the hospital's governing body approves, after considering the medical staff's recommendations, medical staff rules and regulations establishing criteria for the qualifications for the director of the anesthesia services. Such criteria must be consistent with State laws and acceptable standards of practice.

As previously mentioned, there is often no bright line, i.e., no clear boundary, between anesthesia and analgesia. This is particularly the case with moderate versus deep sedation, but also with respect to labor epidurals. However, the anesthesia services CoP establishes certain requirements that apply only when anesthesia is administered. Consequently, each hospital that provides anesthesia services must establish policies and procedures, based on nationally recognized guidelines that address whether specific clinical situations involve anesthesia versus analgesia. (It is important to note that anesthesia services are usually an integral part of "surgery," as we have defined that term in our guidance. Because the surgical services CoP at §482.51 requires provision of surgical services in accordance with acceptable standards of practice, this provides additional support for the expectation that anesthesia services policies and procedures concerning anesthesia are based on nationally recognized guidelines.) We encourage hospitals to address whether the sedation typically provided in the emergency department or procedure rooms involves anesthesia or analgesia. In establishing such policies, the hospital is expected to take into account the characteristics of the patients served, the skill set of the clinical staff in providing the services, as well as the characteristics of the sedation medications used in the various clinical settings.

The regulation at 42 CFR 482.52(a) establishes the qualifications and, where applicable, supervision requirements for personnel who administer anesthesia. However, hospital anesthesia services policies and procedures are expected to also address the minimum qualifications and supervision requirements for each category of practitioner who is permitted to provide analgesia services, particularly moderate sedation. This expectation is consistent not only with the requirement under this CoP to provide anesthesia services in a well-organized manner, but also with various provisions of the Medical Staff CoP at §482.22 and the Nursing Services CoP at §482.23 related to qualifications of personnel providing care to patients. Taken together, these regulations require the hospital to assure that any staff administering drugs for analgesia must be appropriately qualified, and that the drugs are administered in accordance with accepted standards of practice. Specifically:

- The Medical Staff CoP at §482.22(c)(6) requires the medical staff bylaws, "Include criteria for determining the privileges to be granted to individual practitioners and a procedure for applying the criteria to individuals requesting privileges."

- The Nursing Services CoP requires at:

  - §482.23(b)(5) that nursing personnel be assigned to provide care based on "the specialized qualifications and competence of the nursing staff available."

  - §482.23(c) that, "Drugs and biologicals must be prepared and administered in accordance with Federal and State laws, …and accepted standards of practice." And

  - §482.23(c)(3) , "… If … intravenous medications are administered by personnel other than doctors of medicine or osteopathy, the personnel must have special training for this duty."

Finally, it is expected that the anesthesia services policies and procedures will undergo periodic re-evaluation that includes analysis of adverse events, medication errors and other quality or safety indicators related not only to anesthesia, but also to the administration of medications in clinical applications that the hospital has determined involve analgesia rather than anesthesia. This expectation is also supported by the provisions of the Quality Assessment and Performance Improvement (QAPI) CoP at §482.21, which requires the hospital to ensure its QAPI program, "…involves all hospital departments and services…"; "…focuses on indicators related to improved health outcomes and the prevention and reduction of medical errors…."; "…track[s] quality indicators, including adverse patient events…"; "… use[s] the data collected to monitor the effectiveness and safety of the services and quality of care…"; and "…take[s] actions aimed at performance improvement…"

Hospitals are free to develop their own specific organizational arrangements in order to deliver all anesthesia services in a well-organized manner. Although not required under the regulation to do so, a well-organized anesthesia service would develop the hospital's anesthesia policies and procedures in collaboration with several other hospital disciplines (e.g., surgery, pharmacy, nursing, safety experts, material management, etc.) that are involved in delivering these services to patients in the various areas in the hospital.

A well-organized anesthesia service must be integrated into the hospital's required Quality Assessment/Performance Improvement program, in order to assure the provision of safe care to patients.

Survey Procedures §482.52

- Request a copy of the organizational chart for anesthesia services.

- Determine that a doctor of medicine or osteopathy has the authority and responsibility for directing all anesthesia services throughout the hospital.

- Look for evidence in the director's file of the director's appointment privileges and qualifications, consistent with the criteria adopted by the hospital's governing body. Review the position description. Confirm that the director's responsibilities include at least the following:

  - Planning, directing, and supervising all activities of the service;

  - Evaluating the quality and appropriateness of the anesthesia services provided to patients as part of the hospital's QAPI program;

- Request a copy of and review the hospital's anesthesia services policies and procedures.

  - Do they apply in all hospital locations where anesthesia services are provided?

  - Do they indicate the necessary qualifications that each clinical practitioner must possess in order to administer anesthesia as well as moderate sedation or other forms of analgesia?

  - Do they address what clinical applications are considered to involve analgesia, in particular moderate sedation, rather than anesthesia, based on identifiable national guidelines? What are the national guidelines that they are following and how is that documented?

- Does the hospital have a system by which adverse events related to the administration of anesthesia and analgesia, including moderate sedation, are tracked and acted upon?

A-1001

(Rev. 59, Issued: 05-21-10, Effective/Implementation: 05-21-10)

§482.52(a) Standard: Organization and Staffing

The organization of anesthesia services must be appropriate to the scope of the services offered. Anesthesia must be administered only by --

(1) A qualified anesthesiologist;

(2) A doctor of medicine or osteopathy (other than an anesthesiologist);

(3) A dentist, oral surgeon, or podiatrist who is qualified to administer anesthesia under State law;

(4) A certified registered nurse anesthetist (CRNA), as defined in §410.69(b) of this chapter, who, unless exempted in accordance with paragraph (c) of this section, is under the supervision of the operating practitioner or of an anesthesiologist who is immediately available if needed; or

(5) An anesthesiologist's assistant, as defined in Sec. 410.69(b) of this chapter, who is under the supervision of an anesthesiologist who is immediately available if needed.

§482.52(c) Standard: State Exemption

(1) A hospital may be exempted from the requirement for MD/DO supervision of CRNAs as described in paragraph (a)(4) of this section, if the State in which the hospital is located submits a letter to CMS signed by the Governor, following consultation with the State's Boards of Medicine and Nursing, requesting exemption from MD/DO supervision of CRNAs. The letter from the Governor must attest that he or she has consulted with State Boards of Medicine and Nursing about issues related to access to and the quality of anesthesia services in the State and has concluded that it is in the best interests of the State's citizens to opt-out of the current MD/DO supervision requirement, and that the opt-out is consistent with State law.

(2) **The request for exemption and recognition of State laws, and the withdrawal of the request may be submitted at any time, and are effective upon submission.**

Interpretive Guidelines §482.52(a) and (c)

Who May Administer Anesthesia

Topical/local anesthetics, minimal sedation, moderate sedation

The requirements at §482.52(a) concerning who may administer anesthesia do not apply to the administration of topical or local anesthetics, minimal sedation, or moderate sedation. However, the hospital must have policies and procedures, consistent with State scope of practice law, governing the provision of these types of anesthesia services. Further, hospitals must assure that all anesthesia services are provided in a safe, well-organized manner by qualified personnel.

General anesthesia, regional anesthesia and monitored anesthesia, including deep sedation/analgesia, may only be administered by:

- A qualified anesthesiologist;
- An MD or DO (other than an anesthesiologist);
- A dentist, oral surgeon or podiatrist who is qualified to administer anesthesia under State law;
- A CRNA who is supervised by the operating practitioner or by an anesthesiologist who is immediately available if needed; or
- An anesthesiologist's assistant under the supervision of an anesthesiologist who is immediately available if needed.

Administration by an MD/DO/dentist/oral surgeon/podiatrist

The hospital's anesthesia services policies must address the circumstances under which an MD or DO who is not an anesthesiologist, a dentist, oral surgeon or podiatrist is permitted to administer anesthesia. In the case of a dentist, oral surgeon or podiatrist, administration of anesthesia must be permissible under State law and comply with all State requirements concerning qualifications. Hospitals should conform to generally accepted standards of anesthesia care when establishing policies governing anesthesia administration by these types of practitioners as well as MDs or DOs who are not anesthesiologists.

Administration by a CRNA

Unless the hospital is located in a State that has chosen to opt out of the CRNA supervision requirements, a CRNA administering general, regional and monitored anesthesia must be supervised either by the operating practitioner who is performing the procedure, or by an anesthesiologist who is immediately available.

Hospitals should conform to generally accepted standards of anesthesia care when establishing policies for supervision by the operating practitioner. An anesthesiologist is considered "immediately available" when needed by a CRNA under the anesthesiologist's supervision only if he/she is physically located within the same area as the CRNA, e.g., in the same operative/ procedural suite, or in the same labor and delivery unit, and not otherwise occupied in a way that prevents him/her from immediately conducting hands-on intervention, if needed.

If the hospital is located in a State where the Governor has submitted a letter to CMS attesting that he or she has consulted with State Boards of Medicine and Nursing about issues related to access to and the quality of anesthesia services in the State and has concluded that it is in the best interests of the State's citizens to opt-out of the current physician supervision requirement, and that the opt-out is consistent with State law, then a hospital may permit a CRNA to administer anesthesia without operating practitioner or anesthesiologist supervision. (A list of States that have opted out of the CRNA supervision requirement may be found at http://www.cms.hhs.gov/CFCsAndCoPs/02_Spotlight.asp)

A CRNA is defined in §410.69(b) as a "registered nurse who:

(1) Is licensed as a registered professional nurse by the State in which the nurse practices;

(2) Meets any licensure requirements the State imposes with respect to non-physician anesthetists;

(3) Has graduated from a nurse anesthesia educational program that meets the standards of the Council on Accreditation of Nurse Anesthesia Programs, or such other accreditation organization as may be designated by the Secretary; and

(4) Meets the following criteria:

(i) Has passed a certification examination of the Council on Certification of Nurse Anesthetists, the Council on Recertification of Nurse Anesthetists, or any other certification organization that may be designated by the Secretary; or

(ii) Is a graduate of a program described in paragraph (3) of this definition and within 24 months after that graduation meets the requirements of paragraph (4)(i) of this definition."

Administration by an Anesthesiologist's Assistant

An anesthesiologist's assistant may administer anesthesia when under the supervision of an anesthesiologist. The anesthesiologist must be immediately available if needed. An anesthesiologist is considered "immediately available" to assist the anesthesiologist's assistant under the anesthesiologist's supervision only if he/she is physically located within the same area as the anesthesiologist's assistant, e.g., in the same operative/procedural suite, or in the same labor and delivery unit, and not otherwise occupied in a way that prevents him/her from immediately conducting hands-on intervention, if needed.

An anesthesiologist's assistant is defined at §410.69(b) as a "person who-

(1) Works under the direction of an anesthesiologist;

(2) Is in compliance with all applicable requirements of State law, including any licensure requirements the State imposes on nonphysician anesthetists; and

(3) Is a graduate of a medical school-based anesthesiologist's assistant education program that –

(a) Is accredited by the Committee on Allied Health Education and Accreditation; and

(b) Includes approximately two years of specialized basic science and clinical education in anesthesia at a level that builds on a premedical undergraduate science background."

Anesthesia Services Policies

The medical staff bylaws or rules and regulations must include criteria for determining the anesthesia service privileges to be granted to an individual practitioner and a procedure for applying the criteria to individuals requesting privileges, as required by the regulations at §482. 22(c)(6) for any type of anesthesia services, including those not subject to the anesthesia administration requirements at §482.52(a). The hospital's governing body must approve the specific anesthesia service privileges for each practitioner who furnishes anesthesia services, addressing the type of supervision, if any, required. The privileges granted must be in accordance with State law and hospital policy. The type and complexity of procedures for which the practitioner may administer anesthesia must be specified in the privileges granted to the individual practitioner. Deficiencies related to these requirements should be cited under §482. 22(c)(6).

When a hospital permits operating practitioners to supervise a CRNA administering anesthesia, the medical staff bylaws or rules and regulations must specify for each category of operating practitioner, the type and complexity of procedures that category of practitioner may supervise. However, individual operating practitioners do not need to be granted specific privileges to supervise a CRNA.

Survey Procedures §482.52(a) and (c)

- Review the qualifications of individuals authorized to administer general anesthesia, regional anesthesia and monitored anesthesia, including deep sedation/analgesia to determine if they satisfy the requirements at §482.52(a) and (c).

- Determine that there is documentation of current licensure and, as applicable, current certification for all persons administering anesthesia.

- Determine if the state is an "opt-out state" and therefore permits CRNAs to administer anesthesia without supervision in accordance with 482.52(c).

- Review the hospital's policies and procedures governing supervision of CRNA's and anesthesiologist's assistants, and determine whether they comply with the regulatory requirements. and

- Review the qualifications of individuals authorized to furnish other anesthesia services, to determine if they are consistent with the hospital's anesthesia service policies.

A-1002
(Rev. 59, Issued: 05-21-10, Effective/Implementation: 05-21-10)

§482.52(b) Standard: Delivery of Services

Anesthesia services must be consistent with needs and resources. Policies on anesthesia procedures must include the delineation of preanesthesia and postanesthesia responsibilities. The policies must ensure that the following are provided for each patient:

Interpretive Guidelines §482.52(b)

Anesthesia services must be delivered in a manner that is consistent with the needs and the resources of the hospital. Anesthesia policies at a minimum must address:

- How the hospital's anesthesia services needs will be met;

- Delivery of anesthesia services consistent with recognized standards for anesthesia care. A well-designed anesthesia services policy would address issues such as:

o   Patient consent;

o   Infection control measures;

o   Safety practices in all anesthetizing areas;

o   Protocol for supportive life functions, e.g., cardiac and respiratory emergencies;

o   Reporting requirements;

o   Documentation requirements;

o   Equipment requirements, as well as the monitoring, inspection, testing, and maintenance of anesthesia equipment in the hospital's biomedical equipment program.

o   Delineation of pre- and post-anesthesia staff responsibilities

Survey Procedures §482.52(b)

Review the policies developed on anesthesia procedures. Determine whether the anesthesia service policies for delivery of care address the issues identified in interpretive guidelines.

A-1003
(Rev. 74, Issued: 12-02-11, Effective: 12-02-11, Implementation: 12-02-11)

[The policies must ensure that the following are provided for each patient:]

§482.52(b) (1) - A pre-anesthesia evaluation completed and documented by an individual qualified to administer anesthesia, as specified in paragraph (a) of this section, performed within 48 hours prior to surgery or a procedure requiring anesthesia services.

Interpretive Guidelines §482.52(b)(1)

A pre-anesthesia evaluation must be performed for each patient who receives general, regional or monitored anesthesia. While current practice dictates that the patient receiving moderate sedation be monitored and evaluated before, during, and after the procedure by trained practitioners, a pre-anesthesia evaluation performed by someone qualified to administer anesthesia as specified in §482.52(a) is not required because moderate sedation is **not** considered to be "anesthesia", and thus is not subject to that requirement under this regulation.

The evaluation must be performed by someone qualified to administer anesthesia as specified in §482.52(a), i.e., only by:

- A qualified anesthesiologist;

- A doctor of medicine or osteopathy (other than an anesthesiologist);

- A dentist, oral surgeon, or podiatrist who is qualified to administer anesthesia under State law;

- A certified registered nurse anesthetist (CRNA), who, unless exempted in accordance with paragraph (c) of this section, is under the supervision of the operating practitioner or of an anesthesiologist who is immediately available if needed; or

- An anesthesiologist's assistant who is under the supervision of an anesthesiologist who is immediately available if needed.

Although §482.12 (c)(1)(i) generally provides broad authority to physicians to delegate tasks to other qualified medical personnel, the more stringent requirements at §482.52(b)(1) do not permit delegation of the pre-anesthesia evaluation to practitioners who are not qualified to administer anesthesia.

The pre-anesthesia evaluation must be completed and documented within 48 hours immediately prior to any inpatient or outpatient surgery or procedure requiring anesthesia services. The delivery of the first dose of medication(s) for the purpose of inducing anesthesia, as defined above, marks the end of the 48 hour time frame.

In accordance with current standards of anesthesia care, some of the individual elements contributing to the pre-anesthesia evaluation may be performed prior to the 48-hour timeframe. However, under no circumstances may these elements be performed more than 30 days prior to surgery or a procedure requiring anesthesia services. Review of these elements must be conducted, and any appropriate updates documented, within the 48-hour timeframe.

The pre-anesthesia evaluation of the patient includes, at a minimum:

Elements that must be performed within the 48-hour timeframe:

- Review of the medical history, including anesthesia, drug and allergy history; and

- Interview, if possible given the patient's condition, and examination of the patient.

Elements that must be reviewed and updated as necessary within 48 hours, but which may also have been performed during or within 30 days prior to the 48-hour time period, in preparation for the procedure:

- Notation of anesthesia risk according to established standards of practice (e.g., ASA classification of risk);

- Identification of potential anesthesia problems, particularly those that may suggest potential complications or contraindications to the planned procedure (e.g., difficult airway, ongoing infection, limited intravascular access);

- Additional pre-anesthesia data or information, if applicable and as required in accordance with standard practice prior to administering anesthesia (e.g., stress tests, additional specialist consultation);

- Development of the plan for the patient's anesthesia care, including the type of medications for induction, maintenance and post-operative care and discussion with the patient (or patient's representative) of the risks and benefits of the delivery of anesthesia.

Survey Procedures §482.52(b)(1)

- Review a sample of inpatient and outpatient medical records for patients who had surgery or a procedure requiring administration of anesthesia.

- Determine whether each patient had a pre-anesthesia evaluation by a practitioner qualified to administer anesthesia.

- Determine whether each patient's pre-anesthesia evaluation included at least the elements described above.

- Determine that the pre-anesthesia evaluation was updated, completed and documented within 48 hours prior to the delivery of the first dose of medication(s) given for the purpose of inducing anesthesia for the surgery or a procedure requiring anesthesia services.

A-1004
(Rev. 59, Issued: 05-21-10, Effective/Implementation: 05-21-10)

[The policies must ensure that the following are provided for each patient:]

§482.52(b)(2) - An intraoperative anesthesia record.

Interpretive Guidelines §482.52(b)(2)

There must be an intraoperative anesthesia record or report for each patient who receives general, regional or monitored anesthesia. While current practice dictates that the patient receiving moderate sedation be monitored and evaluated before, during, and after the procedure by trained practitioners, an intraoperative anesthesia report is not required because, as explained above , moderate sedation is not "anesthesia". Current standard of care stipulates that an intraoperative anesthesia record, at a minimum, includes:

- Name and hospital identification number of the patient;

- Name(s) of practitioner(s) who administered anesthesia, and as applicable, the name and profession of the supervising anesthesiologist or operating practitioner;

- Name, dosage, route and time of administration of drugs and anesthesia agents;

- Techniques(s) used and patient position(s), including the insertion/use of any intravascular or airway devices;

- Name and amounts of IV fluids, including blood or blood products if applicable;

- Timed-based documentation of vital signs as well as oxygenation and ventilation parameters; and

- Any complications, adverse reactions, or problems occurring during anesthesia, including time and description of symptoms, vital signs, treatments rendered, and patient's response to treatment.

Survey Procedures §482.52(b)(2)

Review records to determine that each patient has an intraoperative anesthesia record that includes the elements described above.

A-1005
(Rev. 74, Issued: 12-02-11, Effective: 12-02-11, Implementation: 12-02-11)

[The policies must ensure that the following are provided for each patient:]

482.52(b)(3) - A postanesthesia evaluation completed and documented by an individual qualified to administer anesthesia, as specified in paragraph (a) of this section, no later than 48 hours after surgery or a procedure requiring anesthesia services. The postanesthesia evaluation for anesthesia recovery must be completed

in accordance with State law and with hospital policies and procedures that have been approved by the medical staff and that reflect current standards of anesthesia care.

Interpretive Guidelines §482.52(b)(3)

A postanesthesia evaluation must be completed and documented no later than 48 hours after surgery or a procedure requiring anesthesia services. The evaluation is required any time general, regional, or monitored anesthesia has been administered to the patient. While current practice dictates that the patient receiving moderate sedation be monitored and evaluated before, during, and after the procedure by trained practitioners, a postanesthesia evaluation performed by someone qualified to administer anesthesia as specified in §482.52(a) is not required under this regulation. (71 FR 68691)

The postanesthesia evaluation must be completed and documented by any practitioner who is qualified to administer anesthesia; this need not be the same practitioner who administered the anesthesia to the patient. In accordance with §482.52(a), anesthesia must be administered only by:

- A qualified anesthesiologist;

- A doctor of medicine or osteopathy (other than an anesthesiologist);

- A dentist, oral surgeon, or podiatrist who is qualified to administer anesthesia under State law;

- A certified registered nurse anesthetist (CRNA), who, unless exempted in accordance with paragraph (c) of this section, is under the supervision of the operating practitioner or of an anesthesiologist who is immediately available if needed; or

- An anesthesiologist's assistant who is under the supervision of an anesthesiologist who is immediately available if needed.

Although §482.12(c)(1)(i) provides broad authority to physicians to delegate tasks to other qualified medical personnel, the more stringent requirements of §482.52(b)(3) do not permit delegation of the postanesthesia evaluation to practitioners who are not qualified to administer anesthesia.

The calculation of the 48-hour timeframe begins at the point the patient is moved into the designated recovery area. The evaluation generally should not be performed immediately at the point of movement from the operative area to the designated recovery area. Rather, accepted standards of anesthesia care indicate that the evaluation should not begin until the patient is sufficiently recovered from the acute administration of the anesthesia so as to participate in the evaluation, e.g., answer questions appropriately, perform simple tasks, etc. While the evaluation should begin in the PACU/ICU or other designated recovery location, it may be completed after the patient is moved to another inpatient location or, for same day surgeries, if State law and hospital policy permits, after the patient is discharged, so long as it is completed within 48 hours. The 48 hour timeframe for completion and documentation of the postanesthesia evaluation is an outside parameter. Individual patient risk factors may dictate that the evaluation be completed and documented sooner than 48 hours. This should be addressed by hospital policies and procedures (71 FR 68690).

For those patients who are unable to participate in the postanesthesia evaluation (e.g., post-operative sedation, mechanical ventilation, etc.), a postanesthesia evaluation should be completed and documented within 48 hours with notation that the patient was unable to participate. This documentation should include the reason for the patient's inability to participate as well as expectations for recovery time, if applicable. For those patients who require long-acting regional anesthesia to ensure optimum medical care of the patient, whose acute effects will last beyond the 48-hour timeframe, a postanesthesia evaluation must still be completed and documented within 48 hours. However, there should be a notation that the patient is otherwise able to participate in the evaluation, but full recovery from regional anesthesia has not occurred and is not expected within the stipulated timeframe for the completion of the evaluation.

The elements of an adequate post-anesthesia evaluation should be clearly documented and conform to current standards of anesthesia care, including:

- Respiratory function, including respiratory rate, airway patency, and oxygen saturation;

- Cardiovascular function, including pulse rate and blood pressure;

- Mental status;

- Temperature;

- Pain;

- Nausea and vomiting; and

- Postoperative hydration.

Depending on the specific surgery or procedure performed, additional types of monitoring and assessment may be necessary.

Survey Procedures §482.52(b)(3)

- Review a sample of medical records for patients who had surgery or a procedure requiring general, regional or monitored anesthesia to determine whether a post anesthesia evaluation was written for each patient.

- Determine whether the evaluation was conducted by a practitioner who is qualified to administer anesthesia.

- Determine whether the evaluation was completed and documented within 48 hours after the surgery or procedure.

- Determine whether the appropriate elements of a postanesthesia evaluation are documented in the medical record.

A-1026
(Rev. 37, Issued: 10-17-08; Effective/Implementation Date: 10-17-08)

§482.53 Condition of Participation: Nuclear Medicine Services

If the hospital provides nuclear medicine services, those services must meet the needs of the patients in accordance with acceptable standards of practice.

Interpretative Guidelines §482.53

This is an optional hospital service. However, if a hospital provides any degree of nuclear medicine services to its patients, the hospital must comply with the requirements of this Condition of Participation.

The hospital's nuclear medicine services must be integrated into its hospital-wide QAPI program.

If nuclear medicine services are provided under arrangement, the governing body must ensure that the services are provided in a safe and effective manner, in accordance with §482.12(e).

Nuclear medicine services must be provided in accordance with acceptable standards of practice. Acceptable standards of practice include maintaining compliance with applicable Federal and State laws, regulations and guidelines governing the use of nuclear medicine, including facility licensure and/or certification requirements, as well as any standards and recommendations promoted by nationally recognized professional organizations (e.g., the American Medical Association, American College of Radiology, etc).

Survey Procedures §482.53

- Determine if the hospital provides nuclear medicine services. If nuclear medicine services are offered, determine the type(s) of services provided and the location where each service is provided.

- Determine if the hospital's nuclear medicine services are integrated into its hospital-wide QAPI program.

A-1027
(Rev. 37, Issued: 10-17-08; Effective/Implementation Date: 10-17-08)
§482.53(a) Standard: Organization and Staffing

The organization of the nuclear medicine service must be appropriate to the scope and complexity of the services offered.

Interpretive Guidelines §482.53(a)

The hospital must provide the appropriate equipment and types and numbers of qualified personnel necessary to furnish the services offered by the hospital in accordance with acceptable standards of practice.

The scope of nuclear medicine services offered by the hospital should be defined in writing, and approved by the Medical staff.

Survey Procedures §482.53(a)

Review the hospital policies & procedures to verify that the scope of the nuclear medicine services offered is defined in writing.

A-1028
(Rev. 37, Issued: 10-17-08; Effective/Implementation Date: 10-17-08)

§482.53(a)(1) - There must be a director who is a doctor of medicine or osteopathy qualified in nuclear medicine.

Interpretive Guidelines §482.53(a)(1)

The nuclear medicine service director must be a doctor of medicine or osteopathy and must demonstrate through education, experience and specialized training that he/she is qualified in nuclear medicine, appropriate to the scope and complexity of services offered.

Survey Procedures §482.53(a)(1)

Review the service director's credentialing file to verify that he/she is a M.D. or D.O. and has the necessary education, experience and specialized training in nuclear medicine, appropriate to the scope and complexity of services offered.

A-1029
(Rev. 37, Issued: 10-17-08; Effective/Implementation Date: 10-17-08)

§482.53(a)(2) - The qualifications, training, functions and responsibilities of the nuclear medicine personnel must be specified by the service director and approved by the medical staff.

Interpretive Guidelines §482.53(a)(2)

The hospital must have written policies, developed and approved by the nuclear medicine service director and medical staff that specify the qualifications, training, functions and experience of personnel responsible for performing each type of nuclear medicine procedure. Qualifications include at a minimum, job title, education, experience, specialized training, and licensure/certification, consistent with Federal and State law.

Survey Procedures §482.53(a)(2)

- Review personnel files for nuclear medicine staff to verify that they meet the necessary qualifications, specified by the medical staff, to perform their specified duties and responsibilities.

- Verify that the qualifications, training, functions and responsibilities of nuclear medicine staff are specified by the director and approved by the medical staff.

A-1035
(Rev. 37, Issued: 10-17-08; Effective/Implementation Date: 10-17-08)
§482.53(b) Standard: Delivery of Service

Radioactive materials must be prepared, labeled, used, transported, stored, and disposed of in accordance with acceptable standards of practice.

Interpretive Guidelines §482.53(b)

The hospital must establish, in writing, safety standards for radioactive materials that address, at a minimum:

- Handling of equipment and radioactive materials;

- Protection of patients and personnel from radiation hazards;

- Labeling of radioactive materials, waste, and hazardous areas;

- Transportation of radioactive materials between locations within the hospital;

- Security of radioactive materials, including determining who may have access to radioactive materials and controlling access to radioactive materials;

- Testing of equipment for radiation hazards;

- Maintenance of personal radiation monitoring devices;

- Storage of radio nuclides and radio pharmaceuticals as well as radioactive waste; and

- Disposal of radio nuclides, unused radio pharmaceuticals, and radioactive waste.

The hospital must implement and ensure compliance with its established safety standard

Survey Procedures §482.53(b)

- Verify that safety precautions are followed in the functioning of the nuclear medicine service and that personnel and patients wear appropriate body shielding (e.g., lead aprons or lead gloves) when appropriate.

- Verify that radioactive materials are prepared, labeled, used, transported, stored and disposed of in accordance with Federal and State laws and regulations and acceptable standards of practice.

A-1036
(Rev. 37, Issued: 10-17-08; Effective/Implementation Date: 10-17-08)

§482.53(b)(1) In-house preparation of radio pharmaceuticals is by, or under, the direct supervision of an appropriately trained registered pharmacist or doctor of medicine or osteopathy.

Interpretive Guidelines §482.53(b)(1)

In-house preparation of radio pharmaceuticals must be performed by, or directly supervised by, a registered pharmacist or MD/DO who is qualified through education, experience and training, in the preparation of radio pharmaceuticals, consistent with Federal and State law.

Survey Procedures §482.53(b)(1)

If radio pharmaceuticals are prepared in-house, determine that the preparation is performed by, or directly supervised by, a registered pharmacist or MD/DO who is qualified through education, experience and training, consistent with Federal and State law.

A-1037
(Rev. 37, Issued: 10-17-08; Effective/Implementation Date: 10-17-08)

§482.53(b)(2) - There is proper storage and disposal of radioactive material.

Survey Procedures §482.53(b)(2)

- Verify through observation and document review that radioactive materials, including radioactive waste, have appropriate storage and disposal.

- Determine how the hospital disposes of unneeded radio nuclides and radio pharmaceuticals.

  o   Are these methods in accordance with Federal and State laws, regulations and guidelines?

  o   Are the methods described in hospital policy?

A-1038
(Rev. 37, Issued: 10-17-08; Effective/Implementation Date: 10-17-08)

§482.53(b)(3) - If laboratory tests are performed in the nuclear medicine service, the service must meet the applicable requirement for laboratory services specified in §482.27.

Interpretive Guidelines §482.53(b)(3)

Refer to the guidelines under §482.27 for independent laboratory if laboratory tests are performed in the nuclear medicine service.

All in vitro tests and all in vivo procedures classified under radio bioassay must be performed in accordance with the requirements of §482.27 including quality control calibration and record retention, etc.

A-1044
(Rev. 37, Issued: 10-17-08; Effective/Implementation Date: 10-17-08)
§482.53(c) Standard: Facilities

Equipment and supplies must be appropriate for the types of nuclear medicine services offered and must be maintained for safe and efficient performance. The equipment must be--

Interpretive Guidelines §482.53(c)

The nuclear medicine service must function in accordance with applicable Federal and State regulations and guidelines governing radiation safety. For more information, see 21 CFR Subpart J, "Radiological Health," and 10 CFR, Chapter 1, Part 20, "U.S. Nuclear Regulatory Commission Standards for Protection Against Ionizing Radiation."

Reagents must be labeled to ensure proper identification, use, storage and safe handling and date of preparation and assay.

A-1045
(Rev. 37, Issued: 10-17-08; Effective/Implementation Date: 10-17-08)

§482.53(c) - [The equipment must be--]

(1) **Maintained in safe operating condition; and**

(2) **Inspected, tested and calibrated at least annually by qualified personnel.**

Interpretive Guidelines §482.53(c)(1-2)

The hospital must develop and implement a preventive maintenance schedule to ensure that nuclear medicine equipment is maintained in safe operating condition to ensure accurate results and patient, staff, and public safety.

Nuclear medicine equipment must be inspected, tested and calibrated at least annually by qualified personnel in accordance with Federal and State laws, regulations and guidelines.

Survey Procedures §482.53(c)(1-2)

Verify that the nuclear medicine service follows its preventive maintenance schedule and that any problems identified are corrected in a timely manner.

Review preventive maintenance records to verify that equipment is inspected, tested and calibrated at least annually by qualified personnel.

A-1051
(Rev. 37, Issued: 10-17-08; Effective/Implementation Date: 10-17-08)
§482.53(d) Standard: Records

The hospital must maintain signed and dated reports of nuclear medicine interpretations, consultations, and procedures.

Interpretive Guidelines §482.53(d)

The hospital must maintain records for all nuclear medicine procedures performed. At a minimum, the records must include signed and dated reports of nuclear medicine interpretations, consultations, and procedures. Nuclear medicine patient records, including interpretations, consultations, and procedures are patient medical records and the hospital must comply with the Medical Records CoP (§482.24).

A-1052
(Rev. 37, Issued: 10-17-08; Effective/Implementation Date: 10-17-08)

§482.53(d)(1) - The hospital must maintain copies of nuclear medicine reports for at least 5 years.

Interpretive Guidelines §482.53(d)(1)

Nuclear medicine patient records, like all patient medical records, must be maintained in accordance with the Medical Records CoP (§482.24).

Survey Procedures §482.53(d)(1)

Verify that copies of nuclear medicine reports are maintained for at least 5 years.

A-1053
(Rev. 37, Issued: 10-17-08; Effective/Implementation Date: 10-17-08)

§482.53(d)(2) - The practitioner approved by the medical staff to interpret diagnostic procedures must sign and date the interpretation of these tests.

Survey Procedures §482.53(d)(2)

Verify that reports of nuclear medicine interpretations are signed and dated only by practitioners authorized by the medical staff to perform these interpretations.

A-1054
(Rev. 37, Issued: 10-17-08; Effective/Implementation Date: 10-17-08)

§482.53(d)(3) - The hospital must maintain records of the receipt and distribution of radio pharmaceuticals.

Survey Procedures §482.53(d)(3)

Verify that the hospital maintains accurate records of the receipt and distribution of radio pharmaceuticals. Request to see the most recent documentation for the delivery of radio pharmaceuticals.

A-1055
(Rev. 37, Issued: 10-17-08; Effective/Implementation Date: 10-17-08)

§482.53(d)(4) - Nuclear medicine services must be ordered only by practitioners whose scope of Federal or State licensure and whose defined staff privileges allow such referrals.

Survey Procedures §482.53(d)(4)

Verify that nuclear medicine services are ordered only by practitioners authorized to do so by the medical staff, consistent with Federal and State law.

A-1076
(Rev. 84, Issued: 06-07-13, Effective: 06-07-13, Implementation: 06-07-13)

§482.54 Condition of Participation: Outpatient Services

If the hospital provides outpatient services, the services must meet the needs of the patients in accordance with acceptable standards of practice.

Interpretive Guidelines §482.54

This is an optional hospital service; however, if a hospital provides any degree of outpatient care to its patients, the hospital must comply with the requirements of this Condition of Participation (CoP).

The Medicare Hospital CoP applies to both inpatient and outpatient services of the hospital. The hospital must be in compliance with the CoP in 42 CFR §482 in all on-campus and off-campus outpatient service locations.

Tag 1080 provides more detailed guidance on the overall requirements for outpatient services and permits standard-level citations for identified deficiencies.

The manner and degree of noncompliance identified in relation to Tags 1077 – 1080 may result in substantial noncompliance with this CoP, requiring citation at the condition level.

A-1077
(Rev. 37, Issued: 10-17-08; Effective/Implementation Date: 10-17-08)

§482.54(a) Standard: Organization

Outpatient services must be appropriately organized and integrated with inpatient services.

Interpretive Guidelines §482.54(a)

The organization of the hospital's outpatient services must be appropriate to the scope and complexity of services offered.

The hospital's outpatient services, at all locations, must be integrated with inpatient services (e.g., medical records, radiology, laboratory, surgical services, anesthesia (including pain management) services, other diagnostic services, etc), as appropriate to the outpatient services offered. The hospital must have written policies in place to assure the integration of outpatient services, including an established method of communication between outpatient service departments to corresponding inpatient services.

The hospital must coordinate the care, treatment and services provided to a patient. In order to provide continuity of care, it should have an established method of communication between inpatient services and outpatient care in order to provide continuity of care to its patients.

Survey Procedures §482.53(a)

- Verify that the outpatient services are organized in a manner appropriate to the scope and complexity of services offered.

- Verify that the hospital has an established method of communication and established procedures to assure integration with inpatient services to provide continuity of care.

- Review medical records of outpatients who were later admitted to the hospital in order to determine that pertinent information from the outpatient record has been included in the inpatient record.

- Determine that each outpatient service location is integrated with the appropriate hospital inpatient services in accordance with the needs of the patient care provided at each of those locations.

A-1079
(Rev. 84, Issued: 06-07-13, Effective: 06-07-13, Implementation: 06-07-13)

§482.54(b) Standard: Personnel

The hospital must --

(1) Assign one or more individuals to be responsible for outpatient services.

(2) Have appropriate professional and nonprofessional personnel available at each location where outpatient services are offered, based on the scope and complexity of outpatient services.

Interpretive Guidelines §482.54(b)

The hospital's outpatient services may be directed by one or more individuals. Hospitals have the flexibility to determine how best to organize their outpatient services, including how direction will be provided. As services offered in outpatient departments become more varied, complex and technologically advanced, hospitals may find it better to have individuals with more specialized expertise providing direction for a specific type of outpatient services.

Hospitals should define in writing the qualifications and competencies necessary for their outpatient services department leader(s). These qualifications should include items such as education, experience, and specialized training consistent with State law and acceptable standards of practice.

The hospital should define in writing the qualifications and competencies necessary to direct each outpatient service for which there is a separate director. Qualifications include necessary education, experience and specialized training consistent with State law and acceptable standards of practice.

Adequate types and numbers of qualified licensed healthcare professionals and other personnel must be available to provide patients with the appropriate level of care for the outpatient services offered by the hospital. The types and numbers of qualified personnel required for area of the hospital's main campus or for each provider-based off-site location must be based on the scope and complexity of the outpatient services offered and the number and types of patients treated as outpatients at each.

Survey Procedures 482.54(b)

- Ask the hospital how it has organized its outpatient services and to identify the individual(s) responsible for providing direction for outpatient services.

- Review the organization's policies and procedures to determine the person's responsibility.

- Review the position description and personnel file of the individual(s) responsible for a selection of outpatient services to ensure that they are qualified, in accordance with State law, acceptable standards of practice and hospital policy to direct the service for which they are responsible.

- Visit several on- and off-campus locations where hospital outpatient services are provided. Given the scope and complexity of the services being offered, are there sufficient personnel with the appropriate education, experience, certifications, current licensure where appropriate, and competencies for assigned responsibilities?

A-1080
(Rev. 84, Issued: 06-07-13, Effective: 06-07-13, Implementation: 06-07-13)

Standard-level Tag for

§482.54 Condition of Participation: Outpatient Services

If the hospital provides outpatient services, the services must meet the needs of the patients in accordance with acceptable standards of practice.

Interpretive Guidelines §482.54

This is an optional hospital service; however, if a hospital provides any degree of outpatient care to its patients, the hospital must comply with the requirements of this Condition of Participation (CoP).

The Medicare Hospital CoP apply to both inpatient and outpatient services of the hospital. The hospital must be in compliance with the CoP in 42 CFR §482 in all on-campus and off-campus outpatient service locations.

All outpatient services provided by the hospital, both on campus and at any provider-based clinics, must meet the needs of the patients, in accordance with acceptable standards of practice. The hospital must ensure that services, equipment, staff, and facilities are adequate to provide the outpatient services offered at each location in accordance with acceptable standards of practice.

Acceptable standards of practice include standards that are set forth in Federal or State laws, regulations or guidelines, as well as standards and recommendations promoted by nationally recognized professional organizations (e.g., the American Medical Association, American College of Radiology, American College of Surgeons, etc).

Orders for outpatient services may be made by any practitioner who is:

- Responsible for the care of the patient;

- Licensed in, or holds a license recognized in, the jurisdiction where he/she sees the patient;

- Acting within his/her scope of practice under State law; and

- Authorized by the medical staff to order the applicable outpatient services under a written hospital policy that is approved by the governing body. This includes both practitioners who are on the hospital medical staff and who hold medical staff privileges that include ordering the services, as well as other practitioners who are not on the hospital medical staff, but who satisfy the hospital's policies for ordering applicable outpatient services.

The hospital's medical staff policy for authorizing practitioners to refer patients to the hospital with orders for specific outpatient services must address how the hospital verifies that the referring/ordering practitioner who is responsible for the patient's care is appropriately licensed and acting within his/her scope of practice. The policy must also make clear whether the policy applies to all hospital outpatient services, or whether there are specific services for which orders may only be accepted from practitioners with medical staff privileges. For example, a hospital may prefer not to accept orders for a regimen of outpatient chemotherapy or outpatient therapeutic nuclear medicine services from a referring physician who does not hold medical staff privileges. In such cases, the hospital's policy must make these exceptions to the general authorization for accepting orders from referring practitioners clear.

If the hospital offers outpatient surgical services, the Surgical Services CoP (§482.5) requires that the offered services must be consistent in quality with inpatient care in accordance with the services offered.

The hospital's outpatient services must be integrated into its hospital-wide QAPI program.

Survey Procedures §482.54

- Verify that equipment, staff and facilities are adequate to provide the outpatient services offered at each location are in accordance with acceptable standards of practice.

- Verify that outpatient services at all locations are in compliance with the hospital CoP.

- Determine locations and type(s) of outpatient services provided.

- Verify that the hospital's outpatient services are integrated into its hospital-wide QAPI program.

- Ask the individual(s) directing outpatient services whether the hospital orders for that type of outpatient service from referring physicians who are not members of the hospital's medical staff. If yes:

- Ask for evidence that the medical staff has approved the policy.

- Ask how the hospital verifies that the order comes from a referring practitioner who is appropriately licensed in the jurisdiction where he/she sees the patient to prescribe such orders. Ask for documentation of such verification efforts.

A-1100
(Rev. 37, Issued: 10-17-08; Effective/Implementation Date: 10-17-08)

§482.55 Condition of Participation: Emergency Services

The hospital must meet the emergency needs of patients in accordance with acceptable standards of practice.

A-1101
(Rev. 37, Issued: 10-17-08; Effective/Implementation Date: 10-17-08)

§482.55(a) Standard: Organization and Direction. If emergency services are provided at the hospital --

Interpretive Guidelines §482.55(a):

If emergency services are provided at the hospital, the hospital must ensure that specific emergency services organization and direction requirements are met.

A-1102
(Rev. 37, Issued: 10-17-08; Effective/Implementation Date: 10-17-08)

§482.55(a) - [If emergency services are provided at the hospital --]
  (1) The services must be organized under the direction of a qualified member of the medical staff;

Interpretive Guidelines §482.55(a)(1)

The hospital's emergency services must be under the direction of a qualified member of the hospital's medical staff. The hospital's medical staff establishes criteria for the qualifications for the director of the hospital's emergency services in accordance with State law and acceptable standards of practice. A single emergency services director must be responsible for the hospital's emergency services.

Survey Procedures §482.55(a)(1)

Verify that emergency services are organized under the direction of a qualified member of the medical staff.

A-1103
(Rev. 37, Issued: 10-17-08; Effective/Implementation Date: 10-17-08)

§482.55(a) - [If emergency services are provided at the hospital --]

(2)   The services must be integrated with other departments of the hospital;

Interpretive Guidelines §482.55(a)(2)

The hospital's emergency service/department must be integrated with the other departments of the hospital such as surgical services, lab, ICU, diagnostic services, etc. The hospital must demonstrate that its emergency services are truly integrated into its other departments. The integration must be such that the hospital can immediately make available the full extent of its patient care resources to assess and render appropriate care for an emergency patient.

Emergency Services integration would include at a minimum:

- Coordination and communication between the Emergency Department and other hospital services/departments;

- Physical access for emergency department patients to the services, equipment, personnel, and resources of other hospital departments/services;

- The immediate availability of services, equipment, personnel, and resources of other hospital departments/services to emergency patients; and

- That the provision of services, equipment, personnel and resources of other hospital departments/services to emergency department patients is within timeframes that protect the health and safety of patients and is within acceptable standards of practice, including:

    o The length of time it takes to transport the emergency patient from the ED to another hospital department where needed interventions or diagnostic services will be rendered.

    o The length of time it takes to deliver equipment or supplies, or for the staff from other departments to travel from their location to the emergency department in order to provide needed interventions, tests, care, or services.

Time is critical in the provision of emergency care. The hospital must be able to demonstrate how the hospital's other departments provide emergency patients the care and services needed within safe and appropriate times.

In emergency care situations, the time needed to provide the patient with appropriate diagnostic and care interventions can have a significant effect on the patient. Delays in diagnosis and the provision of needed interventions is likely to adversely affect the health and safety of patients who require emergency care. Therefore, a hospital that cannot demonstrate integration of its emergency services with its other departments (including radiological services, OR, intensive care, laboratory, etc) would not be in compliance with the Emergency Services CoP.

Many hospitals offer urgent care services on the hospital campus or in provider-based clinics in the communities they serve. Those clinics must be in compliance with the hospital CoP. Hospitals may organize their **urgent care clinics** as part of their outpatient department or emergency services department. An urgent care clinic that:

- The hospital holds out to the public as providing only urgent care services and possibly other services;

- Clearly advises the public that the urgent care clinic is not an emergency services department; and

- Does not meet the EMTALA definition of dedicated emergency department;

would be evaluated for compliance with the integration requirement in the Outpatient Services CoP (§482.54(a)) rather than the integration requirement in the Emergency Services CoP. In most urgent care situations, the time, qualified personnel, equipment, and other resources needed to provide the patient with appropriate diagnostic and care interventions are less than needed in emergency situations.

Survey Procedures §482.55(a)(2)

Verify that there are established procedures to assure integration with either hospital services including laboratory, radiology, and operating services to provide continuity of care.

A-1104
(Rev. 37, Issued: 10-17-08; Effective/Implementation Date: 10-17-08)

§482.55(a) - [If emergency services are provided at the hospital --]

(3) **The policies and procedures governing medical care provided in the emergency service or department are established by and are a continuing responsibility of the medical staff.**

Interpretive Guidelines §482.55(a)(3)

The hospital's medical staff must establish policies and procedures governing the medical care provided in the emergency service or emergency department. The medical staff must have had ongoing/continuing assessment of the medical care provided in the emergency service or department. Emergency service or emergency department policies must be current and revised as necessary based on the ongoing monitoring conducted by the medical staff and the emergency service or department QAPI activities.

Survey Procedures §482.55(a)(3)

Verify that procedures and policies for emergency medical services (including triage of patients) are established, evaluated, and updated on an ongoing basis.

A-1110
(Rev. 37, Issued: 10-17-08; Effective/Implementation Date: 10-17-08)
§482.55(b) Standard: Personnel

Interpretive Guidelines §482.55(b):

The hospital must ensure the emergency services personnel requirements are met.

A-1111
(Rev. 37, Issued: 10-17-08; Effective/Implementation Date: 10-17-08)

§482.55(b)(1) - The emergency services must be supervised by a qualified member of the medical staff.

Interpretive Guidelines §482.55(b)(1)

A qualified member of the medical staff must supervise the provision of emergency services. Since §482.55(a)(1) requires that emergency services must be organized under the **direction** of a qualified member of the medical staff, the requirement for **supervision** at§482.55(b)(1) must be distinguished from the prior requirement. In this context, "supervision" implies a more immediate form of oversight by a qualified member of the medical staff during all times the hospital makes emergency services available. A supervisor may be briefly absent from the emergency department, but is expected to be in the hospital and immediately available to provide direction and/or direct care during the operating hours of the emergency department.

The medical staff must establish criteria, in accordance with State law, regulations, and guidelines, delineating the qualifications a medical staff member must possess in order to be granted privileges for the supervision of the provision of emergency care services. Qualifications include necessary education, experience and specialized training, consistent with State law and acceptable standards of practice.

Survey Procedures §482.55(b)(1)

Verify that a qualified member of the medical staff is designated to supervise emergency services.

A-1112
(Rev. 37, Issued: 10-17-08; Effective/Implementation Date: 10-17-08)

§482.55(b)(2) - There must be adequate medical and nursing personnel qualified in emergency care to meet the written emergency procedures and needs anticipated by the facility.

Interpretive Guidelines §482.55(b)(2)

The hospital must staff the emergency department with the appropriate numbers and types of professionals and other staff who possess the skills, education, certifications, specialized training and experience in emergency care to meet the written emergency procedures and needs anticipated by the facility.

The hospital must determine the categories and numbers of MD/DOs, specialists, RNs, EMTs, and emergency department support staff the hospital needs to met its anticipated emergency needs.

The medical staff must establish criteria, in accordance with State law and regulations and acceptable standards of practice delineating the qualifications required for each category of emergency services staff (e.g., emergency physicians, specialist MD/DO, RNs, EMTs, mid-level practitioners, etc.).

As a suggested prudent practice the hospital should conduct periodic assessments of its emergency needs in order to anticipate the policies, procedures, staffing, training, and other resources that may be needed to address likely demands.

Additionally, the hospital should work cooperatively with Federal, State and local emergency preparedness agencies and officials in order to identify likely risks to the community (e.g., natural disasters, mass casualties, terrorist acts, etc.), to anticipate demands and resources needed by the hospital emergency services, and to develop plans, methods and coordinating networks to address those anticipated needs.

Survey Procedures §482.55(b)(2)

- Verify that there are sufficient medical and nursing personnel qualified in the needs anticipated by the facility and that there are specific assigned duties for emergency care personnel and a clear chain of command.

- Interview staff to determine that they are knowledgeable, within their own level of participation in emergency care including:

  o Parenteral administration of electrolytes, fluids, blood and blood components;

  o Care and management of injuries to extremities and central nervous system;

  o Prevention of contamination and cross infection.

A-1123
(Rev. 37, Issued: 10-17-08; Effective/Implementation Date: 10-17-08)

§482.56 Condition of Participation: Rehabilitation Services

If the hospital provides rehabilitation, physical therapy, occupational therapy, audiology, or speech pathology services, the services must be organized and staffed to ensure the health and safety of patients.

Interpretive Guidelines §482.56

This is an optional hospital service. However, if a hospital provides any degree of rehabilitative services to its patients, the hospital must comply with the requirements of the Condition of Participation.

If rehabilitative services are provided, they must be organized and staffed in such a manner to ensure the health and safety of patients. This includes providing rehabilitative services in accordance with practitioner orders and acceptable standards of practice.

Acceptable standards of practice include compliance with any applicable Federal or State laws, regulations or guidelines, as well as standards and recommendations promoted by nationally recognized professional organizations (e.g., American Physical Therapy Association, American Speech and Hearing Association, American Occupational Therapy Association, American College of Physicians, American Medical Association, etc.).

The hospital's rehabilitation services must be integrated into its hospital-wide QAPI program.

Survey Procedures §482.56

- Determine if the hospital provides any degree of rehabilitation services.

- Determine if the hospital's rehabilitation services are integrated into its hospital-wide QAPI program.

A-1124
(Rev. 37, Issued: 10-17-08; Effective/Implementation Date: 10-17-08)

§482.56(a) Standard: Organization and Staffing

The organization of the service must be appropriate to the scope of the services offered.

Interpretive Guidelines §482.56(a)

The hospital must provide the appropriate equipment and types and numbers of qualified personnel necessary to furnish the rehabilitation services offered by the hospital in accordance with acceptable standards of practice.

The scope of rehabilitation services offered by the hospital should be defined in written policies and procedures, and approved by the Medical staff.

Each service, whether provided through a single discipline department or within a multi-discipline department, must function with established lines of authority and responsibility to ensure the health and safety of patients. There must be an adequate number of qualified staff available when needed to evaluate each patient, initiate the plan of treatment, and supervise supportive personnel when they furnish rehabilitation services. The number of qualified staff is based on the type of patients treated and the frequency, duration, and complexity of the treatment required.

Survey Procedures §482.56(a)

- Review the hospital's policies and procedures to verify that the scope of rehabilitation services offered is defined in writing.

- If services are provided under an arrangement, review policies and contracts.

- For each service, determine that adequate types and numbers of qualified staff are available to ensure safe and efficient provision of treatment.

- Review medical records to verify that a qualified professional evaluates the patient and initiates each treatment episode.

- Review a sample of personnel files to verify current licensure, certifications and ongoing training, consistent with applicable State laws.

A-1125
(Rev. 37, Issued: 10-17-08; Effective/Implementation Date: 10-17-08)

§482.56(a)(1) - The director of the services must have the necessary knowledge, experience, and capabilities to properly supervise and administer the services.

Interpretive Guidelines §482.56(a)(1)

Each service must be accountable to an individual that directs the overall hospital-wide operation of that service. An individual may serve as the director of a multi-service department or as director of single service departments.

The service director must demonstrate through education, experience, and/or specialized training that he/she has the necessary knowledge, experience and capabilities to properly supervise and administer the service(s).

The director may be part-time or full time. In all situations the director retains professional and administrative responsibility for personnel providing the service. If the director is part-time, the time spent directing the service should be appropriate to the scope of the services provided.

Survey Procedures §482.56(a)(1)

- Verify that each service is accountable to an individual who directs the overall operation of that service.

- Review the service director's position description to verify that he/she has been granted the authority and responsibility for operation of the service, consistent with hospital policies, State law, and accepted standards of practice.

- If the director does not work full-time, determine that the number of hours (review timesheets) spent working is appropriate to the scope of services provided.

- Review the director's personnel file to determine that he/she has the necessary education, experience and specialized training to properly supervise and administer the service. This includes maintaining current licensure and certifications as required by State law.

- Interview the director to determine if he/she has the necessary knowledge, experience and capabilities to properly supervise and administer the service.

A-1126
(Rev. 37, Issued: 10-17-08; Effective/Implementation Date: 10-17-08)

§482.56(a)(2) Physical therapy, occupational therapy, or speech-language pathology or audiology services, if provided, must be provided by qualified physical therapists, physical therapist assistants, occupational therapists, occupational therapy assistants, speech-language pathologists, or audiologists as defined in part 484 of this chapter.

A-1132
(Rev. 81, Issued, 03-23-12, Effective: 03-23-12, Implementation: 03-23-12)

§482.56(b) Standard: Delivery of Services

Services must only be provided under the orders of a qualified and licensed practitioner who is responsible for the care of the patient, acting within his or her scope of practice under State law, and who is authorized by the hospital's medical staff to order the services in accordance with hospital policies and procedures and State laws.

A-1133
(Rev. 72, Issued: 11-18-11, Effective: 11-18-11, Implementation: 11-18-11)

§482.56(b)(1) All rehabilitation services orders must be documented in the patient's medical record in accordance with the requirements at §482.24.

Interpretive Guidelines §482.56(b)(1)

The patient's medical record must contain documentation of all rehabilitation services ordered. The medical record entries must comply with regulations at §482.24.

Survey Procedures §482.56(b)(1)

Review a sample of patient medical records who received rehabilitation services. Determine whether the rehabilitation service orders are legible, complete, dated, timed, authenticated, and meet all other medical record requirements specified at §482.24.

A-1134

§482.56(b)(2) The provision of care and the personnel qualifications must be in accordance with national acceptable standards of practice and must also meet the requirements of §409.17 of this chapter.

Interpretive Guidelines §482.56(b)(2)

The provision of rehabilitation services care and development of the plan of care for rehabilitation services can be initiated only after the order is written for services by a qualified licensed practitioner responsible for the care of the patient. Physical therapy, occupational therapy, or speech-language pathology must be furnished under a plan of care. The regulation at 42 CFR 409.17 specifies the following rehabilitation services plan of care requirements:

Establishment of the plan: "The plan must be established before treatment begins by one of the following: (1) A physician. (2) A nurse practitioner, a clinical nurse specialist or a physician assistant. (3) The physical therapist furnishing the physical therapy services. (4) A speech-language pathologist furnishing the speech-language pathology services. (5) An occupational therapist furnishing the occupational therapy services."

Content of the plan: "The plan: (1) Prescribes the type, amount, frequency, and duration of the physical therapy, occupational therapy, or speech-language pathology services to be furnished to the individual; and (2) Indicates the diagnosis and anticipated goals."

Changes in the plan: "Any changes in the plan are implemented in accordance with hospital policies and procedures."

Also in accordance with 42 CFR 409.17, rehabilitation services must be provided by qualified physical therapists, physical therapy assistants, occupational therapists, occupational therapy assistants, and/or speech-language pathologists who meet the personnel qualifications defined in 42 CFR 484.4. Hospitals must have policies and procedures consistent with State law.

Rehabilitation services must be provided according to national standards of practice as established by professional organizations such as, but not limited to, the American Physical Therapy Association, the American Occupational Therapy Association, and the American Speech-Language-Hearing Association.

Survey Procedures §482.56(b)(2)

Review medical records of patients who received rehabilitation services. Determine whether the required care plan was developed and implemented.

Review employee personnel files to verify the rehabilitation service providers (i.e., physical therapists, physical therapy assistants, occupational therapists, occupational therapy assistants, and/or speech-language pathologists) have the necessary education, experience, training, and documented competencies to provide rehabilitation services.

Ask the hospital what national standards of rehabilitation practice provide the basis for its rehabilitation services. Is there supporting documentation?

A-1151
(Rev. 37, Issued: 10-17-08; Effective/Implementation Date: 10-17-08)

§482.57 Condition of Participation: Respiratory Services

The hospital must meet the needs of the patients in accordance with acceptable standards of practice. The following requirements apply if the hospital provides respiratory care services.

Interpretive Guidelines §482.57

If a hospital provides care to patients who require respiratory care services, the hospital must meet the needs of those patients, in accordance with acceptable standards of practice. This is an optional hospital service. However, if a hospital provides any degree of respiratory care to its patients, the hospital must comply with the requirements of this Condition of Participation.

Acceptable standards of practice include compliance with applicable standards that are set forth in Federal or State laws, regulations or guidelines, as well as standards and recommendations promoted by nationally recognized professional organizations (e.g., American Medical Association, American Association for Respiratory Care, American Thoracic Association, etc).

The hospital's respiratory services must be integrated into its hospital-wide QAPI program.

Survey Procedures §482.57

- Determine if the hospital provides any degree of respiratory care services.

- Determine that the type and amount of respiratory care provided meets the needs of the patients and is delivered in accordance with acceptable standards of practice.
- Determine if the hospital's respiratory services are integrated into its hospital-wide QAPI program.

A-1152
(Rev. 37, Issued: 10-17-08; Effective/Implementation Date: 10-17-08)
§482.57(a) Standard: Organization and Staffing

The organization of the respiratory care services must be appropriate to the scope and complexity of the services offered.

Interpretive Guidelines §482.57(a)

The hospital must provide the appropriate equipment and types and numbers of qualified personnel necessary to furnish the services offered by the hospital in accordance with acceptable standards of practice.

The scope of diagnostic and/or therapeutic respiratory services offered by the hospital should be defined in writing, and approved by the Medical staff.

Survey Procedures §482.57(a)

- Review the hospital's organizational chart to determine the relationship of respiratory care services to other services provided by the hospital.

- Review the hospital policies and procedures to verify that the scope of the diagnostic and/or therapeutic respiratory care services provided is defined in writing.

A-1153
(Rev. 37, Issued: 10-17-08; Effective/Implementation Date: 10-17-08)

§482.57(a)(1) - There must be a director of respiratory care services who is a doctor of medicine or osteopathy with the knowledge, experience and capabilities to supervise and administer the service properly. The director may serve on either a full-time or part-time basis.

Interpretive Guidelines §482.57(a)(1)

The service director must be a doctor of medicine or osteopathy and must demonstrate through education, experience and specialized training that he/she has the qualifications necessary to supervise and administer the service properly, appropriate to the scope and complexity of services offered.

If the director serves on a part-time basis, the time spent directing the department should be appropriate to the scope and complexity of services provided.

Survey Procedures §482.57(a)(1)

- Verify that a director has been appointed and that he/she has fixed lines of authority and delegated responsibility for operation of the service.

- Interview staff regarding the role and oversight activities conducted by the director.

- Review the service director's credentialing file to determine that he/she is a M.D. or D.O. and has the necessary education, experience and specialized training to supervise and administer the service properly.

A-1154
(Rev. 37, Issued: 10-17-08; Effective/Implementation Date: 10-17-08)

§482.57(a)(2) - There must be adequate numbers of respiratory therapists, respiratory therapy technicians, and other personnel who meet the qualifications specified by the medical staff, consistent with State law.

Interpretive Guidelines §482.57(a)(2)

There must be sufficient personnel available to respond to the respiratory care needs of the patient population being served.

Survey Procedures §482.57(a)(2)

- Interview respiratory care staff regarding: services provided, schedules, and availability of respiratory care staff throughout the day and week to determine that the number and type of staff available is appropriate to the volume and types of treatments furnished. If needed, review staffing and on-call schedules.

- Review a sample of personnel files for respiratory care staff to determine that the personnel meet the qualifications specified by the medical staff, consistent with State law.

A-1160
(Rev. 37, Issued: 10-17-08; Effective/Implementation Date: 10-17-08)
§482.57(b) Standard: Delivery of Services

Services must be delivered in accordance with medical staff directives.

Interpretive Guidelines §482.57(b)

There should be written policies for the delivery of respiratory care services that are developed and approved by the medical staff. Appropriate to the scope of services provided, the written policies should address at least the following:

- Equipment assembly, operation, and preventive maintenance;

- Safety practices, including infection control measures for equipment, sterile supplies, biohazardous waste, posting of signs, and gas line identification;

- Handling, storage, and dispensing of therapeutic gases to both inpatients and outpatients;

- Cardiopulmonary resuscitation;

- Procedures to follow in the advent of adverse reactions to treatments or interventions;

- Pulmonary function testing;

- Therapeutic percussion and vibration;

- Bronchopulmonary drainage;

- Mechanical ventilatory and oxygenation support;

- Aerosol, humidification, and therapeutic gas administration;

- Storage, access, control, administration of medications and medication errors; and

- Procedures for obtaining and analyzing blood samples (e.g., arterial blood gases).

A-1161
(Rev. 37, Issued: 10-17-08; Effective/Implementation Date: 10-17-08)

§482.57(b)(1) - Personnel qualified to perform specific procedures and the amount of supervision required for personnel to carry out specific procedures must be designated in writing.

Interpretive Guidelines §482.57(b)(1)

The hospital must have written policies to address, at a minimum:

- Each type of respiratory care service provided by the hospital;

- The qualifications, including job title, licensure consistent with State law, education, training and experience of personnel authorized to perform each type of respiratory care service and whether they may perform it without supervision; and

- The type of personnel qualified to provide the direct supervision.

Survey Procedures §482.57(b)(1)

- Review treatment logs, job descriptions of respiratory care staff, and policies and procedures to determine the following:

    o Duties and responsibilities of staff;

    o Qualifications and education required, including licensure, consistent with State law;

    o Specialized training or experience needed to perform specific duties.

A-1162
(Rev. 37, Issued: 10-17-08; Effective/Implementation Date: 10-17-08)

§482.57(b)(2) - If blood gases or other clinical laboratory tests are performed in the respiratory care unit, the unit must meet the applicable requirements for laboratory services specified in §482.27.

Interpretive Guidelines §482.57(b)(2)

Refer to the guidelines under §482.27 for independent laboratory if blood gases and laboratory tests are performed in the respiratory care unit.

A-1163
(Rev. 81, Issued, 03-23-12, Effective: 03-23-12, Implementation: 03-23-12)

§482.57(b)(3) - Services must only be provided under the orders of a qualified and licensed practitioner who is responsible for the care of the patient, acting within his or her scope of practice under State law, and who is authorized by the hospital's

medical staff to order the services in accordance with hospital policies and procedures and State laws.

A-1164
(Rev. 72, Issued: 11-18-11, Effective: 11-18-11, Implementation: 11-18-11)

§482.57(b)(4)- All respiratory care services orders must be documented in the patient's medical record in accordance with the requirements at §482.24.

Interpretive Guidelines §482.57(b)(4)

The patient's medical record must contain documentation of all respiratory care services ordered. The medical record entries must comply with regulations at 42 CFR 482.24.

Survey Procedures §482.57(b)(4)

Review a sample of patient medical records who received respiratory care services. Determine whether the respiratory care services orders are legible, complete, dated, timed, authenticated, and meet all other medical record requirements as specified at §484.24.

Transmittals Issued for this Appendix

Rev #	Issue Date	Subject	Impl Date	CR#
R89SOM	08/30/2013	Revised State Operations Manual (SOM) Appendices A, I, L, and W	08/30/2013	N/A
R87SOM	07/19/2013	Revised Appendix A, Interpretive Guidelines for Hospitals, Condition of Participation: Discharge Planning	07/19/2013	N/A
R84SOM	06/07/2013	Revised Appendix A, Interpretive Guidelines for Hospitals, Appendix L, Interpretive Guidelines for Ambulatory Surgical Centers and Appendix W, Interpretive Guidelines for Critical Access Hospitals	06/07/2013	N/A
R81SOM	03/23/2012	Revisions to State Operations Manual (SOM), Appendix A, Hospitals	03/23/2012	N/A
R78SOM	12/22/2011	Revised Appendix A, Interpretive Guidelines for Hospitals and Appendix W, Interpretive Guidelines for Critical Access Hospitals(CAH)	12/22/2011	N/A
R77SOM	12/22/2011	Revised Appendix A, "Interpretive Guidelines for Hospitals"	12/22/2011	N/A
R75SOM	12/02/2011	Revised Appendix A, Interpretive Guidelines for Hospitals and Appendix W, Interpretive Guidelines for Critical Access Hospitals(CAH)	12/02/2011	N/A
R74SOM	12/02/2011	Revised Appendix A, "Interpretive Guidelines for Hospitals"	12/02/2011	N/A
R72SOM	11/18/2011	Revised Appendix A: Conditions of Participation and Interpretive Guidelines for Hospitals	11/18/2011	N/A
R59SOM	05/21/2010	Clarification of the Interpretive Guidelines for the Anesthesia Services Condition of Participation	05/21/2010	N/A
R47SOM	06/05/2009	Revised Appendix A, "Interpretive Guidelines for Hospitals"	06/05/2009	N/A
R37SOM	10/17/2008	Revised Appendix A, "Interpretive Guidelines for Hospitals"	10/17/2008	N/A
R01SOM	05/21/2004	Initial Release of Pub. 100-07	N/A	N/A